LONG + LIVE + MATH

Middle School Math Solution
Course 3

Student Edition

Sandy Bartle Finocchi and Amy Jones Lewis

with Kelly Edenfield and Josh Fisher

501 Grant St., Suite 1075
Pittsburgh, PA 15219
Phone 888.851.7094
Customer Service Phone 412.690.2444
Fax 412.690.2444

www.carnegielearning.com

Cover Design by Anne Milliron

ISBN: 978-1-60972-891-5
Student Edition

Printed in the United States of America
1 2 3 4 5 6 7 8 9 B&B 21 20 19 18

Dear Student,

You are about to begin an exciting journey! These mathematical materials were written specifically for you, a middle school student. The book you are holding is your book. There is lots of space for writing, sketching, drawing, cutting, pasting, and constructing new mathematical ideas.

Connections are important in life. The popularity of social networks shows the importance of connections. In much the same way, mathematics connects with so many activities in our lives. Throughout the lessons, you will build new knowledge based upon your prior knowledge. You will apply math to real-world situations so that you can see why it's meaningful. You will encounter models that portray mathematical concepts. Models will be presented in all sorts of ways—from pictures, to different student methods and approaches to problem solving. You will also use manipulatives, which are objects that you can use to model or reinforce key mathematical concepts.

I bet the folks at home would like to know what we're going to do this year!

Keep in mind, no professional athlete practices by just playing an entire game—ballet dancers repeat some basic steps, moves, and dances; basketball players practice dribbling, shooting, and defending; even writers jot ideas for novels in their spare time—all to improve their skills. Mathematics is no different and these materials enable and encourage you to practice.

Don't worry—you will not be working alone. We encourage students to work together in pairs or in groups because it gets you talking about your insights. Everyone will share his or her ideas and thoughts in class. Sometimes you will help your classmates, and other times they will help you.

We have designed this book to help you build a deep understanding of mathematics. Enjoy the journey and share your thoughts with others. Have fun while Learning by Doing!

The Carnegie Learning® Instructional Design Team

Acknowledgments

Middle School Math Solution Authors
- Sandy Bartle Finocchi, Senior Academic Officer
- Amy Jones Lewis, Director of Instructional Design
- Kelly Edenfield, Instructional Designer
- Josh Fisher, Instructional Designer

Foundation Authors (2010)
- William S. Hadley, Algebra and Proportional Reasoning
- Mary Lou Metz, Data Analysis and Probability
- Mary Lynn Raith, Number and Operations
- Janet Sinopoli, Algebra
- Jaclyn Snyder, Geometry and Measurement

Vendors
- Lumina Datamatics, Ltd.
- Cenveo Publisher Services, Inc.

Images
- www.pixabay.com

Special Thanks
- Alison Huettner for project management and editorial review.
- Jacyln Snyder and Janet Sinopoli for their contributions to the Teacher's Implementation Guide facilitation notes.
- Victoria Fisher for her review of content and contributions to all the ancillary materials.
- Valerie Muller for her contributions and review of content.
- The members of Carnegie Learning's Cognitive Scientist Team—Brendon Towle, John Connelly, Bob Hausmann, Chas Murray, and Martina Pavelko—for their insight in learning science and review of content.
- Bob Hausmann for his contributions to the Family Guide.
- John Jorgenson, Chief Marketing Officer, for all his insight and messaging.
- Carnegie Learning's Education Services Team for content review and providing customer feedback.
- In Memory of David Dengler, Director of Curriculum Development (Deceased), who made substantial contributions to conceptualizing Carnegie Learning's middle school software.

"Mathematics is so much more than memorizing rules. It is learning to reason, to make connections, and to make sense of the world. We believe in Learning by Doing™—you need to actively engage with the content if you are to benefit from it. The lessons were designed to take you from your intuitive understanding of the world and build on your prior experiences to then learn new concepts. My hope is that these instructional materials help you build a deep understanding of math.

Sandy Bartle Finocchi, Senior Academic Officer

"My hope is that as you work through this course, you feel capable—capable of exploring new ideas that build upon what you already know, capable of struggling through challenging problems, capable of thinking creatively about how to fix mistakes, and capable of thinking like a mathematician.

Amy Jones Lewis, Director of Instructional Design

"At Carnegie Learning we have created an organization whose mission and culture is defined by your success. Our passion is creating products that make sense of the world of mathematics and ignite a passion in you. Our hope is that you will enjoy our resources as much as we enjoyed creating them.

Barry Malkin, CEO

Table of Contents

Module 1: Transforming Geometric Objects

Module 2: Developing Function Foundations

Topic 1: From Proportions to Linear Relationships

Topic 2: Linear Relationships

Topic 3: Introduction to Functions

Topic 4: Patterns in Bivariate Data

Module 3: Modeling Linear Equations

Topic 1: Solving Linear Equations

Topic 2: Systems of Linear Equations

Module 4: Expanding Number Systems

Topic 1: The Real Number System

Module 5: Applying Powers

Topic 1: Exponents and Scientific Notation

Topic 2: Volume of Curved Figures

Habits of Mind

Mathematical Practices

The types of activities within this book require you to make sense of mathematics and to demonstrate your reasoning through problem solving, writing, discussing, and presenting. Effective communication and collaboration are essential skills of a successful learner.

Each activity is denoted with an icon that represents a practice or pair of practices intentionally being developed. To help develop these habits of mind ask yourself the types of questions listed as you work.

With practice, you can develop the habits of mind of a productive mathematical thinker.

► Make sense of problems and persevere in solving them.

This practice is evident every day in every lesson. No icon used.

Questions to ask:
- What is this problem asking and what is my plan for answering it?
- What tools do I need to solve this problem?
- Does my answer make sense?

► Reason abstractly and quantitatively.
► Construct viable arguments and critique the reasoning of others.

Questions to ask:
- What representation can I use to solve this problem?
- How can this problem be represented with symbols and numbers?
- How can I explain my thinking?
- How does my strategy compare to my partner's?

> I hope that every once in a while you will see something that you weren't quite expecting. These are my favorite parts! Because I <3 being confused at first, and then figuring it out.
>
> Josh Fisher, Instructional Designer

▶ **Model with mathematics.**
▶ **Use appropriate tools strategically.**

Questions to ask:

- What expression or equation could represent this situation?
- What tools would help me solve this problem?
- What representations best show my thinking?
- How does this answer make sense in the context of the original problem?

▶ **Attend to precision.**

Questions to ask:

- Is my answer accurate?
- Did I use the correct units or labels?
- Is there a more efficient way to solve this problem?
- Is there more sophisticated vocabulary that I could use in my explanation?

▶ **Look for and make use of structure.**
▶ **Look for and express regularity in repeated reasoning.**

Questions to ask:

- What characteristics of this expression or equation are made clear through this representation?
- How can I use what I know to explain why this works?
- Can I develop a more efficient method?
- How could this problem help me to solve another problem?

"This book is your place to record your thoughts, your conjectures, your mistakes, your strategies, and your 'ah-has' about the mathematics you need to learn this year. Don't erase when you make mistakes; cross it out so that you can still see your original thinking. Learn from your mistakes and grow your brain."

Kelly Edenfield, Instructional Designer

The Crew

The Crew is here to help you on your journey. Sometimes they will remind you about things you already learned. Sometimes they will ask you questions to help you think about different strategies. Sometimes they will share fun facts. They are members of your group—someone you can rely on!

Teacher aides will guide you along your journey. They will help you make connections and remind you to think about the details.

Academic Glossary

There are important terms you will encounter throughout this book. It is important that you have an understanding of these words as you get started on your journey through the mathematical concepts. Knowing what is meant by these terms and using these terms will help you think, reason, and communicate your ideas.

ANALYZE

Definition

To study or look closely for patterns. Analyzing can involve examining or breaking a concept down into smaller parts to gain a better understanding of it.

Ask Yourself

- Do I see any patterns?
- Have I seen something like this before?
- What happens if the shape, representation, or numbers change?

Related Phrases

- Examine
- Evaluate
- Determine
- Observe
- Consider
- Investigate
- What do you notice?
- What do you think?
- Sort and match

EXPLAIN YOUR REASONING

Definition

To give details or describe how to determine an answer or solution. Explaining your reasoning helps justify conclusions.

Ask Yourself

- How should I organize my thoughts?
- Is my explanation logical?
- Does my reasoning make sense?
- How can I justify my answer to others?

Related Phrases

- Show your work
- Explain your calculation
- Justify
- Why or why not?

REPRESENT

Related Phrases

- Show
- Sketch
- Draw
- Create
- Plot
- Graph
- Write an equation
- Complete the table

Definition

To display information in various ways. Representing mathematics can be done using words, tables, graphs, or symbols.

Ask Yourself

- How should I organize my thoughts?
- How do I use this model to show a concept or idea?
- What does this representation tell me?
- Is my representation accurate?

ESTIMATE

Related Phrases

- Predict
- Approximate
- Expect
- About how much?

Definition

To make an educated guess based on the analysis of given data. Estimating first helps inform reasoning.

Ask Yourself

- Does my reasoning make sense?
- Is my solution close to my estimation?

DESCRIBE

Related Phrases

- Demonstrate
- Label
- Display
- Compare
- Determine
- Define
- What are the advantages?
- What are the disadvantages?
- What is similar?
- What is different?

Definition

To represent or give an account of in words. Describing communicates mathematical ideas to others.

Ask Yourself

- How should I organize my thoughts?
- Is my explanation logical?
- Did I consider the context of the situation?
- Does my reasoning make sense?

Problem Types You Will See

WORKED EXAMPLE

The first right triangle has sides of length 3 units, 4 units, and 5 units, where the sides of length 3 units and 4 units are the legs and the side with length 5 units is the hypotenuse.

The sum of the squares of the
lengths of the legs: $\quad 3^2 + 4^2 = 9 + 16$
$$= 25$$
The square of the hypotenuse: $5^2 = 25$

Therefore $3^2 + 4^2 = 5^2$, which verifies the Pythagorean Theorem, holds true.

Worked Example

When you see a Worked Example:
- Take your time to read through it.
- Question your own understanding.
- Think about the connections between steps.

Ask Yourself:
- What is the main idea?
- How would this work if I changed the numbers?
- Have I used these strategies before?

Thumbs Up

When you see a Thumbs Up icon:
- Take your time to read through the correct solution.
- Think about the connections between steps.

Ask Yourself:
- Why is this method correct?
- Have I used this method before?

Thumbs Down

When you see a Thumbs Down icon:
- Take your time to read through the incorrect solution.
- Think about what error was made.

Ask Yourself:
- Where is the error?
- Why is it an error?
- How can I correct it?

The Pythagorean Theorem can be used to determine unknown side lengths in a right triangle. Evan and Sophi are using the theorem to determine the length of the hypotenuse, c, with leg lengths of 2 and 4. Examine their work.

Sophi

$c^2 = 2^2 + 4^2$
$c^2 = 4 + 16 = 20$
$c = \sqrt{20} \approx 4.5$

The length of the hypotenuse is approximately 4.5 units.

Evan

$c^2 = 2^2 + 4^2$
$c^2 = 6^2$
$c = 6$

The length of the hypotenuse is 6 units.

Who's Correct

When you see a Who's Correct icon:

- Take your time to read through the situation.
- Question the strategy or reason given.
- Determine correct or not correct.

Ask Yourself:

- Does the reasoning make sense?
- If the reasoning makes sense, what is the justification?
- If the reasoning does not make sense, what error was made?

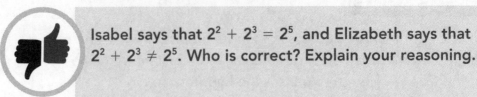

Isabel says that $2^2 + 2^3 = 2^5$, and Elizabeth says that $2^2 + 2^3 \neq 2^5$. Who is correct? Explain your reasoning.

MODULE 1

TRANSFORMING GEOMETRIC OBJECTS

The lessons in this module build on your experience with rational numbers, proportionality, scale drawings, triangles, and angle pairs formed when two lines intersect. You will use patty paper to investigate transformations of geometric objects to develop an understanding of congruence and similarity. You will then use this new knowledge about transformations to establish facts about triangles and relationships between special angle pairs.

TOPIC 1
Rigid Motion Transformations

You can see geometric transformations everywhere. What reflections, rotations, and translations can you see in this picture?

Module 1: Transforming Geometric Objects

TOPIC 1: RIGID MOTION TRANSFORMATIONS

In this topic, students use patty paper and the coordinate plane to investigate congruent figures. Throughout the topic, students are expected to make conjectures, investigate conjectures, and justify true results about transformations. They learn that transformations are mappings of a plane and all the points of a figure in a plane according to a common action or operation. They also learn that rigid motions preserve the size and shape of a figure, but that reflections change the orientation of the vertices of a figure.

Where have we been?

Students review using patty paper to compare figures in a coordinate plane. They review how to compare side lengths and angle measures and how to locate the midpoint of a segment using patty paper. They sort figures according to shape and then according to size and shape, using patty paper and informal transformation language to verify their sorts.

Where are we going?

This topic begins the study of congruence and sets the stage for similarity. In high school, students will continue to formalize their knowledge of congruent triangles and use congruence to prove a wide variety of geometric theorems and justify constructions.

Verifying Congruence Using Translations

A translation "slides" a geometric figure in some direction. Translations can be used to verify that two figures are congruent. For example, Quadrilateral CDEF can be translated up 2 units and left 5 units. This will show that it is congruent to Quadrilateral C'D'E'F'.

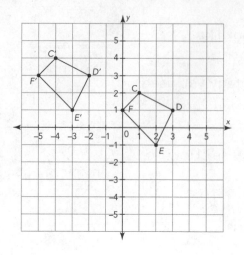

Myth: "I don't have the math gene."

Let's be clear about something. There isn't **a** gene that controls the development of mathematical thinking. Instead, there are probably **hundreds** of genes that contribute to our ability to reason mathematically. Moreover, a recent study suggests that mathematical thinking arises from the ability to learn a language. Given the right input from the environment, children learn to speak without any formal instruction. They can use number sense and pattern recognition the same way.

To further nurture your child's mathematical growth, attend to the learning environment. You can think of it as providing a nutritious mathematical diet that includes: discussing math in the real world, offering the right kind of encouragement, being available to answer questions, allowing your student to struggle with difficult concepts, and giving them space for plenty of practice.

#mathmythbusted

Talking Points

You can further support your student's learning by asking questions about the work they do in class or at home. Your student is becoming familiar with movements (called transformations) of geometric figures and reasoning about these movements.

Questions to Ask

- How does this problem look like something you did in class?
- Can you show me the strategy you used to solve this problem? Do you know another way to solve it?
- Does your answer make sense? How do you know?
- Is there anything you don't understand? How can you use today's lesson to help?

Key Terms

corresponding sides
Corresponding sides are sides that have the same relative position in geometric figures.

transformation
A transformation is the movement of a plane and all the points of a figure on a plane according to a common action or operation.

pre-image
The original figure in a transformation is called the pre-image.

image
The new figure created from a transformation is called the image.

Patty Paper, Patty Paper

Introduction to Congruent Figures

WARM UP

Draw an example of each shape.

1. parallelogram

2. trapezoid

3. pentagon

4. regular hexagon

LEARNING GOALS

- Define congruent figures.
- Use patty paper to verify experimentally that two figures are congruent by obtaining the second figure from the first using a sequence of slides, flips, and/or turns.
- Use patty paper to determine if two figures are congruent.

KEY TERMS

- congruent figures
- corresponding sides
- corresponding angles

You have studied figures that have the same shape or measure. How do you determine if two figures have the same size and the same shape?

It's Transparent!

Let's use patty paper to investigate the figure shown.

Patty paper is great paper to investigate geometric properties. You can write on it, trace with it, and see creases when you fold it.

1. List everything you know about the shape.

   — It has six sides

   — It has six connection points

   — called a pentagon

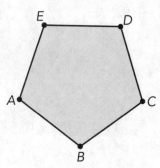

2. Use patty paper to compare the sizes of the sides and angles in the figure.

   a. What do you notice about the side lengths?

   b. What do you notice about the angle measures?

   c. What can you say about the figure based on this investigation?

Patty paper was originally created for separating patties of meat! Little did the inventors know that it could also serve as a powerful geometric tool.

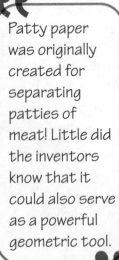

Trace the polygon onto a sheet of patty paper.

3. Use five folds of your patty paper to determine the center of each side of the shape. What do you notice about where the folds intersect?

Analyzing Size and Shape

Cut out each of the figures provided at the end of the lesson.

1. Sort the figures into at least two categories. Provide a rationale for your classification. List your categories and the letters of the figures that belong in each category.

> Figures with the same shape but not necessarily the same size are *similar figures*, which you will study in later lessons.

2. List the figures that are the same shape as Figure A. How do you know they are the same shape?

3. List the figures that are both the same shape and the same size as Figure A. How do you know they are the same shape and same size?

Figures that have the same size and shape are **congruent figures**. If two figures are congruent, all *corresponding sides* and all *corresponding angles* have the same measure.

4. List the figures that are congruent to Figure C.

> **Corresponding sides** are sides that have the same relative position in geometric figures.

> **Corresponding angles** are angles that have the same relative position in geometric figures.

ACTIVITY 1.2

Congruent or Not?

Throughout the study of geometry, as you reason about relationships, study how figures change under specific conditions, and generalize patterns, you will engage in the geometric process of

- making a conjecture about what you think is true,
- investigating to confirm or refute your conjecture, and
- justifying the geometric idea.

In many cases, you will need to make and investigate conjectures a few times before reaching a true result that can be justified.

Let's use this process to investigate congruent figures.

If two figures are congruent, you can slide, flip, and spin one figure until it lies on the other figure.

1. **Consider the flowers shown following the table. For each flower, make a conjecture about which are congruent to the original flower, which is shaded in the center. Then, use patty paper to investigate your conjecture. Finally, justify your conjecture by stating how you can move from the shaded flower to each congruent flower by sliding, flipping, or spinning the original flower.**

Flower	Congruent to original flower?	How Do You Move the Original Flower onto the Congruent Flower?
A		
B		
C		
D		
E		
F		
G		
H		

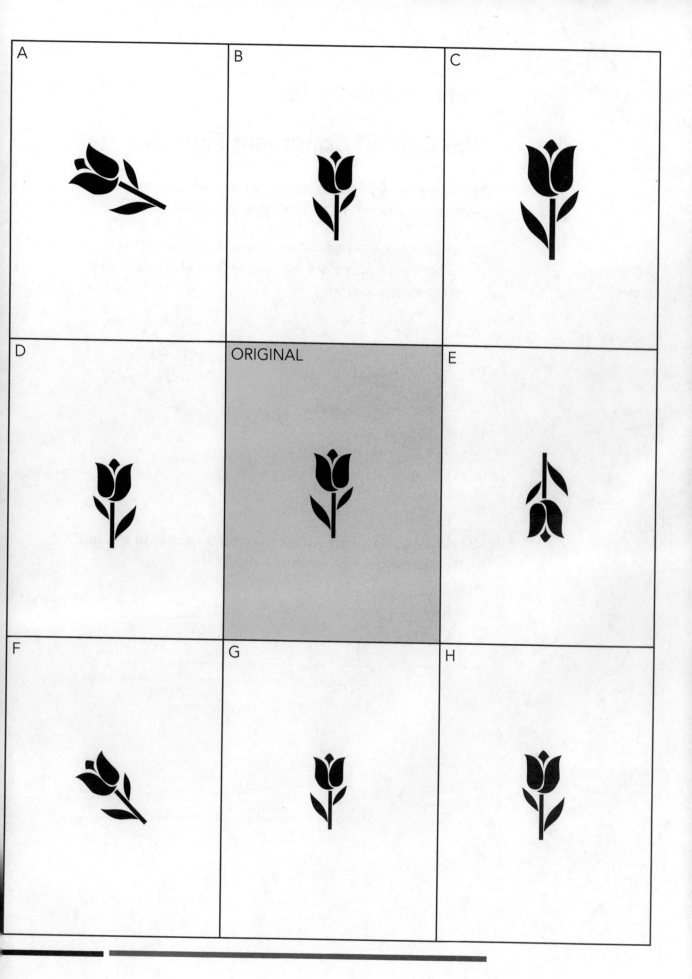

A

B

C

D

ORIGINAL

E

F

G

H

TALK the TALK

The Core of Congruent Figures

Recall that if two figures are congruent, all corresponding sides and all corresponding angles have the same measure.

1. Use patty paper to determine which sides of the congruent figures are corresponding and which angles are corresponding.

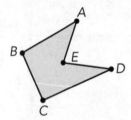
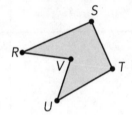

2. How can you slide, flip, or spin the figure on the left to obtain the figure on the right?

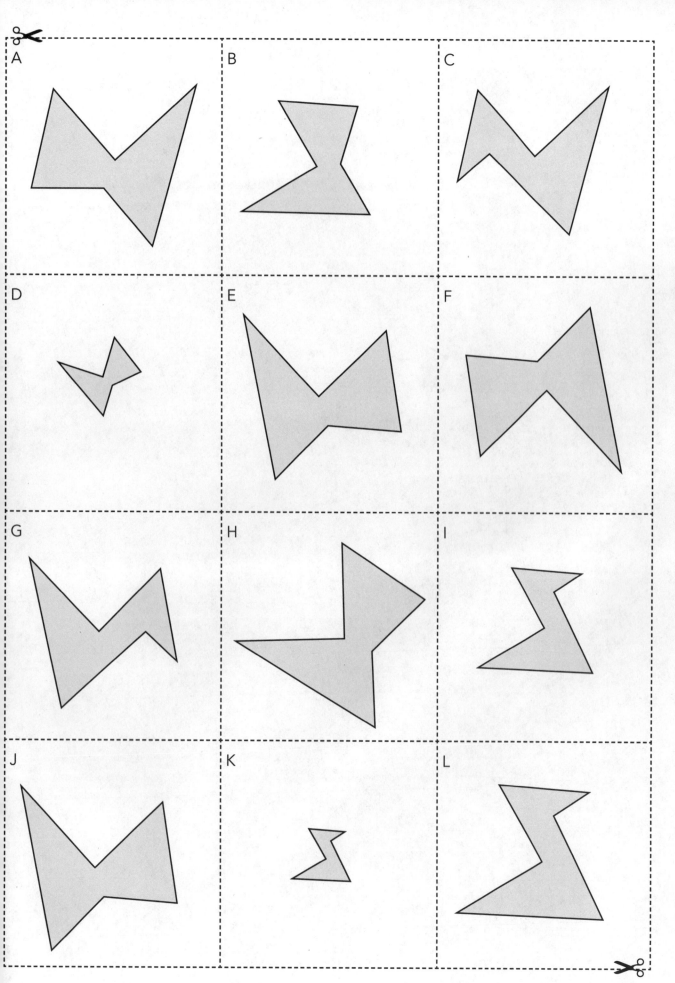

A

B

C

D

E

F

G

H

I

J

K

L

Assignment

Write

Explain what a conjecture is and how it is used in math.

Remember

If two figures are congruent, all corresponding sides and all corresponding angles have the same measure.

Practice

1. Determine which figures are congruent to Figure A. Follow the steps given as you investigate each shape.

- Make a conjecture about which figures are congruent to Figure A.
- Use patty paper to investigate your conjecture.
- Justify your conjecture by stating how you can move from Figure A to each congruent figure by sliding, flipping, or spinning Figure A.

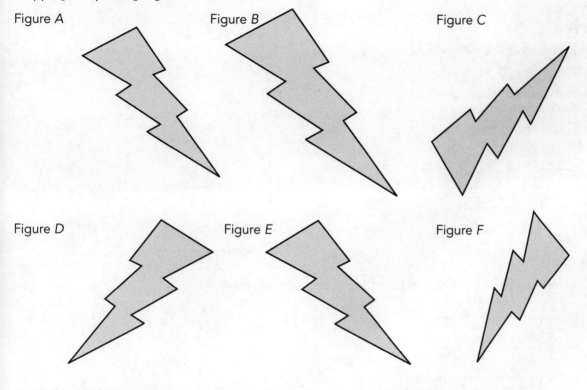

Figure A   Figure B   Figure C

Figure D   Figure E   Figure F

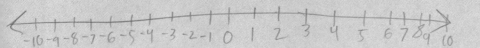

Stretch

The figure on the left was reflected, or flipped, over a *line of reflection* to create the figure on the right. Determine the location of the line of reflection.

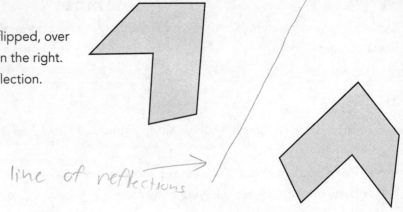

line of reflections

Review

1. Determine each sum or difference.

   a. −14 + 25 =

   b. −14 − 25 =

2. Calculate the area of each figure.

   a.

   15 in.

   7 in.   105 inches   7 in.

   6 in.   15 in   6 in.

   3 in.   81 inches   3 in.

   27 in.

   $\begin{array}{r} 3 \\ 15 \\ \times\ 7 \\ \hline 105 \end{array}$

   $\begin{array}{r} 2 \\ 27 \\ \times\ 3 \\ \hline 81 \end{array}$

   b.

   22 cm   7 cm

   10 cm

   17 cm

3. Write the ordered pair for each point plotted on the coordinate plane.

   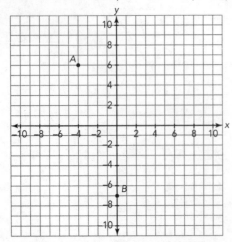

   (x, y)

   A = (−4, 6)

   B = (0, −7)

Slides, Flips, and Spins

2

Introduction to Rigid Motions

WARM UP

Draw all lines of symmetry for each letter.

1. A

2. B

3. H

4. X

LEARNING GOALS

- Model transformations of a plane.
- Translate geometric objects on the plane.
- Reflect geometric objects on the plane.
- Rotate geometric objects on the plane.
- Describe a single rigid motion that maps a figure onto a congruent figure.

KEY TERMS

- plane
- transformation
- rigid motion
- pre-image
- image
- translation
- reflection
- line of reflection
- rotation
- center of rotation
- angle of rotation

When you investigated shapes with patty paper, you used slides, flips, and spins to determine if shapes are congruent. What are the formal names for the actions used to carry a figure onto a congruent figure and what are the properties of those actions?

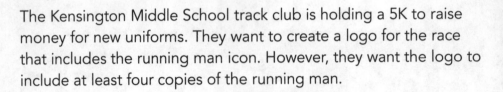
Design Competition

The Kensington Middle School track club is holding a 5K to raise money for new uniforms. They want to create a logo for the race that includes the running man icon. However, they want the logo to include at least four copies of the running man.

1. Trace the running man onto a sheet of patty paper. Create a logo for the track team on another sheet of patty paper that includes the original running man and three copies, one example each of sliding, flipping, and spinning the picture of the running man.

2. What do you know about the copies of the running man compared with the original picture of the running man?

Are all of the copies of the icon turned the same way?

Each sheet of patty paper represents a model of a geometric *plane*. A **plane** extends infinitely in all directions in two dimensions and has no thickness.

Translations on the Plane

In this module, you will explore different ways to transform, or change, planes and figures in planes. A **transformation** is the mapping, or movement, of a plane and all the points of a figure on a plane according to a common action or operation. A **rigid motion** is a special type of transformation that preserves the size and shape of the figure. Each of the actions you used to make the running man logo—slide, flip, spin—is a rigid motion transformation.

You are going to start by exploring translations on the plane using the trapezoid shown. Trapezoid *ABCD* has angles *A*, *B*, *C*, and *D*, and sides $\overline{AB}$, $\overline{BC}$, $\overline{CD}$, and $\overline{DA}$.

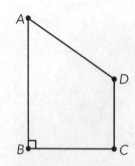

1. What else do you know about Trapezoid *ABCD*?

2. Use the Translations Mat at the end of the lesson for this exploration.

   a. Use a straightedge to trace the trapezoid on the shiny side of a sheet of patty paper.

   b. Slide the patty paper containing the trapezoid to align $\overline{AB}$ with one of the segments $\overline{A'B'}$.

   c. Record the location of the *image* of Trapezoid *ABCD* on the mat. This image is called Trapezoid *A'B'C'D'*.

Once you have traced the trapezoid on one side, turn the patty paper over and, using a pencil, copy the lines on the back side as well. This will help you to transfer the translated trapezoid back onto the Translations Mat.

$\overline{AB}$ is read, "line segment *AB*." *A'* is read, "*A* prime."

The original trapezoid
on the mat is called
the **pre-image**.

The traced trapezoid
is the **image**. It is
the new figure that
results from the
transformation.

3. Examine your pre-image and image.

   a. Which angle in Trapezoid *ABCD* maps to each angle of
      Trapezoid *A'B'C'D'*? Label the vertices on your drawing of
      the image of Trapezoid *ABCD*.

   b. Which side of Trapezoid *ABCD* maps to each side of
      Trapezoid *A'B'C'D'*?

   c. What do you notice about the measures of the
      corresponding angles in the pre-image and the image?

   d. What do you notice about the lengths of the corresponding
      sides in the pre-image and the image?

   e. What do you notice about the relationship of $\overline{A'B'}$ to $\overline{C'D'}$?
      How does this relate to the corresponding sides of
      the pre-image?

   f. Is the image congruent to the pre-image?
      Explain your reasoning.

This type of movement of a plane containing a figure is called a *translation*. A **translation** is a rigid motion transformation that "slides" each point of a figure the same distance and direction. Let's verify this definition.

4. On the mat, draw segments to connect corresponding vertices of the pre-image and image.

   a. Use a ruler to measure each segment. What do you notice?

   b. Compare your translations and measures with your classmates' translations and measures. What do you notice?

5. Consider the translation you created, as well as your classmates' translations.

   a. What changes about a figure after a translation?

   A figure can be translated in any direction. Two special translations are vertical and horizontal translations. Sliding a figure only left or right is a horizontal translation, and sliding it only up or down is a vertical translation.

   b. What stays the same about a figure after a translation?

   c. What information do you need to perform a translation?

ACTIVITY 2.2

Reflections on the Plane

The first transformation you explored was a translation. Now, let's see what happens when you flip, or reflect, the trapezoid. Trace Trapezoid *ABCD* onto a sheet of patty paper. Imagine tracing the trapezoid on one side of the patty paper, folding the patty paper in half, and tracing the trapezoid on the other half of the patty paper.

1. **Make a conjecture about how the image and pre-image will be alike and different.**

To verify or refine your conjecture, let's explore a reflection using patty paper and the Reflections Mat located at the end of the lesson. Trace the trapezoid from the previous activity on the lower left corner of a new piece of patty paper.

2. **Align the trapezoid on the patty paper with the trapezoid on the Reflections Mat. Fold the patty paper along ℓ_1. Trace the trapezoid on the other side of the crease and transfer it onto the Reflections Mat. Label the vertices of the image, Trapezoid *A'B'C'D'*.**

3. **Compare the pre-image and image that you created.**

   a. **What do you notice about the measures of the corresponding angles in the pre-image and the image?**

   b. **What do you notice about the lengths of the corresponding sides in the pre-image and the image?**

c. What do you notice about the relationship of $\overline{A'B'}$ to $\overline{C'D'}$? How does this relate to the corresponding sides of the pre-image?

d. Is the image congruent to the pre-image? Explain your reasoning.

e. Draw segments connecting corresponding vertices of the pre-image and image. Measure the lengths of these segments and the distance from each vertex to the fold. What do you notice?

Notice that the segments you drew are perpendicular to the crease of the patty paper. Why do you think this is true?

4. Repeat the reflection investigation using Trapezoid *ABCD* and folding along ℓ_2. Record your observations.

5. Repeat the reflection investigation using Trapezoid *ABCD* and folding along ℓ_3. Record your observations.

How is a reflection in geometry like your reflection in a mirror?

Are the vertices of the image in the same relative order as the vertices of the pre-image?

This type of movement of a plane containing a figure is called a *reflection*. A **reflection** is a rigid motion transformation that "flips" a figure across a *line of reflection*. A **line of reflection** is a line that acts as a mirror so that corresponding points are the same distance from the line.

6. Consider the reflections you created.

    a. What changes about a figure after a reflection?

    b. What stays the same about a figure after a reflection?

    c. What information do you need to perform a reflection?

How can you be sure that you spin the patty paper 90°?

ACTIVITY 2.3	Rotations on the Plane

You have now investigated translating and reflecting a trapezoid on the plane. Let's see what happens when you spin, or rotate, the trapezoid. You are going to use the Rotations Mat found at the end of the lesson for this investigation.

Trace Trapezoid *ABCD* onto the center of a sheet of patty paper. Imagine spinning the patty paper so that the trapezoid was no longer aligned with the trapezoid on the mat.

1. Make a conjecture about how the image and pre-image will be alike and different.

Let's investigate with patty paper to verify or refine your conjecture.

2. Align your trapezoid with the trapezoid on the Rotations Mat.

   Put your pencil on point O_1 and spin the patty paper 90° in a clockwise direction.

   Then copy the rotated trapezoid onto the Rotations Mat and label the vertices.

3. Compare the pre-image and image created by the rotation.

   a. What do you notice about the measures of the corresponding angles in the pre-image and the image?

   b. What do you notice about the lengths of the corresponding sides in the pre-image and the image?

   c. What do you notice about the relationship of $\overline{A'B'}$ to $\overline{C'D'}$? How does this relate to the corresponding sides of the pre-image?

   d. Is the image congruent to the pre-image? Explain your reasoning.

4. Draw two segments: one to connect point O_1 to A and another to connect point O_1 to A'.

   a. Measure the lengths of these segments. What do you notice?

   b. Measure the angle formed by the segments. What do you notice?

5. Repeat the process from the previous question with
   B and *B'*. What do you notice about the segment lengths
   and angle measures?

6. What do you think is true about the segments connecting *C*
   and *C'* and the segments connecting *D* and *D'*?

7. Repeat the rotations investigation using Trapezoid *ABCD* and
   spinning the patty paper 90° in a counterclockwise direction
   around O_2. Record your observations.

Why don't the
instructions for
a 180-degree
turn say whether
it is clockwise or
counterclockwise?

8. Repeat the rotations investigation using Trapezoid *ABCD*
   and spinning the patty paper 180° around O_3. Record your
   observations.

his type of movement of a plane containing a figure is called a *rotation*.
rotation is a rigid motion transformation that turns a figure on a plane
bout a fixed point, called the **center of rotation**, through a given
ngle, called the **angle of rotation**. The center of rotation can be a
oint outside the figure, inside the figure, or on the figure.

Rotations can be clockwise or counterclockwise.

. Consider the rotations you created.

a. Describe the centers of rotation used for each investigation.

b. How do you identify the angle of rotation, including the direction, in your patty paper rotations?

c. What changes about a figure after a rotation?

d. What stays the same about a figure after a rotation?

e. What information do you need to perform a rotation?

Use your investigations about the properties of rigid motions to complete each transformation.

1. **Rotate Ali the Alien 180°. Be sure to identify your center of rotation.**

2. **Translate the googly eyes horizontally to the right.**

3. Rotate the letter **E** 90° clockwise. Be sure to identify your center of rotation.

4. Transform the running man so that he is running in the opposite direction.

TALK the TALK

Congruence in Motion

1. Describe a transformation that maps one figure onto the other. Be as specific as possible.

   a. Figure A onto Figure B

   b. Figure A onto Figure C

   c. Figure A onto Figure E

   d. Figure C onto Figure D

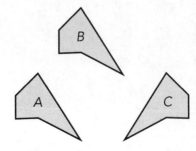
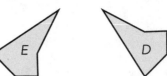

2. Explain what you know about the images that result from translating, reflecting, and rotating the same pre-image. How are the images related to each other and to the pre-image?

3. If Figure A is congruent to Figure C and Figure C is congruent to Figure D, answer each question.

   a. What is true about the relationship between Figures A and D?

   b. How could you use multiple transformations to map Figure A onto Figure D?

   c. How could you use a single transformation to map Figure A onto Figure D?

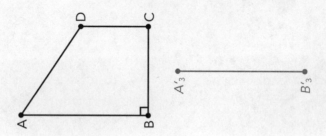

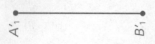

Reflections Mat

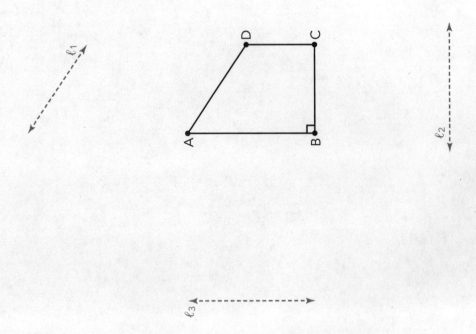

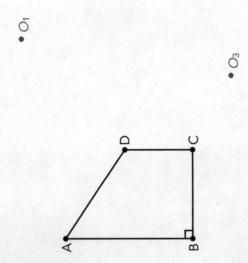

O_1

O_3

O_2

Assignment

Write

Explain each term or set of terms in your own words.

1. transformation
2. pre-image and image
3. translation
4. reflection and line of reflection
5. rotation, angle of rotation, and center of rotation

Remember

Rigid motions are transformations that preserve the size and shape of figures. Translations and rotations also preserve the orientation of a figure. The relative order of the vertices is the same in the pre-image and the image of a translation and of a rotation.

Practice

1. Complete each rigid motion transformation of the provided figure. In each case, be sure to label the vertices of the image and label your transformation to demonstrate at least one property of the transformation.

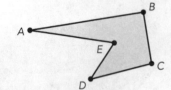

   a. Translate the figure in a horizontal direction.
   b. Translate the figure in a vertical direction.
   c. Translate the figure in a diagonal direction.
   d. Reflect the figure across a vertical line of reflection.
   e. Reflect the figure across a horizontal line of reflection.
   f. Reflect the figure across a diagonal line of reflection.
   g. Rotate the figure 90° clockwise. Be sure to label the center of rotation.
   h. Rotate the figure 90° counterclockwise. Be sure to label the center of rotation.
   i. Rotate the figure 180° Be sure to label the center of rotation.

2. Figure B is the image of Figure A.
   a. What is the relationship between the figures?
   b. Explain how Figure A was transformed to create Figure B.

Figure A

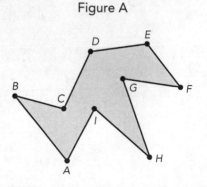

Figure B

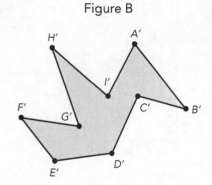

Stretch

Assume that an image is created by rotating another figure 180°. Explain how you could determine the location of the center of rotation.

Review

1. Determine which figures are congruent to Figure A. Follow the steps given as you investigate each shape.
   - Make a conjecture about which figures are congruent to Figure A.
   - Justify your conjecture by stating how you can move from Figure A to each congruent figure by translating, reflecting, or rotating Figure A.

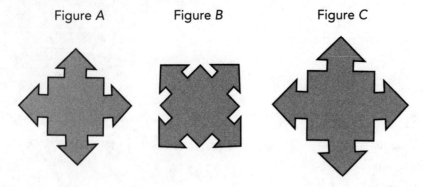

Figure A   Figure B   Figure C

2. Complete each sum or difference.
   a. $-3.25 + 4.5$
   b. $-15 - 3.5$

3. Plot each point on the coordinate plane. Connect the points and identify the shape.

   $A(7, 0)$ $B(-1, 0)$ $C(-1, 4)$ $D(4, 4)$

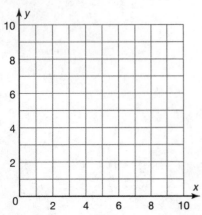

Lateral Moves

Translations of Figures on the Coordinate Plane

WARM UP

1. Identify the ordered pairs associated with each of the five labeled points of the star.

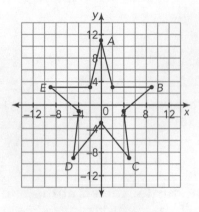

LEARNING GOALS

- Translate geometric figures on the coordinate plane.
- Identify and describe the effect of geometric translations on two-dimensional figures using coordinates.
- Identify congruent figures by obtaining one figure from another using a sequence of translations.

You have learned to model transformations, such as translations, rotations, and reflections. How can you model and describe these transformations on the coordinate plane?

Stopping for Directions

Consider the maze shown.

1. Navigate this maze to help the turtle move to the end. Justify your solution by writing the steps you used to solve the maze.

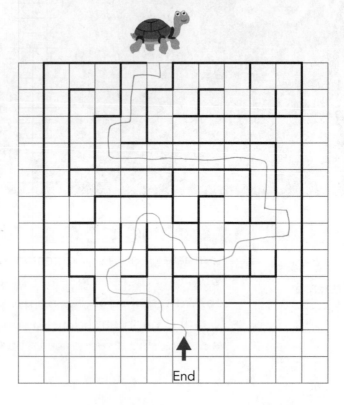

2. How would your steps change if the turtle started at the end and had to make its way to the start of the maze?

You know that translations are transformations that "slide" each point of a figure the same distance and the same direction. Each point moves in a line. You can describe translations more precisely by using coordinates.

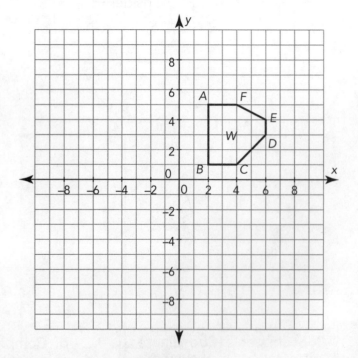

1. Place patty paper on the coordinate plane, trace Figure *W*, and copy the labels for the vertices on the patty paper.

   a. Translate the figure down 6 units. Then, identify the coordinates of the translated figure.

   b. Draw the translated figure on the coordinate plane with a different color, and label it as Figure *W'*. Then identify the pre-image and the image.

   c. Did translating Figure *W* vertically change the size or shape of the figure? Justify your answer.

   d. Complete the table with the coordinates of Figure *W'*.

   e. Compare the coordinates of Figure *W'* with the coordinates of Figure *W*. How are the values of the coordinates the same? How are they different? Explain your reasoning.

Coordinates of *W*	Coordinates of *W'*
A (2, 5)	
B (2, 1)	
C (4, 1)	
D (6, 3)	
E (6, 4)	
F (4, 5)	

Now, let's investigate translating Figure *W* horizontally.

2. Place patty paper on the coordinate plane, trace Figure *W*, and write and copy the labels for the vertices.

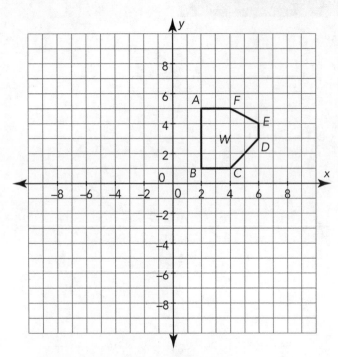

a. Translate the figure left 5 units.

b. Draw the translated figure on the coordinate plane with a different color, and label it as Figure *W*″. Then identify the pre-image and the image.

c. Did translating Figure *W* horizontally change the size or shape of the figure? Justify your answer.

d. Complete the table with the coordinates of Figure *W*″.

Coordinates of *W*	Coordinates of *W*″
A (2, 5)	
B (2, 1)	
C (4, 1)	
D (6, 3)	
E (6, 4)	
F (4, 5)	

e. Compare the coordinates of Figure *W*″ with the coordinates of Figure *W*. How are the values of the coordinates the same? How are they different? Explain your reasoning.

3. Make a conjecture about how a vertical or horizontal translation affects the coordinates of any point (*x*, *y*).

Consider the point (x, y) located anywhere in the first quadrant on the coordinate plane.

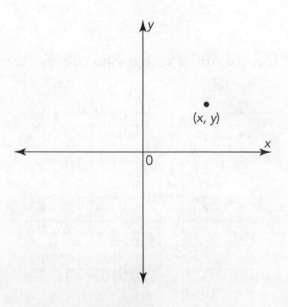

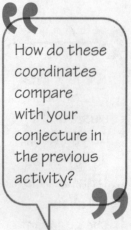

How do these coordinates compare with your conjecture in the previous activity?

1. Consider each translation of the point (x, y) according to the descriptions in the table shown. Record the coordinates of the translated points in terms of x and y.

Translation	Coordinates of Translated Point
3 units to the left	
3 units down	
3 units to the right	
3 units up	

2. Describe a translation in terms of *x* and *y* that would move any point (*x*, *y*) in Quadrant I into each quadrant.

a. Quadrant II

b. Quadrant III

c. Quadrant IV

Let's consider Triangle *ABC* shown on the coordinate plane.

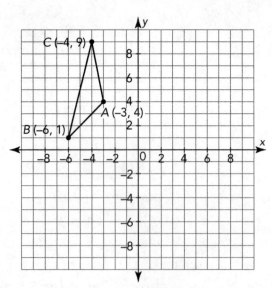

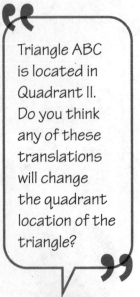

Triangle ABC is located in Quadrant II. Do you think any of these translations will change the quadrant location of the triangle?

3. Use the table to record the coordinates of the vertices of each translated triangle.

a. Translate Triangle *ABC* 5 units to the right to form Triangle *A'B'C'*. List the coordinates of points *A'*, *B'*, and *C'*. Then graph Triangle *A'B'C'*.

b. Translate Triangle *ABC* 8 units down to form Triangle *A"B"C"*. List the coordinates of points *A"*, *B"*, and *C"*. Then graph Triangle *A"B"C"*.

Original Triangle	Triangle Translated 5 Units to the Right	Triangle Translated 8 Units Down
△ABC	△A′B′C′	△A″B″C″
A (−3, 4)		
B (−6, 1)		
C (−4, 9)		

Let's consider translations of a different triangle without graphing.

4. The vertices of Triangle *DEF* are *D* (−7, 10), *E* (−5, 5), and *F* (−8, 1).

   a. If Triangle *DEF* is translated to the right 12 units, what are the coordinates of the vertices of the image? Name the triangle.

   b. How did you determine the coordinates of the image without graphing the triangle?

   c. If Triangle *DEF* is translated up 9 units, what are the coordinates of the vertices of the image? Name the triangle.

   d. How did you determine the coordinates of the image without graphing the triangle?

One way to verify that two figures are congruent is to show that the same sequence of translations moves all of the points of one figure to all the points of the other figure.

Consider the two quadrilaterals shown on the coordinate plane.

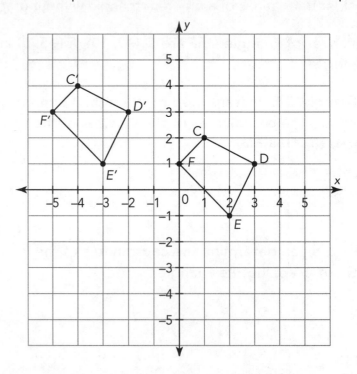

1. Complete the table with the coordinates of each figure and the translation from each vertex in Quadrilateral *CDEF* to the corresponding vertex in Quadrilateral *C'D'E'F'*.

Coordinates of Quadrilateral *CDEF*	Coordinates of Quadrilateral *C'D'E'F'*	Translations

2. Is Quadrilateral *CDEF* congruent to Quadrilateral *C'D'E'F'*?
   Explain how you know.

3. Describe a sequence of translations that can be used to show
   that Figures *A* and *A'* are congruent and that Figures *B* and *B'*
   are congruent. Show your work and explain your reasoning.

a.

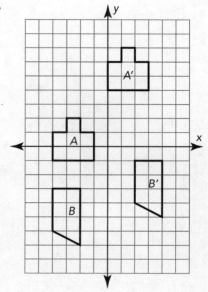

b.

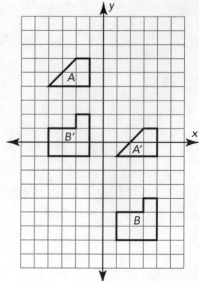

4. For each example, decide whether the figures given are congruent or not congruent using translations. Show your work and explain your reasoning.

a.

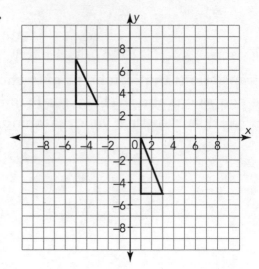

b.

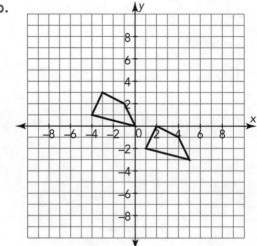

c.

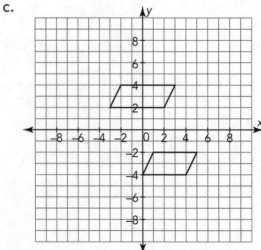

TALK the TALK 💬

Left and Right, Up and Down

1. Suppose the point (x, y) is translated horizontally c units.

   a. How do you know if the point is translated left or right?

   b. Write the coordinates of the image of the point.

2. Suppose the point (x, y) is translated vertically d units.

   a. How do you know if the point is translated up or down?

   b. Write the coordinates of the image of the point.

3. Suppose a point is translated repeatedly up 2 units and right 1 unit. Does the point remain on a straight line as it is translated? Draw an example to explain your answer.

4. Can you verify that these two figures are congruent using only translations? Explain why or why not.

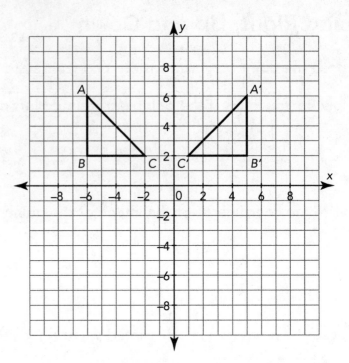

Assignment

Write

In your own words, explain how horizontal and vertical translations each affect the coordinates of the points of a figure.

Remember

A translation "slides" a figure along a line. A translation is a rigid motion that preserves the size and shape of figures.

Practice

1. Use the figures shown to complete parts (a) through (d).

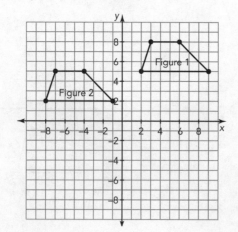

a. Describe the sequence of translations used to move Figure 1 onto Figure 2.

b. Determine the coordinates of the image of Figure 1 if it is translated 1 unit horizontally and −8 units vertically.

c. Explain how you determined the coordinates in part (b).

d. Verify your answer to part (b) by graphing the image. Label it Figure 3.

2. Use a coordinate plane to complete parts (a) through (d).

a. Plot the given points and connect them with straight lines in the order in which they are given. Connect the last point to the first point to complete the figure. Label the figure A.

(−3, −6), (−3, −3), (0, 0), (3, −3), (3, −6), (0, −3)

b. Translate the figure in part (a) −3 units vertically. Label the image B.

c. Translate the figure in part (a) 6 units vertically and 3 units horizontally. Label the image C.

d. Translate the figure in part (a) −3 units horizontally and 6 units vertically. Label the image D.

Stretch

A point at the origin is repeatedly translated c units horizontally and d units vertically. Write the coordinates of the translated point if the translation sequence is repeated n times.

Review

1. Sketch the translation of each figure.

   a. Translate the figure to the left.

   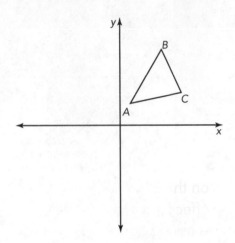

   b. Translate the figure up.

   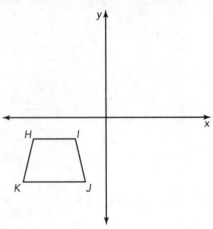

2. What is true about the relationship between the image and pre-image in each translation?

3. Use the order of operations to evaluate each expression.

   a. $-10 + 3(-8)$

   b. $\dfrac{-4(-12)}{3}$

Mirror, Mirror 4

Reflections of Figures on the Coordinate Plane

WARM UP

Determine each product.

1. -1×6

2. $-\frac{3}{5}(-1)$

3. -1×4.33

4. $4h(-1)$

LEARNING GOALS

- Reflect geometric figures on the coordinate plane.
- Identify and describe the effect of geometric reflections on two-dimensional figures using coordinates.
- Identify congruent figures by obtaining one figure from another using a sequence of translations and reflections.

You have learned to model transformations, such as translations, rotations, and reflections. How can you model and describe these transformations on the coordinate plane?

Ambulance

The image shows the front of a typical ambulance.

1. **Why does the word "ambulance" appear like this on the front?**

2. **Suppose you are going to replace the word *ambulance* with your name. Write your name as it appears on the front of the vehicle. How can you check that it is written correctly?**

ACTIVITY 4.1

Modeling Reflections on the Coordinate Plane

In this activity, you will reflect pre-images across the x-axis and y-axis and explore how the reflection affects the coordinates.

1. Place patty paper on the coordinate plane, trace Figure J, and copy the labels for the vertices on the patty paper.

   a. Reflect the Figure J across the x-axis. Then, complete the table with the coordinates of the reflected figure.

Coordinates of J	Coordinates of J' Reflected Across x-Axis
A (2, 5)	
B (2, 1)	
C (4, 1)	
D (6, 3)	
E (5, 4)	
F (6, 6)	

   b. Compare the coordinates of Figure J' with the coordinates of Figure J. How are the values of the coordinates the same? How are they different? Explain your reasoning.

2. Reflect Figure *J* across the *y*-axis.

   a. Complete the table with the coordinates of the reflected figure.

Coordinates of J	Coordinates of J" Reflected Across y-Axis
A (2, 5)	
B (2, 1)	
C (4, 1)	
D (6, 3)	
E (5, 4)	
F (6, 6)	

   b. Compare the coordinates of Figure *J"* with the coordinates of Figure *J*. How are the values of the coordinates the same? How are they different? Explain your reasoning.

Let's consider a new figure situated differently on the coordinate plane.

3. Reflect Quadrilateral *PQRS* across the *x*-axis.

   Make a conjecture about the ordered pairs for the reflection of the quadrilateral across the *x*-axis.

Make a conjecture, investigate, and then use the results to verify or justify your conjecture.

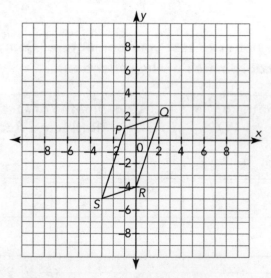

4. Use patty paper to test your conjecture.

   a. Complete the table with the coordinates of the reflection.

Coordinates of Quadrilateral *PQRS*	Coordinates of Quadrilateral *P'Q'R'S'* Reflected Across the *x*-Axis
P (−1, 1)	
Q (2, 2)	
R (0, −4)	
S (−3, −5)	

   b. Compare the coordinates of Quadrilateral *P'Q'R'S'* with the coordinates of Quadrilateral *PQRS*. How are the values of the coordinates the same? How are they different? Explain your reasoning.

5. Reflect Quadrilateral *PQRS* across the *y*-axis.

a. Make a conjecture about the ordered pairs for the reflection of the quadrilateral across the *y*-axis.

b. Use patty paper to test your conjecture. Complete the table with the coordinates of the reflection.

Coordinates of Quadrilateral *PQRS*	Coordinates of Quadrilateral *P"Q"R"S"* Reflected Across the *y*-Axis
P (−1, 1)	
Q (2, 2)	
R (0, −4)	
S (−3, −5)	

6. Compare the coordinates of Quadrilateral *P"Q"R"S"* with the coordinates of Quadrilateral *PQRS*. How are the values of the coordinates the same? How are they different?
Explain your reasoning.

Consider the point (x, y) located anywhere in the first quadrant.

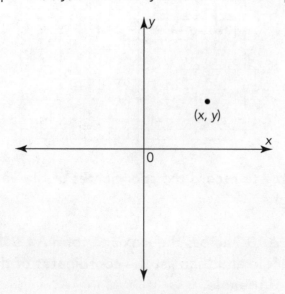

1. Use the table to record the coordinates of each point.

   a. Reflect and graph the point (x, y) across the x-axis on the
      coordinate plane. What are the new coordinates of the
      reflected point in terms of x and y?

   b. Reflect and graph the point (x, y) across the y-axis on the
      coordinate plane. What are the new coordinates of the
      reflected point in terms of x and y?

Original Point	Reflection Across the x-Axis	Reflection Across the y-Axis
(x, y)		

2. Graph △ABC by plotting the points A (3, 4), B (6, 1), and C (4, 9).

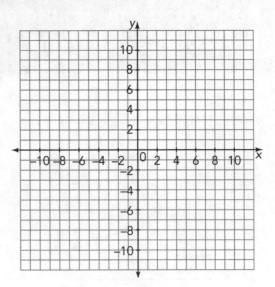

3. Use the table to record the coordinates of the vertices of each triangle.

   a. Reflect △ABC across the x-axis to form △A'B'C'. Graph the triangle and then list the coordinates of the reflected triangle.

Do you see any patterns?

   b. Reflect △ABC across the y-axis to form △A"B"C". Graph the triangle and then list the coordinates of the reflected triangle.

Original Triangle	Triangle Reflected Across the x-Axis	Triangle Reflected Across the y-Axis
△ABC	△A'B'C'	△A"B"C"
A (3, 4)		
B (6, 1)		
C (4, 9)		

Let's consider reflections of a different triangle without graphing.

4. The vertices of ∆*DEF* are *D* (−7, 10), *E* (−5, 5), and *F* (−1, −8).

   a. If ∆*DEF* is reflected across the *x*-axis, what are the
       coordinates of the vertices of the image?
       Name the triangle.

   b. How did you determine the coordinates of the image
       without graphing the triangle?

   c. If ∆*DEF* is reflected across the *y*-axis, what are the
       coordinates of the vertices of the image?
       Name the triangle.

   d. How did you determine the coordinates of the image
       without graphing the triangle?

ACTIVITY 4.3

Verifying Congruence Using Reflections and Translations

Just as with translations, one way to verify that two figures are congruent is to show that the same sequence of reflections moves all the points of one figure onto all the points of the other figure.

1. Consider the two figures shown.

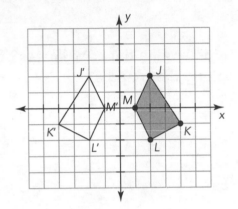

a. Complete the table with the corresponding coordinates of each figure.

Coordinates of *JKLM*	Coordinates of *J'K'L'M'*

Remember, a rigid motion is a transformation that preserves the size and shape of the figure.

b. Is Quadrilateral *JKLM* congruent to Quadrilateral *J'K'L'M'*? Describe the sequence of rigid motions to verify your conclusion.

2. Study the figures shown on the coordinate plane.

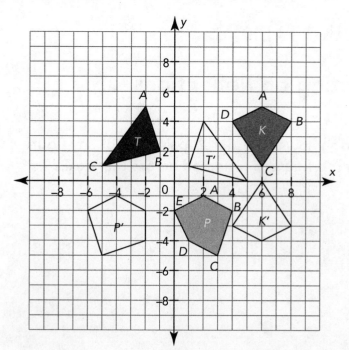

Determine whether each pair of figures are congruent.
Then describe the sequence of rigid motions to verify
your conclusion.

a. Is Figure *K* congruent to Figure *K'*?

b. Is Figure *P* congruent to Figure *P'*?

c. Is Figure *T* congruent to Figure *T'*?

TALK the TALK 💬

Reflecting on Reflections

1. Describe how the ordered pair (x, y) of any figure changes when the figure is reflected across the x-axis.

2. Describe how the ordered pair (x, y) of any figure changes when the figure is reflected across the y-axis.

Assignment

Write

In your own words, explain how reflections across the x-axis and across the y-axis each affect the coordinates of the points of a figure.

Remember

A reflection "flips" a figure across a line of reflection. A reflection is a rigid motion that preserves the size and shape of figures.

Practice

1. Use a coordinate plane to complete parts (a) through (i).

   a. Plot the points (0, 0), (–7, 5), (–7, 8), (–4, 8) and connect them with straight lines in the order in which they are given. Connect the last point to the first point to complete the figure. Label it 1.

   b. List the ordered pairs of Quadrilateral 1 if it is reflected across the y-axis. Explain how you can determine the ordered pairs of the reflection without graphing it. Plot the reflection described. Label it 2.

   c. List the ordered pairs of Quadrilateral 2 if it is reflected over the x-axis. Explain how you can determine the ordered pairs of the reflection without graphing it. Plot the reflection described. Label it 3.

   d. List the ordered pairs of Quadrilateral 1 if it is reflected over the x-axis. Explain how you can determine the ordered pairs of the reflection without graphing it. Plot the reflection described. Label it 4.

2. Write a general statement about how to determine the ordered pairs of the vertices of a figure if it is reflected across the x-axis.

3. Write a general statement about how to determine the ordered pairs of the vertices of a figure if it is reflected across the y-axis.

Stretch

1. Reflect the quadrilateral across the line $y = -2$.

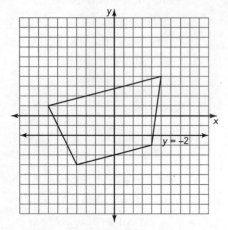

2. Reflect the triangle across the line $x = -3$.

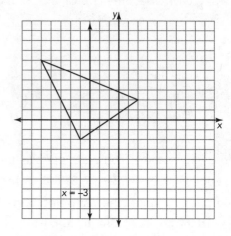

Review

Determine the coordinates of the image following each given translation.

1. Triangle *ABC* with coordinates *A* (2, 4), *B* (3, 6), and *C* (5, 1) is translated 4 units horizontally.

2. Parallelogram *DEFG* with coordinates *D* (0, 2), *E* (1, 5), *F* (6, 5), and *G* (5, 2) is translated −7 units horizontally.

3. For each translation described, what is the relationship between the image and pre-image?

Calculate each product or quotient.

4. $\frac{-24.6}{-6}$

5. 4.3(−2.1)

Half Turns and Quarter Turns

5

Rotations of Figures on the Coordinate Plane

WARM UP

1. Redraw each given figure as described.
   a. so that it is turned 180° clockwise
      Before: After:

   b. so that it is turned 90° counterclockwise
      Before: After:

   c. so that it is turned 90° clockwise
      Before: After:

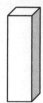

LEARNING GOALS

- Rotate geometric figures on the coordinate plane 90° and 180°.
- Identify and describe the effect of geometric rotations of 90° and 180° on two-dimensional figures using coordinates.
- Identify congruent figures by obtaining one figure from another using a sequence of translations, reflections, and rotations.

You have learned to model rigid motions, such as translations, rotations, and reflections. How can you model and describe these transformations on the coordinate plane?

Jigsaw Transformations

There are just two pieces left to complete this jigsaw puzzle.

1. Which puzzle piece fills the missing spot at 1? Describe the translations, reflections, and rotations needed to move the piece into the spot.

2. Which puzzle piece fills the missing spot at 2? Describe the translations, reflections, and rotations needed to move the piece into the spot.

Modeling Rotations on the Coordinate Plane

In this activity, you will investigate rotating pre-images to understand how the rotation affects the coordinates of the image.

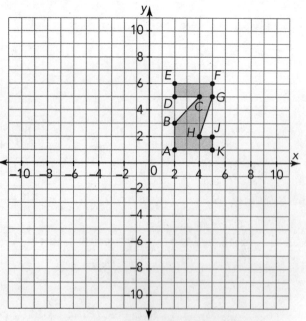

1. Rotate the figure 180° about the origin.

   a. Place patty paper on the coordinate plane, trace the figure, and copy the labels for the vertices on the patty paper.

   b. Mark the origin, (0, 0), as the center of rotation. Trace a ray from the origin on the x-axis. This ray will track the angle of rotation.

   c. Rotate the figure 180° about the center of rotation. Then, identify the coordinates of the rotated figure and draw the rotated figure on the coordinate plane. Finally, complete the table with the coordinates of the rotated figure.

   d. Compare the coordinates of the rotated figure with the coordinates of the original figure. How are the values of the coordinates the same? How are they different? Explain your reasoning.

Coordinates of Pre-Image	Coordinates of Image
A (2, 1)	
B (2, 3)	
C (4, 5)	
D (2, 5)	
E (2, 6)	
F (5, 6)	
G (5, 5)	
H (4, 2)	
J (5, 2)	
K (5, 1)	

Now, let's investigate rotating a figure 90° about the origin.

2. Consider the parallelogram shown on the coordinate plane.

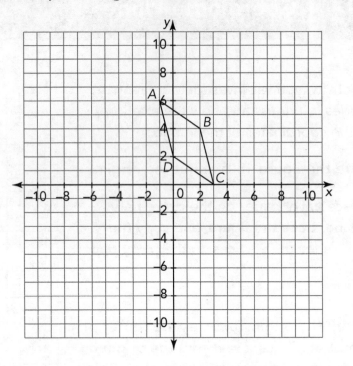

a. Place patty paper on the coordinate plane, trace the parallelogram, and then copy the labels for the vertices.

b. Rotate the figure 90° counterclockwise about the origin. Then, identify the coordinates of the rotated figure and draw the rotated figure on the coordinate plane.

c. Complete the table with the coordinates of the pre-image and the image.

Coordinates of Pre-Image	Coordinates of Image

d. Compare the coordinates of the image with the coordinates of the pre-image. How are the values of the coordinates the same? How are they different? Explain your reasoning.

3. Make conjectures about how a counterclockwise 90° rotation and a 180° rotation affect the coordinates of any point (x, y).

You can use steps to help you rotate geometric objects on the coordinate plane.

Let's rotate a point 90° counterclockwise about the origin.

Step 1: Draw a "hook" from the origin to point A, using the coordinates and horizontal and vertical line segments as shown.

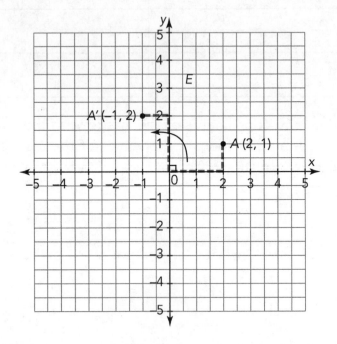

Step 2: Rotate the "hook" 90° counterclockwise as shown.

Point A' is located at $(-1, 2)$. Point A has been rotated 90° counterclockwise about the origin.

4. **What do you notice about the coordinates of the rotated point? How does this compare with your conjecture?**

Rotating Any Points on the Coordinate Plane

Consider the point (x, y) located anywhere in the first quadrant.

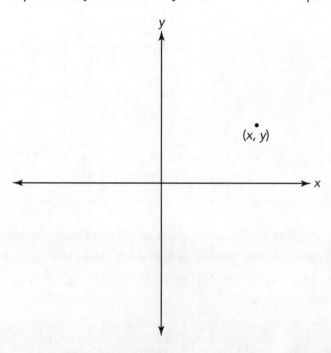

1. Use the origin, (0, 0), as the point of rotation. Rotate the point (x, y) as described in the table and plot and label the new point. Then record the coordinates of each rotated point in terms of x and y.

> If your point was at $(5, 0)$, and you rotated it 90°, where would it end up? What about if it was at $(5, 1)$?

Original Point	Rotation About the Origin 90° Counterclockwise	Rotation About the Origin 90° Clockwise	Rotation About the Origin 180°
(x, y)			

2. Graph △ABC by plotting the points A (3, 4), B (6, 1), and C (4, 9).

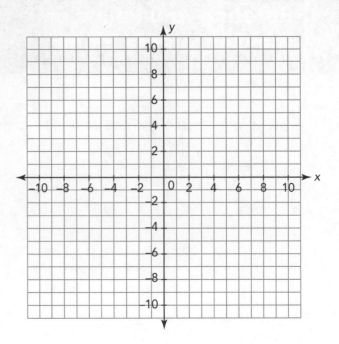

Use the origin, (0, 0), as the point of rotation. Rotate △ABC as described in the table, graph and label the new triangle. Then record the coordinates of the vertices of each triangle in the table.

Original Triangle	Rotation About the Origin 90° Counterclockwise	Rotation About the Origin 90° Clockwise	Rotation About the Origin 180°
△ABC	△A′B′C′	△A″B″C″	△A‴B‴C‴
A (3, 4)			
B (6, 1)			
C (4, 9)			

Let's consider rotations of a different triangle without graphing.

. The vertices of ΔDEF are D (−7, 10), E (−5, 5), and
F (−1, −8).

a. If ΔDEF is rotated 90° counterclockwise about the origin,
what are the coordinates of the vertices of the image?
Name the rotated triangle.

b. How did you determine the coordinates of the image
without graphing the triangle?

c. If ΔDEF is rotated 90° clockwise about the origin, what are
the coordinates of the vertices of the image? Name the
rotated triangle.

d. How did you determine the coordinates of the image without graphing the triangle?

e. If △DEF is rotated 180° about the origin, what are the coordinates of the vertices of the image? Name the rotated triangle.

f. How did you determine the coordinates of the image without graphing the triangle?

Verifying Congruence Using Rigid Motions

Describe a sequence of rigid motions that can be used to verify that the shaded pre-image is congruent to the image.

1.

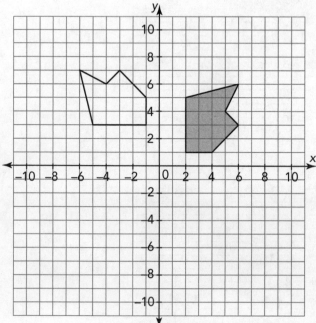

2.

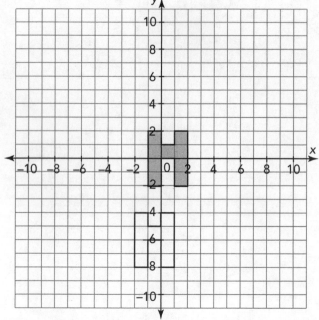

3.

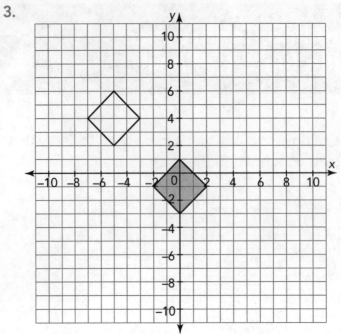

4.

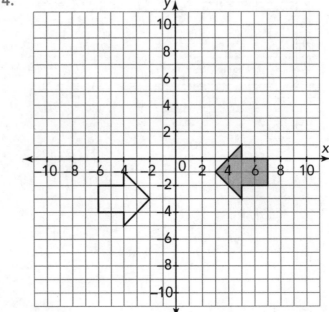

TALK the TALK 💬

Just the Coordinates

Using what you know about rigid motions, verify that the figures represented by the coordinates are congruent. Describe the sequence of rigid motions to explain your reasoning.

1. △QRS has coordinates Q (1, −1), R (3, −2), and S (2, −3). △Q′R′S′ has coordinates Q′ (5, −4), R′ (6, −2), and S′ (7, −3).

2. Rectangle MNPQ has coordinates M (3, −2), N (5, −2), P (5, −6), and Q (3, −6). Rectangle M′N′P′Q′ has coordinates M′ (0, 0), N′ (−2, 0), P′ (−2, 4), and Q′ (0, 4).

Assignment

Write

In your own words, explain how each rotation about the origin affects the coordinate points of a figure.

    a. a counterclockwise rotation of 90°

    b. a clockwise rotation of 90°

    c. a rotation of 180°

Remember

A rotation "turns" a figure about a point. A rotation is a rigid motion that preserves the size and shape of figures.

Practice

1. Use △JKL and the coordinate plane to answer each question.

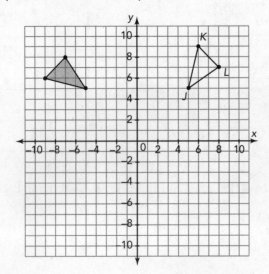

    a. List the coordinates of each vertex of △JKL.

    b. Describe the rotation that you can use to move △JKL onto the shaded area on the coordinate plane. Use the origin as the point of rotation.

    c. Determine what the coordinates of the vertices of the rotated △J'K'L' will be if you perform the rotation you described in your answer to part (b). Explain how you determined your answers.

    d. Verify your answers by graphing △J'K'L' on the coordinate plane.

2. Determine the coordinates of each triangle's image after the given transformation.

    a. Triangle ABC with coordinates A (3, 4), B (7, 7), and C (8, 1) is translated 6 units left and 7 units down.

    b. Triangle DEF with coordinates D (−2, 2), E (1, 5), and F (4, −1) is rotated 90° counterclockwise about the origin.

    c. Triangle GHJ with coordinates G (2, −9), H (3, 8), and J (1, 6) is reflected across the x-axis.

    d. Triangle KLM with coordinates K (−4, 2), L (−8, 7), and M (3, −3) is translated 4 units right and 9 units up.

    e. Triangle NPQ with coordinates N (12, −3), P (1, 2), and Q (9, 0) is rotated 180° about the origin.

Stretch

1. Rotate Trapezoid GHJK 90° clockwise around point G.

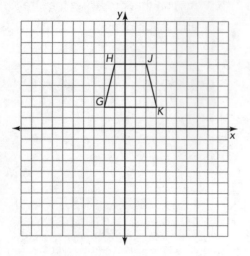

2. Rotate △ABC 135° clockwise around point C.

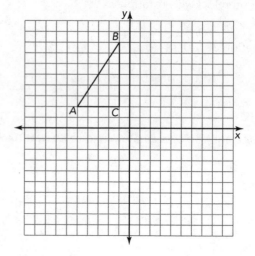

Review

Given a triangle with the vertices A (1, 3), B (4, 8), and C (5, 2). Determine the vertices of each described transformation.

1. A reflection across the x-axis.

2. A reflection across the y-axis.

3. A translation 5 units horizontally.

4. A translation −4 units vertically.

Rewrite each expression using properties.

5. $2(x + 4) - 3(x - 5)$

6. $10 - 8(2x - 7)$

Every Which Way

Combining Rigid Motions

6

WARM UP

Determine the distance between each pair of points.

1. (2, 3) and (−5, 3)

2. (−1, −4) and (−1, 8)

3. (6, −2.5) and (6, 5)

4. (−8.2, 5.6) and (−4.3, 5.6)

LEARNING GOALS

- Use coordinates to identify rigid motion transformations.
- Write congruence statements.
- Determine a sequence of rigid motions that maps a figure onto a congruent figure.
- Generalize the effects of rigid motion transformations on the coordinates of two-dimensional figures.

KEY TERMS

- congruent line segments
- congruent angles

You have determined coordinates of images by translating, reflecting, and rotating pre-images. How can you use the coordinates of an image to determine the rigid motion transformations applied to the pre-image?

Going Backwards

Use your knowledge of rigid motions and their effects on the coordinates of two-dimensional figures to answer each question.

The line of reflection will be an axis, and the center of rotation will be the origin.

1. **The pre-image and image of three different single transformations are given. Determine the transformation that maps the pre-image, the labeled figure, to the image. Label the vertices of the image. Explain your reasoning.**

a.

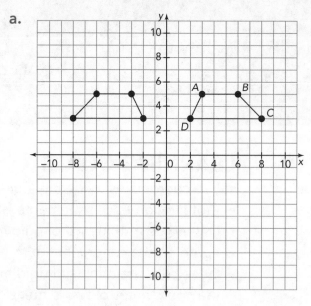

b.

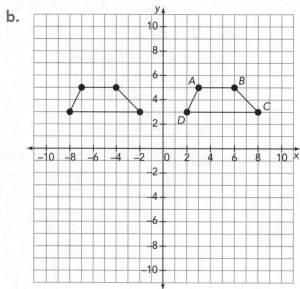

c.

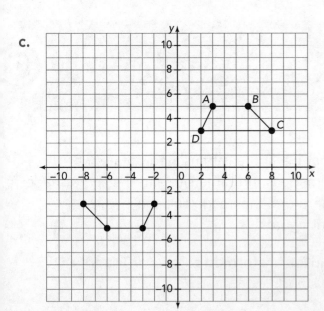

2. Compare the order of the vertices, starting from A′, in each image with the order of the vertices, starting from A, in the pre-image.

Congruence Statements

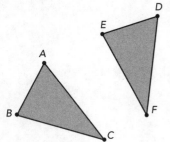

You have determined that if a figure is translated, rotated, or reflected, the resulting image is the same size and the same shape as the original figure; therefore, the image and the pre-image are congruent figures.

1. How was Triangle *ABC* transformed to create Triangle *DEF*?

Congruent line segments are line segments that have the same length.

Think about congruent figures as a mapping of one figure onto the other. When naming congruent segments, write the vertices in a way that shows the mapping.

Because Triangle *DEF* was created using a rigid motion transformation of Triangle *ABC*, the triangles are congruent. Therefore, all corresponding sides and all corresponding angles have the same measure. In congruent figures, the corresponding sides are *congruent line segments*.

WORKED EXAMPLE

If the length of line segment *AB* is equal to the length of line segment *DE*, the relationship can be expressed using symbols. These are a few examples.

- $AB = DE$ is read "the distance between *A* and *B* is equal to the distance between *D* and *E*"

- $m\overline{AB} = m\overline{DE}$ is read "the measure of line segment *AB* is equal to the measure of line segment *DE*."

If the sides of two different triangles are equal in length, for example, the length of side *AB* in Triangle *ABC* is equal to the length of side *DE* in Triangle *DEF*, these sides are said to be congruent. This relationship can be expressed using symbols.

- $\overline{AB} \cong \overline{DE}$ is read "line segment *AB* is congruent to line segment *DE*."

2. Write congruence statements for the other two sets of corresponding sides of the triangles.

Likewise, if corresponding angles have the same measure, they are *congruent angles*. **Congruent angles** are angles that are equal in measure.

WORKED EXAMPLE

If the measure of angle A is equal to the measure of angle D, the relationship can be expressed using symbols.

- $m\angle A = m\angle D$ is read "the measure of angle A is equal to the measure of angle D."

If the angles of two different triangles are equal in measure, for example, the measure of angle A in Triangle ABC is equal to the measure of angle D in Triangle DEF, these angles are said to be congruent. This relationship can be expressed using symbols.

- $\angle A \cong \angle D$ is read "angle A is congruent to angle D."

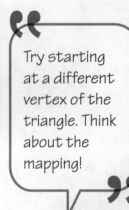

Try starting at a different vertex of the triangle. Think about the mapping!

3. Write congruence statements for the other two sets of corresponding angles of the triangles.

You can write a single congruence statement about the triangles that shows the correspondence between the two figures. For the triangles in this activity, $\triangle ABC \cong \triangle DEF$.

4. Write two additional correct congruence statements for these triangles.

ACTIVITY 6.2

Using Rigid Motions to Verify Congruence

You can determine if two figures are congruent by determining if one figure can be mapped onto the other through a sequence of rigid motions. Therefore, if you know that two figures are congruent, you should be able to determine a sequence of rigid motions that maps one figure onto the other.

1. Analyze the two congruent triangles shown.

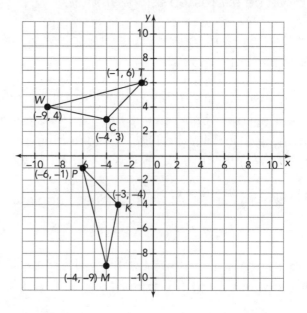

a. Identify the transformation used to create △PMK from △TWC.

b. Write a triangle congruence statement.

c. Write congruence statements to identify the congruent angles.

d. Write congruence statements to identify the congruent sides.

2. Analyze the two congruent triangles shown.

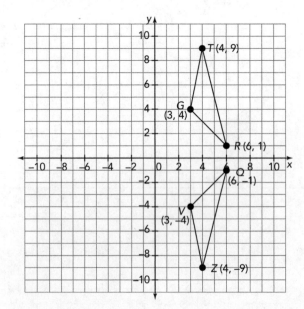

a. Identify the transformation used to create ΔZQV from ΔTRG.

b. Write a triangle congruence statement.

c. Write congruence statements to identify the
   congruent angles.

d. Write congruence statements to identify the
   congruent sides.

3. Analyze the two congruent triangles.

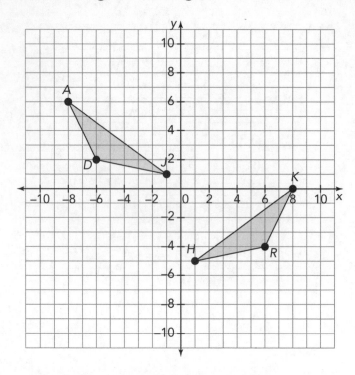

a. Write a congruence statement for the triangles. How did you determine the corresponding angles?

Conjecture, investigate, verify! If your conjecture isn't correct, try again.

b. Identify a sequence of translations, reflections, and/or rotations that could be used to map one triangle onto the other triangle.

c. Reverse the order of the transformations that you used in part (b). Does this order map one figure onto the other?

d. Explain why it is not possible to map one figure onto the other using only rotations and translations.

4. Analyze the two congruent triangles.

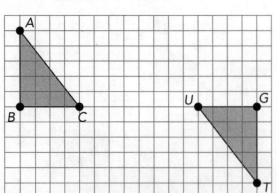

a. Write a congruence statement for the triangles.

b. Identify a sequence of translations, reflections, and/or rotations that could be used to map one triangle onto the other triangle.

c. Reverse the order of the transformations that you used in part (b). Does this order map one figure onto the other?

d. Can you determine a way to map one triangle onto the other in a single transformation? Explain your reasoning.

5. Analyze the two congruent rectangles.

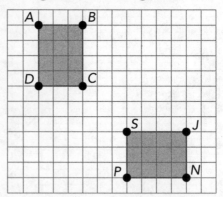

a. Identify a sequence of translations, reflections, and/or rotations that could be used to verify that the rectangles are congruent.

b. Can you determine a way to map one rectangle onto the other in a single transformation? Explain your reasoning.

ACTIVITY
6.3

Transformations with Coordinates

For the triangles in this activity, $\triangle PQR \cong \triangle JME \cong \triangle DLG$.

1. Suppose the vertices of $\triangle PQR$ are P (4, 3), Q (−2, 2), and R (0, 0). Describe the translation used to form each triangle. Explain your reasoning.

   a. J (0, 3), M (−6, 2), and E (−4, 0)

   b. D (4, 5.5), L (−2, 4.5), and G (0, 2.5)

2. Suppose the vertices of △PQR are P (1, 3), Q (6, 5), and R (8, 1). Describe the rotation used to form each triangle. Explain your reasoning.

   a. J (−3, 1), M (−5, 6), and E (−1, 8)

   b. D (−1, −3), L (−6, −5), and G (−8, −1)

3. Suppose the vertices of △PQR are P (12, 4), Q (14, 1), and R (20, 9). Describe the reflection used to form each triangle. Explain your reasoning.

   a. J (−12, 4), M (−14, 1), and E (−20, 9)

Remember, rigid motions preserve size and shape.

   b. D (12, −4), L (14, −1), and G (20, −9)

4. Suppose the vertices of △PQR are P (3, 2), Q (7, 3), and R (1, 7).

   a. Describe a sequence of a translation and reflection to form △JME with coordinates J (8, −2), M (12, −3), and E (6, −7).

   b. Describe a sequence of a translation and a rotation to form △DLG with coordinates D (2, −6), L (3, −10), and G (7, −4).

5. Are the images that result from a translation, rotation, or reflection always, sometimes, or never congruent to the original figure?

TALK the TALK

Transformation Match-Up

Suppose a point (x, y) undergoes a rigid motion transformation. The possible new coordinates of the point are shown. Assume c is a positive rational number.

$(y, -x)$	$(x, y - c)$	$(x, -y)$
$(x + c, y)$	$(x - c, y)$	$(-y, x)$
$(-x, -y)$	$(-x, y)$	$(x, y + c)$

1. Record each set of new coordinates in the appropriate section of the table, and then write a verbal description of the transformation. Be as specific as possible.

Translations		Reflections		Rotations	
Coordinates	Description	Coordinates	Description	Coordinates	Description

2. Describe a single transformation that could be created from a sequence of at least two transformations. Use the coordinates to justify your answer.

Assignment

Write

Draw and label a pair of congruent triangles. Write a congruence statement for the triangles, and then write congruence statements for each set of corresponding sides and angles.

Remember

A single rigid motion or a sequence of rigid motions produces congruent figures. There is often more than one sequence of transformations that can be used to verify that two figures are congruent.

Practice

1. Triangle ABC has coordinates A (1, −8), B (5, −4), and C (8, −9).
   a. Describe a transformation that can be performed on △ABC that will result in a triangle in the first quadrant.
   b. Perform the transformation and name the new △DEF.
   c. List the coordinates for the vertices for △DEF.
   d. Write a triangle congruence statement for the triangles.
2. Triangle ABC has coordinates A (1, −8), B (5, −4), and C (8, −9).
   a. Describe a transformation that can be performed on △ABC that will result in a triangle in the third quadrant.
   b. Perform the transformation and name the new △DEF.
   c. List the coordinates for the vertices for △DEF.
   d. Write a triangle congruence statement for the triangles.
3. Identify the transformation used to create △XYZ in each.

a.

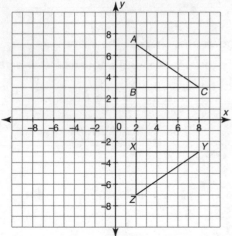

b.

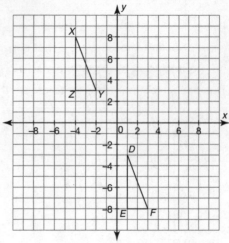

c.

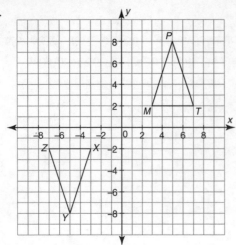

d.

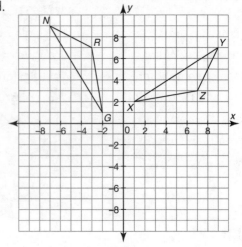

4. Use the coordinates to determine the transformation or sequence of transformations used to map the first triangle onto the second triangle.

a. Triangle ABC with coordinates A (−8, 1), B (−4, 6), and C (0, 3) maps onto △XYZ with coordinates X (−1, −8), Y (−6, −4), and Z (−3, 0).

b. Triangle PRG with coordinates P (2, 8), R (−7, 5), and G (2, 5) maps onto △YOB with coordinates Y (−2, 8), O (7, 5), and B (−2, 5).

c. Triangle JCE with coordinates J (−6, 0), C (−4, −2), and E (0, 2) maps onto △RAN with coordinates R (6, −3), A (4, −1), and N (0, −5).

d. Triangle EFG with coordinates E (2, −1), F (8, −2), and G (8, −5) maps onto △ZOQ with coordinates Z (−6, 1), O (0, 2), and Q (0, 5).

Stretch

The tangram is a popular Chinese puzzle that consists of seven geometric shapes. The shapes are composed into figures using all seven pieces. The seven pieces fit together to form a square. Determine the transformations of each shape required to create the candle pictured.

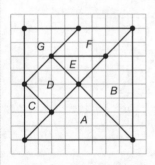

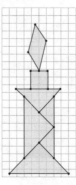

Review

1. Triangle *HOP* has coordinates *H* (2, 1), *O* (−3, 4), and *P* (5, 7). Determine the coordinates of the image of △*HOP* after each rotation.

   a. Rotation 90° clockwise about the origin

   b. Rotation 90° counterclockwise about the origin

   c. Rotation 180° about the origin

2. Combine like terms to rewrite each expression.

   a. $(4\frac{1}{2}x - 3) + (-2 + 1\frac{3}{4}x)$

   b. $4 - (2.3x - 7)$

Rigid Motion Transformations Summary

KEY TERMS

- congruent figures
- corresponding sides
- corresponding angles
- plane
- transformation
- rigid motion

- pre-image
- image
- translation
- reflection
- line of reflection
- rotation

- center of rotation
- angle of rotation
- congruent line segments
- congruent angles

<table>
<tr><td>LESSON
1</td><td>Patty Paper, Patty Paper</td></tr>
</table>

Figures that have the same size and shape are **congruent figures**. If two figures are congruent, all corresponding sides and all corresponding angles have the same measures. **Corresponding sides** are sides that have the same relative position in geometric figures and **corresponding angles** are angles that have the same relative position in geometric figures.

If two figures are congruent, you can obtain one figure by a combination of sliding, flipping, and spinning the figure until it lies on the other figure.

For example, Figure A is congruent to Figure C, but it is not congruent to Figure B or Figure D.

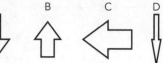

A **plane** extends infinitely in all directions in two dimensions and has no thickness. A **transformation** is the mapping, or movement, of a plane and all the points of a figure on a plane according to a common action or operation. A **rigid motion** is a special type of transformation that preserves the size and shape of each figure.

The original figure on the plane is called the **pre-image** and the new figure that results from a transformation is called the **image**. The labels for the vertices of an image use the symbol ('), which is read as "prime."

A **translation** is a rigid motion transformation that slides each point of a figure the same distance and direction along a line. A figure can be translated in any direction. Two special translations are vertical and horizontal translations. Sliding a figure left or right is a horizontal translation, and sliding it up or down is a vertical translation.

A **reflection** is a rigid motion transformation that flips a figure across a line of reflection. A **line of reflection** is a line that acts as a mirror so that corresponding points are the same distance from the line.

A **rotation** is a rigid motion transformation that turns a figure on a plane about a fixed point, called the **center of rotation**, through a given angle, called the **angle of rotation**. The center of rotation can be a point outside of the figure, inside of the figure, or on the figure itself. Rotation can be clockwise or counterclockwise.

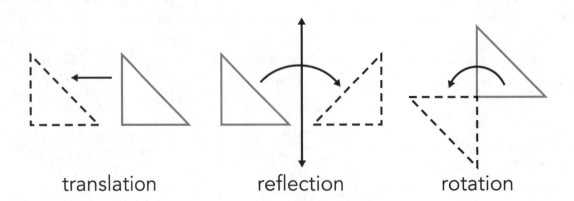

translation   reflection   rotation

A translation slides an image on the coordinate plane. When an image is horizontally translated c units on the coordinate plane, the value of the x-coordinates change by c units. When an image is vertically translated c units on the coordinate plane, the value of the y-coordinate changes by c-units. The coordinates of an image after a translation are summarized in the table.

Original Point	Horizontal Translation to the Left	Horizontal Translation to the Right	Vertical Translation Up	Vertical Translation Down
(x, y)	$(x - c, y)$	$(x + c, y)$	$(x, y + c)$	$(x, y - c)$

For example, the coordinates of △ABC are A (0, 2), B (2, 6), and C(3, 3).

When △ABC is translated down 8 units, the coordinates of the image are A' (0, −6), B' (2, −2), and C' (3, −5).

When △ABC is translated right 6 units, the coordinates of the image are A'' (6, 2), B'' (8, 6), and C'' (9, 3).

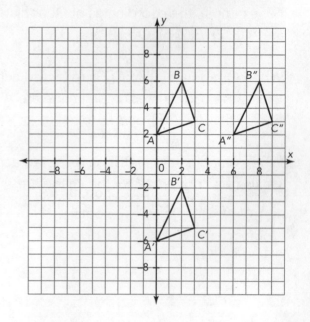

A reflection flips an image across a line of reflection. When an image on the coordinate plane is reflected across the y-axis, the value of the x-coordinate of the image is opposite the x-coordinate of the pre-image. When an image on the coordinate plane is reflected across the x-axis, the value of the y-coordinate of the image is opposite the y-coordinate of the pre-image. The coordinates of an image after a reflection on the coordinate plane are summarized in the table.

Original Point	Reflection Over x-Axis	Reflection Over y-Axis
(x, y)	(x, −y)	(−x, y)

For example, the coordinates of Quadrilateral ABCD are A (3, 2), B (2, 5), C(5, 7), and D (6, 1).

When Quadrilateral ABCD is reflected across the x-axis, the coordinates of the image are A' (3, −2), B' (2, −5), C' (5, −7), and D' (6, −1).

When Quadrilateral ABCD is reflected across the y-axis, the coordinates of the image are A" (−3, 2), B" (−2, 5), C" (−5, 7), and D" (−6, 1).

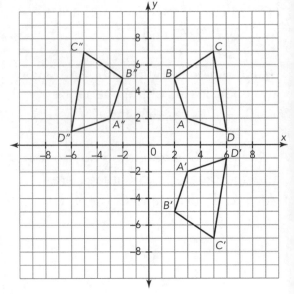

Half Turns and Quarter Turns

A rotation turns a figure about a point through an angle of rotation. When the center of rotation is at the origin (0, 0), and the angle of rotation is 90° or 180°, the coordinates of an image can be determined using the rules summarized in the table.

Original Point	Rotation About the Origin 90° Counterclockwise	Rotation About the Origin 90° Clockwise	Rotation About the Origin 180°
(x, y)	(−y, x)	(y, −x)	(−x, −y)

For example, the coordinates of △ABC are A (2, 1), B (5, 8), and C (6, 4).

When △ABC is rotated 90° counterclockwise about the origin, the coordinates of the image are A′ (−1, 2), B′ (−8, 5), and C′ (−4, 6).

When △ABC is rotated 180° about the origin, the coordinates of the image are A″ (−2, −1), B″ (−5, −8), and C″ (−6, −4).

When △ABC is rotated 90° clockwise about the origin, the coordinates of the image are A″ (1, −2), B″ (8, −5), and C″ (4, −6).

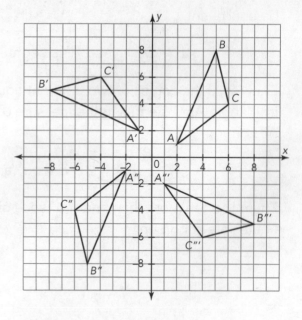

LESSON 6

Every Which Way

Because rigid motions maintain the size and shape of an image, you can use a sequence of translations, reflections, and rotations to verify that two figures are congruent.

In congruent figures, the corresponding sides are congruent line segments. **Congruent line segments** are line segments that have the same length. Likewise, if corresponding angles have the same measure, they are congruent angles. **Congruent angles** are angles that are equal in measure.

For example, if the sides of two different figures are equal in length, the length of side AB in Triangle ABC is equal to the length of side DE in Triangle DEF, these sides are said to be congruent.

$$\overline{AB} \cong \overline{DE} \text{ is read "line segment } AB \text{ is congruent to line segment } DE."$$

Likewise, if the angles of two different figures are equal in measure, the measure of angle A in Triangle ABC is equal to the measure of angle D in Triangle DEF, these angles are said to be congruent.

$$\angle A \cong \angle D \text{ is read "angle } A \text{ is congruent to angle } D."$$

There is often more than one sequence of transformations that can be used to verify that two figures are congruent.

TOPIC 2
Similarity

Another type of transformation scales a figure up or down in size. The original figure and the new figure are similar to each other.

Module 1: Transforming Geometric Objects

TOPIC 2: SIMILARITY

In this topic, students investigate dilations. They make connections between scale factors and dilation factors by examining worked examples of Euclidean dilations. Then they define similar figures. Throughout the topic, students relate dilations to scale factors and scaling up and down. Finally, students use dilations to map from a figure to a similar figure, eventually identifying a sequence of transformations that map from a figure to a similar figure.

Where have we been?

This topic connects grade 7 scale drawings with similarity. Students first review content about scale factors from grade 7 and determine that, after an enlargement or reduction, the ratios of corresponding side lengths are equal and the corresponding angles have the same measure.

Where are we going?

The properties of similar figures are useful for solving real-world problems about scale factors. Similar triangles will also be used later in the course to explain properties of the slope of a line.

Using Technology to Create Similar Figures

Graphic design and word processing programs have methods for scaling images and other objects. This scaling, shown here as a percent of the size of the original figure, produces a similar figure by dilating the image or object. A dilation of 100% is the same as doing nothing to the original figure.

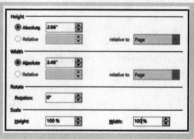

Myth: "If I can get the right answer, then I should not have to explain why."

Sometimes you get the right answer for the wrong reasons. Suppose a student is asked, "What is 4 divided by 2?" and she confidently answers "2!" If she does not explain any further, then it might be assumed that she understands how to divide whole numbers. But, what if she used the following rule to solve that problem? "Subtract 2 from 4 one time." Even though she gave the right answer, she has an incomplete understanding of division.

However, if she is asked to explain her reasoning, by drawing a picture, creating a model, or giving a different example, the teacher has a chance to remediate her flawed understanding. If teachers aren't exposed to their students' reasoning for both right and wrong answers, then they won't know about or be able to address misconceptions. This is important because mathematics is cumulative in the sense that new lessons build upon previous understandings.

You should ask your student to explain his or her thinking, when possible, even if you don't know whether the explanation is correct. When children (and adults!) explain something to someone else, it helps them learn. Just the process of trying to explain is helpful.

#mathmythbusted

Talking Points

You can further support your student's learning by asking questions about the work they do in class or at home. Your student is learning to think about mathematical similarity and scaling.

Questions to Ask

- How does this problem look like something you did in class?
- Can you show me the strategy you used to solve this problem? Do you know another way to solve it?
- Does your answer make sense? How do you know?
- Is there anything you don't understand? How can you use today's lesson to help?

Key Terms

dilation
Dilations are transformations that produce figures that are the same shape as the original figure, but not necessarily the same size.

similar
When two figures are similar, the ratios of their corresponding side lengths are all equal. This means that you can create a similar figure by multiplying or dividing all of the side lengths of a figure by the same scale factor (except 0).

Pinch-Zoom Geometry

Dilations of Figures

WARM UP

A billboard advertises a watch. The face of the watch is 2 meters wide on the billboard. The face of the actual watch is 2 centimeters wide. What scale factor was used to create the billboard?

LEARNING GOALS

- Dilate figures given a center of dilation and scale factor such that the resulting dilation is an enlargement or a reduction of the original figure.
- Identify the scale factor used in a dilation of a figure.
- Determine whether a two-dimensional figure is similar to another by obtaining one from the other using a sequence of dilations.
- Describe a sequence of dilations that demonstrates that two figures are similar.

KEY TERMS

- dilation
- center of dilation
- scale factor
- enlargement
- reduction
- similar

You have learned about geometric transformations that preserve the size and shape of figures. You also know how to use scale factors to produce scale drawings. Is there a geometric transformation that changes the scale of a figure?

Scale Drawing by Doing

Recall that a scale drawing is a representation of a real object or place that is in proportion to the real object or place it represents. The ratios of corresponding side lengths between the drawing and the object are all the same.

Consider the logo shown on the tablet screen.

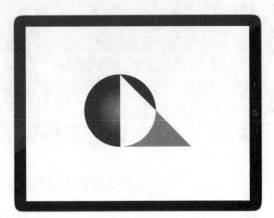

1. **When the logo on the tablet screen appears on the smartphone screen, it will be reduced by a scale factor of $\frac{1}{2}$. Sketch the logo on the smartphone screen and explain your process.**

2. When the logo on the tablet screen appears on the desktop
   screen, it will be enlarged by a scale factor of 2. Sketch the
   logo on the desktop screen and explain your process.

ACTIVITY 1.1

Dilating Figures with a Scale Factor Greater Than 1

The image of a dilation can also be called a scale drawing.

Dilations are transformations that produce figures that are the same shape as the original figure, but not necessarily the same size. Each point on the original figure is moved along a straight line, and the straight line is drawn from a fixed point known as the **center of dilation**. The distance each point moves is determined by the *scale factor* used.

The **scale factor** is the ratio of the distance of the new figure from the center of dilation to the distance of the original figure from the center of dilation. When the scale factor is greater than 1, the new figure is called an **enlargement**.

WORKED EXAMPLE

This image of a logo was dilated to produce an enlargement using point *P* as the center of dilation.

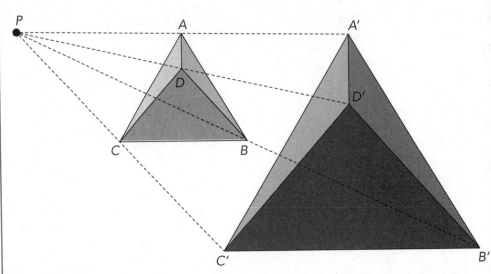

The scale factor can be expressed as $\frac{PA'}{PA} = \frac{PB'}{PB} = \frac{PC'}{PC} = \frac{PD'}{PD}$.

1. In the worked example, the scale factor is represented by 4 equivalent ratios. What distances are represented by each part of those ratios? Is the scale factor less than 1, equal to 1, or greater than 1? Explain your reasoning.

2. Measure the segment lengths of the original logo in millimeters.

   $m\overline{AB}$ = _____ $m\overline{AC}$ = _____

   $m\overline{BC}$ = _____ $m\overline{AD}$ = _____

3. Measure the segment lengths of the new logo in millimeters.

   $m\overline{A'B'}$ = _____ $m\overline{B'C'}$ = _____

   $m\overline{A'C'}$ = _____ $m\overline{A'D'}$ = _____

   _____

   The notation $\overline{AB}$ means "segment AB." The notation AB means "the length of segment AB."

   _____

4. Measure each line segment in millimeters.

   $m\overline{A'P}$ = _____ $m\overline{AP}$ = _____

   $m\overline{B'P}$ = _____ $m\overline{BP}$ = _____

   $m\overline{C'P}$ = _____ $m\overline{CP}$ = _____

   $m\overline{D'P}$ = _____ $m\overline{DP}$ = _____

   _____

   To indicate the measure of the segment, you can write AB or $m\overline{AB}$.

   _____

5. Determine each ratio.

   $\dfrac{A'P}{AP}$ = _____ $\dfrac{B'P}{BP}$ = _____

   $\dfrac{C'P}{CP}$ = _____ $\dfrac{D'P}{DP}$ = _____

   $\dfrac{B'C'}{BC}$ = _____ $\dfrac{A'B'}{AB}$ = _____

   $\dfrac{A'D'}{AD}$ = _____ $\dfrac{A'C'}{AC}$ = _____

6. How do you think the angle measures of the new logo will compare with those of the old logo? Make a conjecture. Then, test your conjecture by measuring various angles in the original and new logos. Describe your conclusion.

7. Compare the original logo and the new logo. What do you notice?

Dilating Figures with a Scale Factor Less Than 1

When the scale factor is less than 1, the new figure is called a **reduction**.

The size of the logo and its distance from point *P* are the same as the worked example showing an enlargement of the logo.

WORKED EXAMPLE

The original logo was dilated to produce a reduction using point *P* as the center of dilation.

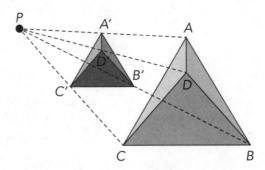

The scale factor can be expressed as $\dfrac{PA'}{PA} = \dfrac{PB'}{PB} = \dfrac{PC'}{PC} = \dfrac{PD'}{PD}$.

1. In the worked example, the scale factor is represented by 4 equivalent ratios. What distances are represented by each part of those ratios? Is the scale factor less than 1, equal to 1, or greater than 1? Explain your reasoning.

2. Measure the segment lengths of the new logo in millimeters.

$m\overline{A'B'}$ = _____ $m\overline{B'C'}$ = _____

$m\overline{A'C'}$ = _____ $m\overline{A'D'}$ = _____

3. Measure each line segment in millimeters.

$m\overline{A'P}$ = _____ $m\overline{B'P}$ = _____

$m\overline{C'P}$ = _____ $m\overline{D'P}$ = _____

4. Determine each ratio.

$\dfrac{A'P}{AP}$ = _____ $\dfrac{B'P}{BP}$ = _____

$\dfrac{C'P}{CP}$ = _____ $\dfrac{D'P}{DP}$ = _____

$\dfrac{B'C'}{BC}$ = _____ $\dfrac{A'B'}{AB}$ = _____

$\dfrac{A'D'}{AD}$ = _____ $\dfrac{A'C'}{AC}$ = _____

5. How do you think the angle measures of the new logo will compare with those of the old logo? Make a conjecture. Then, test your conjecture by measuring various angles in the original and new logos. Describe your conclusion.

6. Compare the original logo and the new logo. What do you notice?

ACTIVITY
1.3

Creating and Verifying Similar Figures

When working with images on a computer, the size of the images can be changed by dragging a corner or side of the image. How you drag the images determines whether or not the scale of the image is maintained.

Anne needs to adjust the original logo to use on different web pages. She plays around with the image to determine how she can adjust the logo and still maintain the same scale.

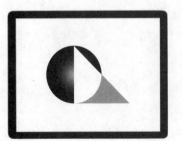

Each image contains an arrow that indicates how Anne adjusts the logo and the resulting logo.

1. Which of the adjusted logos do you think are dilations of the
   original? Which are not? Explain your thinking.

A.

B.

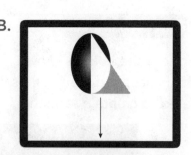

C.

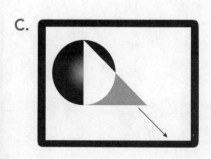

D.

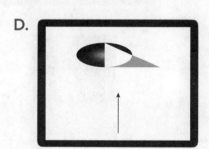

E.

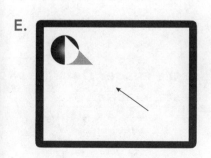

F.

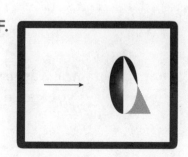

When you dilate a figure, you create a *similar* figure. When two
figures are **similar**, the ratios of their corresponding side lengths are
equal. This means that you can create a similar figure by multiplying
or dividing all of the side lengths of a figure by the same scale
factor (except 0). You can multiply or divide by 1 to create a similar
figure, too. In that case, the similar figures are congruent figures.
Corresponding angles in similar figures are congruent.

Many word processing and graphics software programs allow users to change the sizes of images.

WORKED EXAMPLE

Consider the images shown. The height of the original image is 2.66 inches, and the width is 3.48 inches. The original image is then dilated to create a reduction.

2. Are the two images similar? Explain how you know.

3. What scale factor was used to reduce the image? Describe two different ways you can determine the scale factor.

4. How can you tell that a height of 2.66 in. and a width of 3.48 in. are the original dimensions of the image?

5. Consider each set of new dimensions or scale percents that show adjustments to this original image. Describe how the image changed and whether the new image is similar to the original. Show your work and explain your reasoning.

a. Scale

Height: 225 % Width: 225 %

b. Scale

Height: 90 % Width: 110 %

c.
Height
- Absolute 1.5"
- Relative

Width
- Absolute 2.25"
- Relative

d.
Height
- Absolute 2"
- Relative

Width
- Absolute 2"
- Relative

6. Explain why Jed's reasoning is not correct. Draw examples to illustrate your explanation.

Jed

I can dilate a rectangular figure by adding the same value to its length and width.

TALK the TALK

It's a Cloud

1. Dilate the figure shown using scale factors of $\frac{4}{3}$ and $\frac{3}{4}$ and point Q as the center of dilation.

Q
•

2. Describe the relationship between the corresponding sides in an original figure and the new figure resulting from a dilation.

3. Describe the relationship between the corresponding angles in an original figure and the new figure resulting from a dilation.

Determine if each statement is true or false. If a statement is false, include a counterexample. Explain your reasoning.

4. True   False   All similar figures are also congruent figures.

5. True   False   All congruent figures are also similar figures.

Assignment

Write

In your own words, describe all of the ways you can tell whether two figures are similar. Use examples to illustrate your description.

Remember

Dilations are transformations that produce figures that are the same shape as the original figure, but not the same size. Each point on the original figure is moved along a straight line, and the straight line is drawn from a fixed point known as the center of dilation. The distance each point moves is determined by the scale factor used.

The scale factor is the ratio of the distance of the new figure from the center of dilation to the distance of the original figure from the center of dilation.

Practice

1. Dilate each triangle with *P* as the center of dilation and the given scale factor.

   a. Scale factor of 3

   b. Scale factor of $\frac{1}{3}$

P

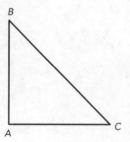

   c. Scale factor of $\frac{1}{4}$

P

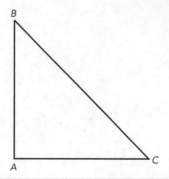

2. The triangles in each pair are similar. Identify the congruent corresponding angles and the corresponding proportional side lengths.

a. Triangle ABC is similar to Triangle A'B'C'.

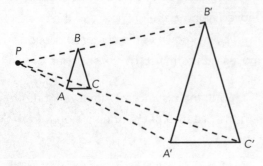

b. Triangle DEF is similar to Triangle D'E'F'.

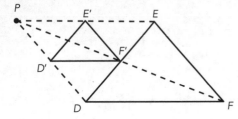

3. Natasha has a photo of a lasagna dish she made, which she wants to post to various websites. The original image has a width of 300 pixels and a height of 450 pixels. Consider each set of new dimensions or scale percents that show adjustments to this original image. Describe how the image changed and whether the new image is similar to the original. Show your work and explain your reasoning.

a. New image: 360 pixels width, 540 pixels height

b. New image: 35% width, 35% height

c. New image: 150 pixels width, 150 pixels height

Stretch

What happens if you dilate a figure by a negative scale factor? Use examples to explain your reasoning and justify your answer.

Review

1. Describe a sequence of transformations that exhibits the congruence between each pair of figures.

a.

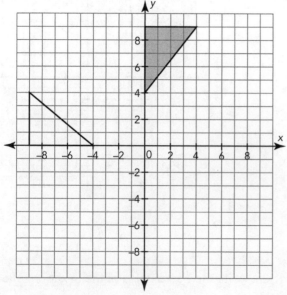

b.

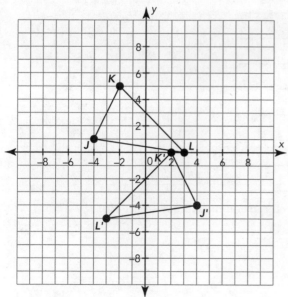

2. Use what you know about reflections to answer each question.

a. Reflect the word MOM across the y-axis. Is it still a word?

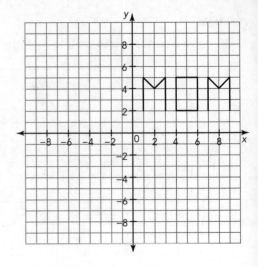

b. The coordinates of the vertices of a hexagon are given. Write the coordinates of the hexagon reflected across the y-axis (Image 1) and across the x-axis (Image 2).

Pre-Image	Image 1	Image 2
A (1, 6)		
B (3, 4)		
C (5, 6)		
D (5, 4)		
E (3, 2)		
F (1, 4)		

3. Calculate the circumference and area of a circle with the given measure. Use 3.14 for π.

a. radius = 3 cm

b. diameter = 4 ft

Rising, Running, Stepping, Scaling

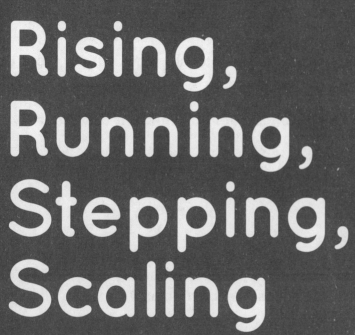

2

Dilating Figures on the Coordinate Plane

WARM UP

Scale up or scale down to determine the value of the variable in each equivalent ratio.

1. $3 : 1 = 25.5 : z$

2. $2 : 5 = a : 30$

3. $1 : 4 = x : 80$

4. $9.9 : 10 = 99 : p$

LEARNING GOALS

- Dilate figures on a coordinate plane.
- Understand the dilation of a figure on the coordinate plane as a scaling up or scaling down of the coordinates of the figure.
- Describe how a dilation of a figure on a coordinate plane affects the coordinates of a figure.
- Distinguish between a dilation centered at the origin and a dilation not centered at the origin.

You have used transformations called dilations to create similar figures. How can you use coordinates to determine whether two figures are similar?

The Escalator or the Stairs

Bob is riding an escalator. The escalator starts at (0, 0) and drops Bob off at (12, 8).

1. Use the coordinate planes given to represent Bob's journey.

    a. Draw a line to show Bob's path on the escalator.

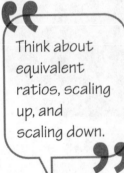

Think about equivalent ratios, scaling up, and scaling down.

    b. Alice takes the stairs. Draw steps starting at the origin that will take Alice to the same location as Bob. Make all of the steps the same.

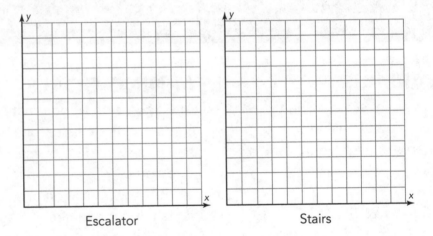

Escalator   Stairs

2. How is taking the stairs similar to riding the escalator? How is it different? Explain your reasoning.

3. Compare the steps that you designed for Alice with your classmates' steps. How are these steps similar to your steps?

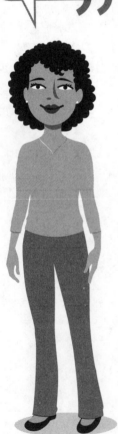

Scaling Up and Down on the Coordinate Plane

You know that a translation moves a point along a line. A sequence of repeated horizontal and/or vertical translations also moves a point along a line. You can use this fact to dilate figures.

WORKED EXAMPLE

Dilate △ABC by a scale factor of 3 using the origin as the center of dilation.

Let's start by dilating Point A, which is located at (2, 1). In other words, Point A is translated from the origin 2 units right and 1 unit up.

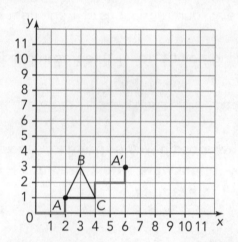

To dilate point A by a scale factor of 3, translate Point A by three repeated sequences: 2 units right and 1 unit up from the origin.

1. Describe the repeated translations you can use to scale point B and point C. Then plot point B' and point C' on the coordinate plane in the worked example.

   a. point B to point B'

   b. point C to point C'

2. Draw △A'B'C' on the coordinate plane in the example. Is △ABC similar to △A'B'C'? Explain your reasoning.

Dilate $\triangle DEF$ by a scale factor of $\frac{1}{4}$ using the origin as the center of dilation.

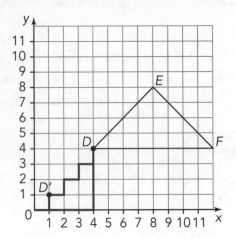

Point D is translated from the origin 4 units right and 4 units up (4, 4). This is the same as four translations of 1 unit right and 1 unit up.

Therefore, scaling point D to (1, 1) represents a dilation by a scale factor of $\frac{1}{4}$.

How do the side lengths and angles of the triangles compare?

3. Determine the coordinates of points E' and F'. Explain how you determined your answers. Then, draw $\triangle D'E'F'$ on the coordinate plane in the example.

4. Is $\triangle DEF$ similar to $\triangle D'E'F'$? Explain your reasoning.

5. How does dilating a figure, using the origin as the center of dilation, affect the coordinates of the original figure? Make a conjecture using the examples in this activity.

Using the Origin as the Center of Dilation

Road signs maintain a constant scale, regardless of whether they are on the road or in the drivers' manual. This sign indicates that the road is bending to the left.

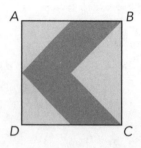

1. Dilate the figure on the coordinate plane using the origin (0, 0) as the center of dilation and a scale factor of 3 to form a new figure.

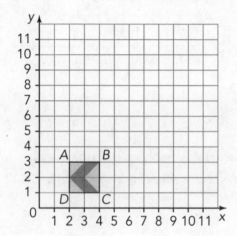

2. List the ordered pairs for the original figure and for the new figure. How are the values in the ordered pairs affected by the dilation?

3. Compare and contrast the corresponding angles and corresponding side lengths of the new figure and the original figure.

Let's consider a different road sign. This sign indicates that the road proceeds to the right.

4. Dilate the figure on the coordinate plane using the origin (0, 0) as the center of dilation and a scale factor of $\frac{1}{2}$ to form a new figure.

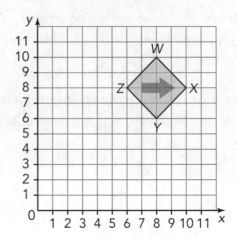

5. List the ordered pairs for the original figure and for the new figure. How are the values in the ordered pairs affected by the dilation?

6. Compare and contrast the corresponding angles and corresponding side lengths of the original figure and the new figure.

Using a Point on the Figure as a Center of Dilation

You can use any point as the center of dilation. The center of dilation can be on the figure, inside the figure, or outside the figure.

1. Consider △*ABC*.

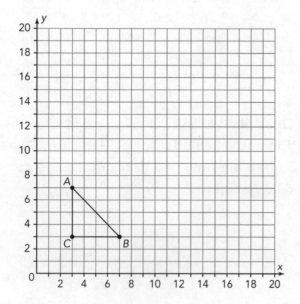

a. Dilate △*ABC* using point *C* as the center of dilation and a scale factor of 3 to form △*A'B'C'*. Explain how you determined the coordinates of the dilated figure.

b. What are the coordinates of points *A'*, *B'* and *C'*?

2. Consider Quadrilateral *ABCD*.

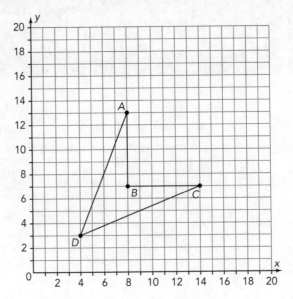

a. Dilate Quadrilateral *ABCD* using point *C* as the center of dilation and a scale factor of $\frac{1}{2}$ to form Quadrilateral *A'B'C'D'*. Explain how you determined the coordinates of the dilated figure.

b. What are the coordinates of points *A'*, *B'*, *C'*, and *D'*?

c. How are the coordinates of a figure affected by a dilation that is not centered at the origin?

Using a Point Inside or Outside the Figure as a Center of Dilation

In this activity, you will explore different center points for dilation to understand how the coordinates of a figure are affected by dilations.

1. Dilate Figure *PQRS* by a scale factor of $\frac{3}{2}$ using the point (4, 6) as the center of dilation. Determine the coordinates of Figure *P'Q'R'S'* and draw the approximate dilation on the coordinate plane.

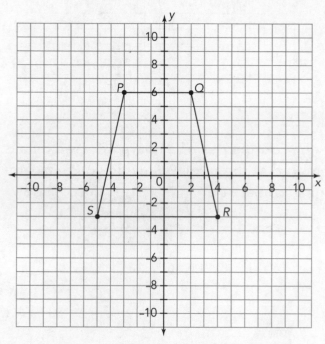

2. Dilate Figure *PQRS* by a scale factor of $\frac{2}{3}$ using the point $(-2, 0)$ as the center of dilation. Determine the coordinates of Figure *P'Q'R'S'* and draw the approximate dilation on the coordinate plane.

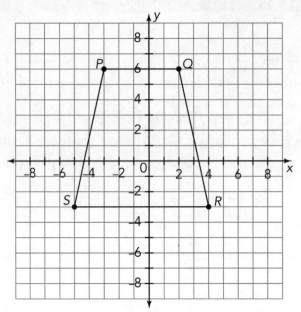

3. How are the coordinates of a figure affected by a dilation that is not centered at the origin? How do you think you can modify your original conjecture?

If the dilation of a figure is centered at the origin, you can multiply the coordinates of the points of the original figure by the scale factor to determine the coordinates of the new figure.

To determine the dilation of a figure not centered at the origin, you can follow these steps:

- Subtract the x- and y-coordinates of the center from the x- and y-coordinates of each point.
- Multiply the new coordinates of each point by the scale factor.
- Add the x- and y-coordinates of the center to the new x- and y-coordinates of each point.

4. Determine the dilation of each triangle using the information given. Verify your answer on the coordinate plane.

a. **Center: (3, 3) Scale factor: 2**

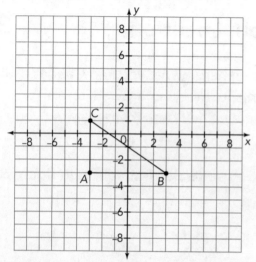

b. **Center: origin Scale factor: $\frac{2}{3}$**

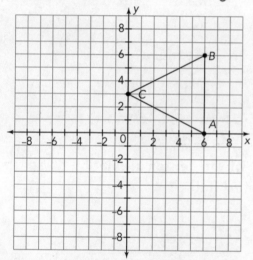

c. **Center: (1, −3) Scale factor: 2**

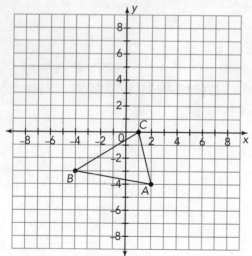

TALK the TALK 💬

Location, Location, Location

Answer each question to summarize what you know about dilating figures on the coordinate plane. Use your answers to plan a presentation for your classmates that demonstrates what you learned in this lesson.

1. What strategies can you use to determine if two figures are similar when they are:

   a. located on a coordinate plane?

   b. not located on a coordinate plane?

2. How does the location of the center of dilation affect the coordinates of the dilated figure?

3. Describe how you can determine whether two figures on the coordinate plane are similar using just their coordinates and the center of dilation.

Assignment

Write

In your own words, explain how to dilate a figure on the coordinate plane using repeated translations. Use examples with scale factors less than and greater than 1 to illustrate your explanation.

Remember

If the dilation of a figure is centered at the origin, you can multiply the coordinates of the points of the original figure by the scale factor to determine the coordinates of the new figure.

To determine the dilation of a figure not centered at the origin, you can follow these steps:

- Subtract the x- and y-coordinates of the center from the x- and y-coordinates of each point.
- Multiply the new coordinates of each point by the scale factor.
- Add the x- and y-coordinates of the center to the new x- and y-coordinates of each point.

Practice

1. Graph Triangle XYZ with the coordinates X (2, 17), Y (17, 17), and Z (17, 8).

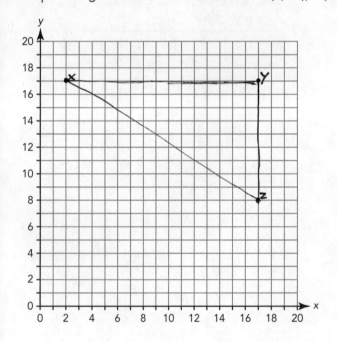

a. Reduce Triangle XYZ on the coordinate plane using the point Y as the center of dilation and a scale factor of $\frac{1}{3}$ to form Triangle X'YZ'.

b. What are the coordinates of points X' and Z'?

2. Dilate Triangle *QRS* on the coordinate plane using the origin (0, 0) as the center of dilation and a scale factor of 3 to form Triangle *Q'R'S'*. Label the coordinates of points *Q'*, *R'*, and *S'*.

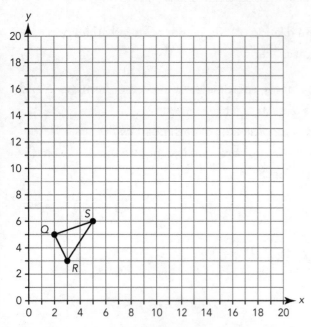

3. Dilate Triangle *ABC* on the coordinate plane using point *A* (2, 1) as the center of dilation and a scale factor of 3.

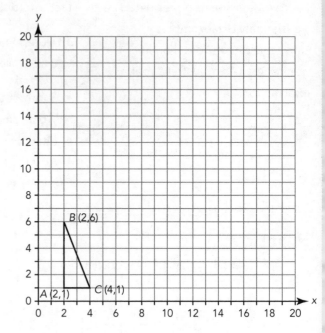

4. Dilate Triangle *ABC* on the coordinate plane using point *A* (3, 3) as the center of dilation and a scale factor of $\frac{1}{3}$.

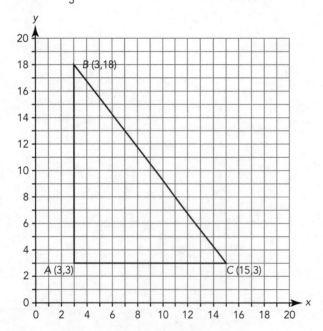

5. Verify that each pair of triangles is similar.

a.

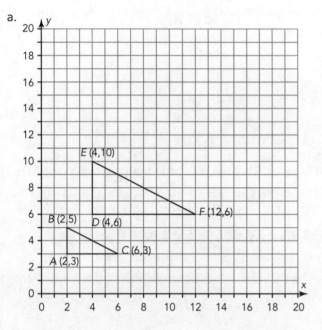

b.

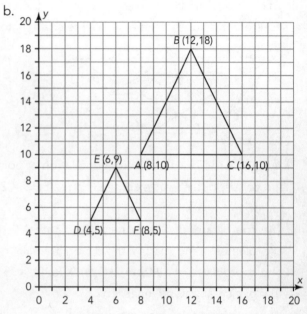

c.

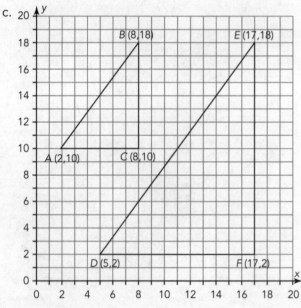

d.

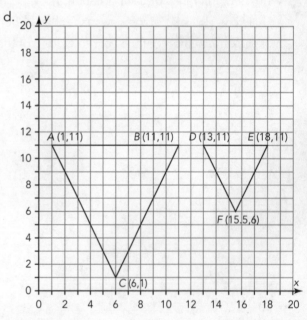

Stretch

Square ABCD has coordinates A (4, 4), B (8, 4), C (8, 0), and D (4, 0). A dilation of Square ABCD has coordinates A' (0, 0), B' (2, 0), C' (2, −2), and D' (0, −2). What is the center of dilation?

Review

1. Triangle *XYZ* has been enlarged with *P* as the center of dilation to form Triangle *X'Y'Z'*. Identify the equivalent ratios that are equal to the scale factor.

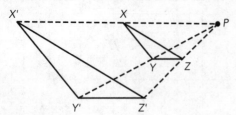

2. A triangle is dilated with center of dilation at point *U*. Point *E* is a vertex of the triangle, and point *E'* is the corresponding vertex of the image. If *UE* = 2 centimeters and *UE'* = 10 centimeters, what is the scale factor?

3. The coordinates of Quadrilateral *ABCD* are *A* (−6, 2), *B* (−5, 3), *C* (7, 3), and *D* (0, −4). What are the coordinates of the image if the quadrilateral is translated 4 units right and 3 units down?

4. The coordinates of ΔJKL are *J* (0, 1), *K* (6, 0), and *L* (−6, 0). What are the coordinates of the image if the triangle is translated 8 units left?

5. Write two unit rates for each situation.
   a. Julie can deliver $\frac{1}{4}$ of the newspapers in $\frac{1}{2}$ hour.
   b. It took the author $\frac{3}{4}$ of the year to write $\frac{1}{4}$ of the book.

From Here to There

Mapping Similar Figures Using Transformations

3

WARM UP

1. Describe at least two different single transformations or sequences of transformations that map Figure *A* to Figure *B*.

2. Describe the geometric relationships between the figures.

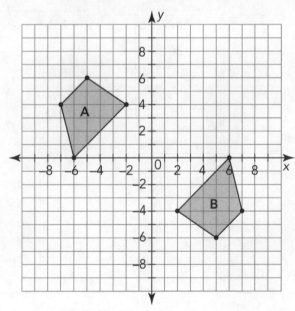

LEARNING GOALS

- Describe a single dilation that maps a two-dimensional figure onto a similar figure.
- Determine a sequence of transformations that maps a two-dimensional figure onto a similar figure.
- Determine the relationship between images of the same pre-image.

You have used sequences of translations, reflections, and rotations to verify that two images are congruent. How can you use transformations to determine if two images are similar and/or congruent?

Same Figure or Same Shape?

When two figures are similar, the same scale factor can be applied to all side lengths to map one figure to the other.

We often say that dilations preserve shape and that rigid motions preserve both size and shape. As a result, it is common to state that similar figures have the same shape, and congruent figures have the same size and shape. However, what does it mean for two figures to have the same shape in this context? Are all rectangles similar? Are all triangles similar?

Use the definition of similar figures to determine which figures are similar.

> Do you think all rectangles are similar to each other? What about squares?

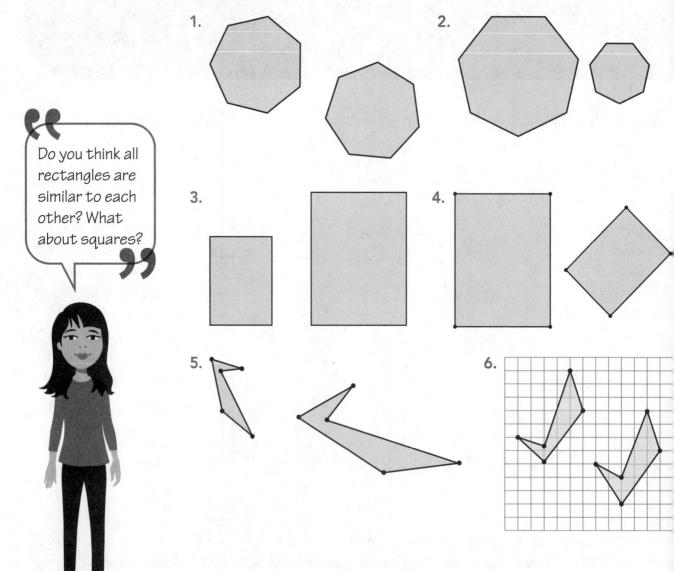

1.

2.

3.

4.

5.

6.

In this activity, you will use what you know about dilations to determine if figures are similar.

1. Determine if the figures are similar. If they are similar, state the scale factor and the center of dilation that maps Figure 1 onto Figure 2.

   a. Figure 1: △ABC

      Figure 2: △DEF

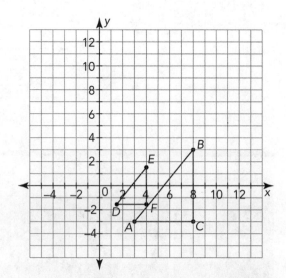

   b. Figure 1: △PWN

      Figure 2: △GKA

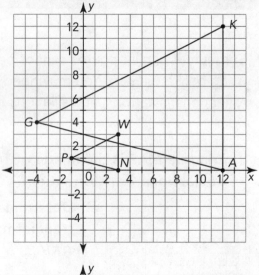

   c. Figure 1: △JDA

      Figure 2: △KGE

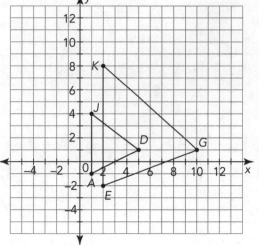

d. Figure 1: △ZEN

Figure 2: △FRB

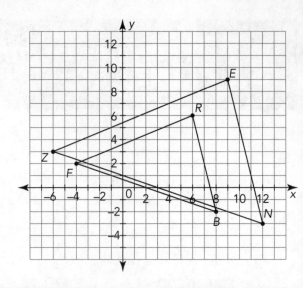

Proving Similarity Through Transformations

Sometimes similar figures cannot be mapped from one to another using only a dilation. You may need a combination of translations, reflections, rotations, and dilations to map a figure onto a similar figure.

1. Triangle *MAP* is the image of Triangle *QRN* after undergoing at least one transformation.

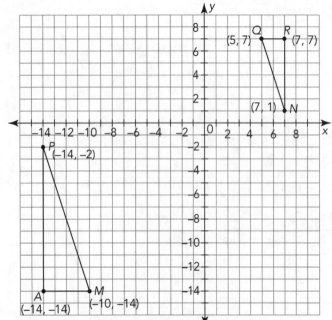

a. Determine a possible sequence of transformations to map △*QRN* onto △*MAP*.

b. Are the triangles congruent? Are they similar? Explain your reasoning.

c. Reverse the order of the sequence of transformations you described in part (b). What do you notice?

2. Triangle XYZ is the image of Triangle ABC after undergoing at least one transformation.

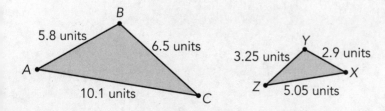

a. List the corresponding sides and angles for △ABC and △XYZ.

b. Determine a possible sequence of transformations to map △ABC onto △XYZ.

c. Reverse the order of the sequence of transformations you described in part (b). What do you notice?

3. Triangle *F"N"R"* is the image of Triangle *FNR* after two transformations.

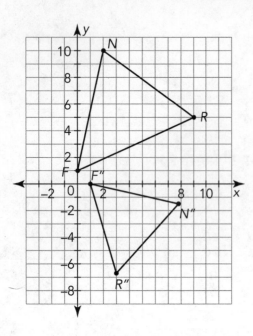

a. Determine a possible sequence of a rotation and dilation to map △*FNR* onto △*F"N"R"*.

b. Reverse the order of the sequence of transformations you described in part (a). Explain any adjustments you need to make in the sequence of transformations to create a correct mapping.

4. Triangle *ABC* was dilated to create Triangle *A'B'C'*. Then Triangle *A'B'C'* was dilated to create Triangle *A"B"C"*. Describe a single transformation that maps △*ABC* onto △*A"B"C"*.

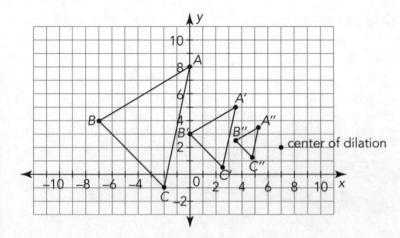

center of dilation

5. Verify that the two houses are similar by describing a sequence of transformations that maps one figure onto the other.

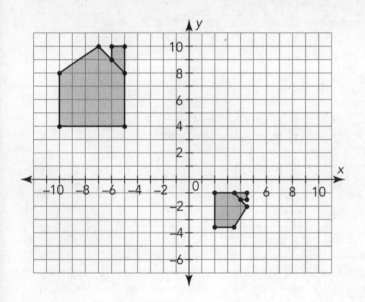

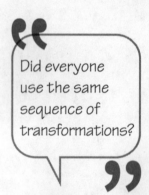

Did everyone use the same sequence of transformations?

6. Use dilations and other transformations to determine if the triangles represented by the coordinates are similar. Show your work and explain your reasoning.

a. A (2, 3) B (2, 9) C (7, 3)
   A′ (−2, −3) B′ (−2, −6) C′ (−4.5, −3)

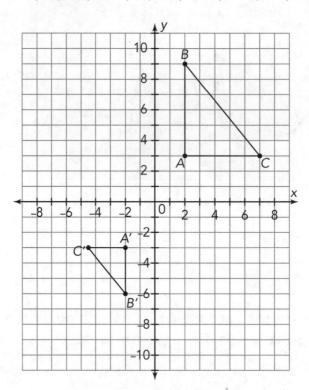

b. A (−2, −1) B (−2, −2) C (1, 1)
   A′ (−5, 2.5) B′ (−5, 5) C′ (2.5, −2.5)

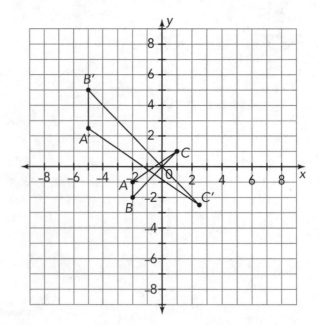

c. $J(-7, 4)$ $K(7, 2)$ $L(1, -2)$
   $J'(-3.5, -2)$ $K'(3.5, 1)$ $L'(0.5, -1)$

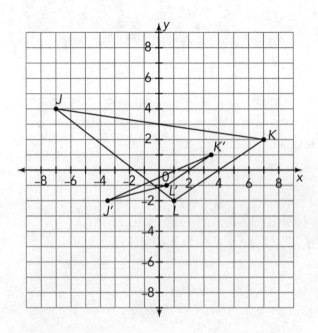

d. $A(-6, 4)$ $B(-4, -2.5)$ $C(-6, -3)$
   $A'(1, 8)$ $B'(5, -5)$ $C'(1, -6)$

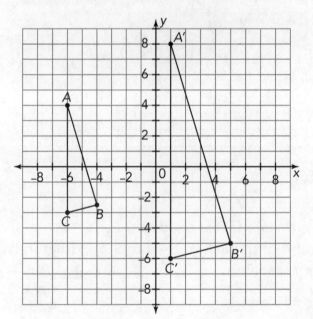

ACTIVITY 3.3 | Comparing Images

You know that similar figures can be mapped from one to another using a sequence of transformations. How are the images of the same pre-image related to each other?

Let's investigate!

1. Quadrilateral *A* is the pre-image used to create Quadrilaterals *B*, *C*, *D*, and *E* using dilations.

Make a conjecture!

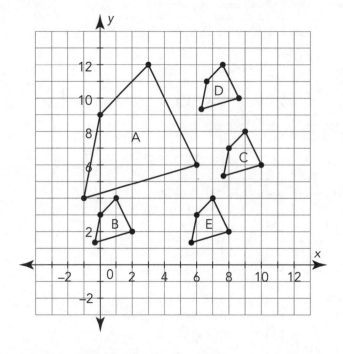

How can you verify your results?

a. Determine the scale factor used to map Quadrilateral *A* onto each of the other quadrilaterals. Explain your reasoning.

b. Was the same center of dilation used to create each of the other quadrilaterals? Explain your reasoning.

c. Are Quadrilaterals *B*, *C*, *D*, and *E* similar? Are they
    congruent? Explain your reasoning.

2. The labeled figure is the pre-image used to create the other
   two figures using dilations.

   a. Determine the scale factor to map the pre-image to each of
       the other figures. Explain your reasoning.

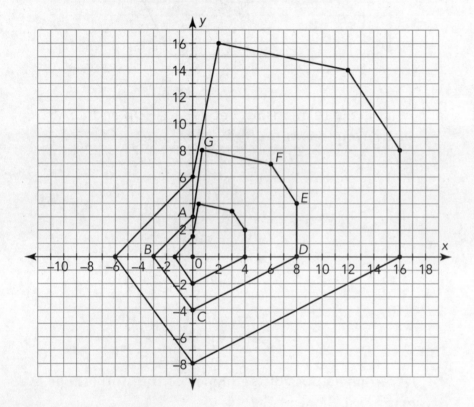

   b. Was the same center of dilation used to create each of the
       other figures? Explain your reasoning.

   c. Are the images similar? Are they congruent? Explain
       your reasoning.

3. Triangle *HUB* was dilated from the origin by a scale factor of $\frac{2}{5}$ to create △*H′U′B′*, and △*H′U′B′* ≅ △*TAP*.

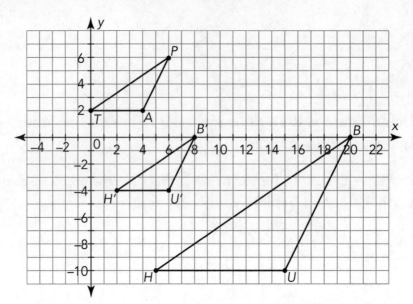

a. What is the relationship between △*HUB* and △*TAP*? Justify your answer.

b. Determine a possible sequence of transformations that maps △*HUB* onto △*TAP*.

4. Triangle *DOT* was dilated from the origin by a scale factor of 3 to create △*D'O'T'*, and △*D'O'T'* ≅ △*JAR*. Determine a possible sequence of transformations that maps △*JAR* onto △*DOT*.

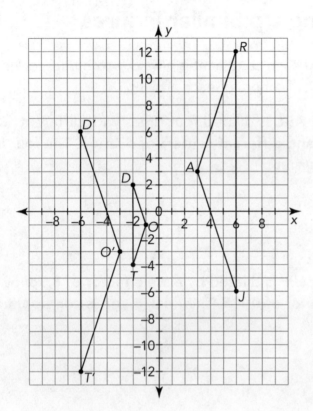

TALK the TALK

Summing Up Similar Figures

Determine if each statement is *always*, *sometimes*, or *never* true. Provide a justification for each answer.

1. Triangle *ABC* is dilated four times with different scale factors and different centers of dilation. The four images are congruent.

2. Triangle *HIP* is dilated by a scale factor of 8, followed by a scale factor of 0.125. The final image is congruent to △*HIP*.

3. The same order for a sequence of transformations can be used to map between two similar figures, regardless of which figure is used as the pre-image.

4. Dilations are used to create congruent figures.

5. Transformations are used to create similar figures.

Assignment

Write

Explain how to use transformations to determine if figures are congruent or similar.

Remember

Images created from the same pre-image are always similar figures.

Practice

Verify that the two figures are similar by describing a dilation that maps one figure onto the other. Be sure to include the scale factor.

1.

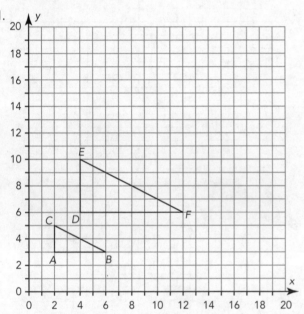

2.

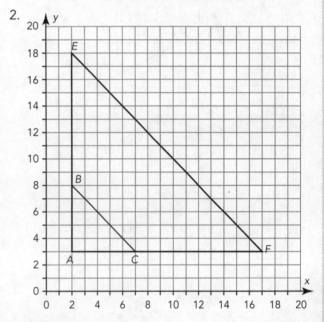

3.

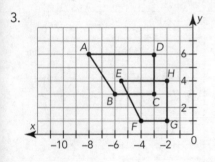

4.

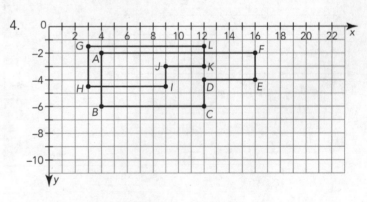

Verify that the figures are similar by describing a sequence of transformations that maps △ABC onto △DEF. Be as specific as possible.

5.

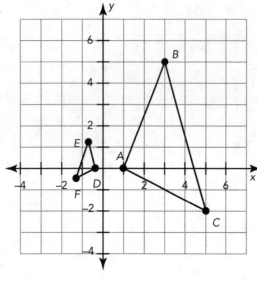

6.

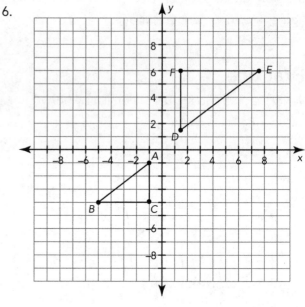

7.

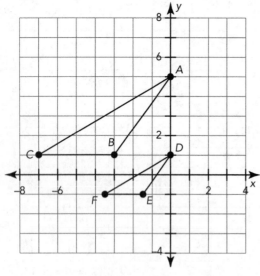

8.

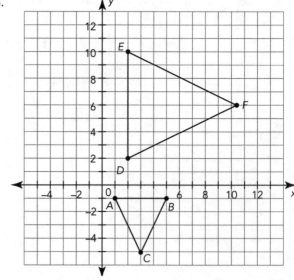

Stretch

Triangle *XYZ* is the image after a dilation of Triangle *ABC*.

1. Determine the scale factor.

2. Determine the center of dilation.

3. Explain how you could verify that the ratio of corresponding sides is constant.

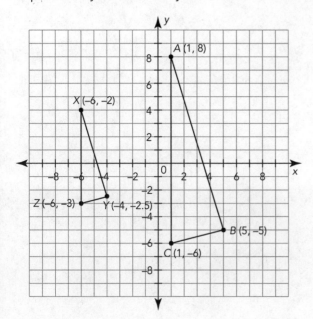

Review

1. Give the coordinates of △*A'B'C'* after a transformation of △*ABC* with the coordinates *A* (6, −3), *B* (9, 5), and *C* (5, 6). Use the origin as the center of dilation or rotation, as needed.

   a. Dilate △*ABC* by a scale factor of $\frac{1}{3}$.

   b. Dilate △*ABC* by a scale factor of 4.

   c. Rotate △*ABC* 180 degrees.

   d. Reflect △*ABC* across the x-axis.

2. Identify the constant of proportionality.

   a. Eight candy bars cost $6.00. Calculate the cost per candy bar.

   b. In the equation *y* = 4*x* + 7, *x* is the number of items and *y* is the total cost. What is the unit rate? Include units in your response.

Similarity Summary

KEY TERMS

- dilation
- center of dilation
- scale factor
- enlargement
- reduction
- similar

LESSON 1   Pinch-Zoom Geometry

Dilations are transformations that produce figures that are the same shape as the original figure, but not necessarily the same size. Each point on the original figure is moved along a straight line, and the straight line is drawn from a fixed point known as the **center of dilation**. The distance each point moves is determined by the scale factor used. The **scale factor** is the ratio of the distance of the new figure from the center of dilation to the distance of the original figure from the center of dilation.

When the scale factor is greater than 1, the new figure is called an **enlargement**.

This image of a logo was dilated to produce an enlargement using point P as the center of dilation.

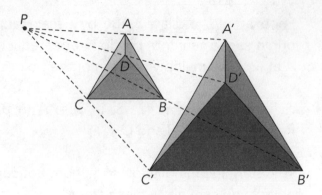

The scale factor can be expressed as

$$\frac{PA'}{PA} = \frac{PB'}{PB} = \frac{PC'}{PC} = \frac{PD'}{PD}.$$

When the scale factor is less than 1, the new figure is called a **reduction**.

For example, the original logo was dilated to produce a reduction using point P as the center of dilation.

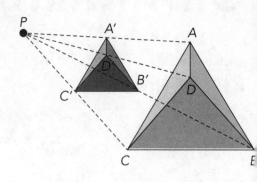

The scale factor can be expressed as

$$\frac{PA'}{PA} = \frac{PB'}{PB} = \frac{PC'}{PC} = \frac{PD'}{PD}.$$

When you dilate a figure, you create a similar figure. When two figures are **similar**, the ratios of their corresponding side lengths are equal. This means that you can create a similar figure by multiplying or dividing all of the side lengths of a figure by the same scale factor (except 0). You can multiply or divide by 1 to create a similar figure, too. In that case, the similar figures are congruent figures. Corresponding angles in similar figures are congruent.

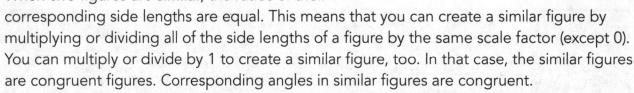

LESSON
2

Rising, Running, Stepping, Scaling

If the dilation of a figure is centered at the origin, you can multiply the coordinates of the points of the original figure by the scale factor to determine the coordinates of the new figure.

For example, to dilate $\triangle ABC$ by a scale factor of 3 using the origin as the center of dilation, repeatedly translate point A at (2, 1) by multiplying each of the point's coordinates by 3.

$$A'\ (2 \cdot 3,\ 1 \cdot 3) \rightarrow A'\ (6, 3)$$

Repeat for points B and C.

To determine the dilation of a figure not centered at the origin, you can follow these steps:

- Subtract the x- and y-coordinates of the center from the x- and y-coordinates of each point.
- Multiply the coordinates of each point by the scale factor.
- Add the x- and y-coordinates of the center to the new x- and y-coordinates of each point.

From Here to There

When two figures are similar, the same scale factor can be applied to all side lengths to map one figure to the other. You can compare the ratios of corresponding side lengths of figures to determine similarity. If the ratio, or scale factor, is the same for all corresponding sides, then the figures are similar.

Sometimes you may need a combination of translations, reflections, rotations, and dilations to map a figure onto a similar figure.

For example, $\triangle MAP$ is similar to $\triangle QRN$.
The ratio of corresponding sides is equal to 2, or
$\frac{1}{2}$. A possible sequence of transformations to
map $\triangle QRN$ onto $\triangle MAP$ is a rotation of 180°
about the origin and a dilation by a scale factor
of 2. Images created from the same
pre-image are always similar figures.

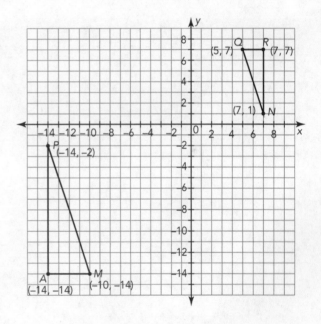

TOPIC 3

Line and Angle Relationships

Crisscrossing roads and interstate highways are common sights in big cities. Interchanges like this cost hundreds of millions of dollars and require millions of worker-hours to complete.

Lesson 1
Pulling a One-Eighty!

Lesson 2
Crisscross Applesauce

Lesson 3
The Vanishing Point

Module 1: Transforming Geometric Objects

TOPIC 3: LINE AND ANGLE RELATIONSHIPS

In this topic, students use their knowledge of transformations, congruence, and similarity to establish the Triangle Sum Theorem, the Exterior Angle Theorem, relationships between angles formed when parallel lines are cut by a transversal, and the Angle-Angle Similarity Theorem for similarity of triangles. Students determine and informally prove the relationships between the special angle pairs formed when parallel lines are cut by a transversal and use these relationships to solve mathematical problems, including writing and solving equations.

Where have we been?

Students use knowledge from grade 7 about supplementary angles and rigid motion transformations when proving theorems in this topic and when exploring the angle relationships formed when parallel lines are cut by a transversal.

Where are we going?

Throughout this topic, students are expected to follow lines of logic to reach conclusions, which is a foundation for formal proof in high school. The geometric results established in the topic via informal arguments will be formally proven in high school, but their experiences in this topic provide students with opportunities to build intuition and justify results.

Using Triangle Similarity to Create Art

Graphic artists can use similarity to create perspective drawings. This is accomplished using a vanishing point, a point at the horizon where all parallel lines intersect. The two triangles shown in this image, which share a common vertex at the vanishing point, are similar triangles.

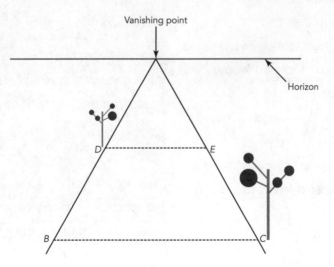

Myth: Asking questions means you don't understand.

It is universally true that, for any given body of knowledge, there are levels to understanding. For example, you might understand the rules of baseball and follow a game without trouble. But there is probably more to the game that you can learn. For example, do you know the 23 ways to get on first base, including the one where the batter strikes out?

Questions don't always indicate a lack of understanding. Instead, they might allow you to learn even more on a subject that you already understand. Asking questions may also give you an opportunity to ensure that you understand a topic correctly. Finally, questions are extremely important to ask yourself. For example, *everyone* should be in the habit of asking themselves, "Does that make sense? How would I explain it to a friend?"

#mathmythbusted

Talking Points

You can further support your student's learning by asking questions about the work they do in class or at home. Your student is learning to think about similar triangles as well as different line and angle theorems from geometry.

Questions to Ask

• How does this problem look like something you did in class?

• Can you show me the strategy you used to solve this problem? Do you know another way to solve it?

• Does your answer make sense? How do you know?

• Is there anything you don't understand? How can you use today's lesson to help?

Key Terms

Triangle Sum Theorem
The Triangle Sum Theorem states that the sum of the measures of the interior angles of a triangle is 180°.

Exterior Angle Theorem
The Exterior Angle Theorem states that the measure of the exterior angle of a triangle is equal to the sum of the measures of the two remote interior angles of the triangle.

transversal
A transversal is a line that intersects two or more lines at distinct points.

Angle-Angle Similarity Theorem
The Angle-Angle (AA) Similarity Theorem states that if two angles of one triangle are congruent to the corresponding angles of another triangle, then the triangles are similar.

Pulling a One-Eighty!

Triangle Sum and Exterior Angle Theorems

WARM UP

Solve each equation for *x*.

1. $x + 105 = 180$

2. $2x + 65 = 180$

3. $x + (x + 30) + 2x = 180$

4. $(90 - x) + 2x + x = 180$

LEARNING GOALS

- Establish the Triangle Sum Theorem.
- Explore the relationship between the interior angle measures and the side lengths of a triangle.
- Identify the remote interior angles of a triangle.
- Identify the exterior angles of a triangle.
- Use informal arguments to establish facts about exterior angles of triangles.
- Explore the relationship between the exterior angle measures and two remote interior angles of a triangle.
- Prove the Exterior Angle Theorem.

KEY TERMS

- Triangle Sum Theorem
- exterior angle of a polygon
- remote interior angles of a triangle
- Exterior Angle Theorem

You already know a lot about triangles. In previous grades you classified triangles by side lengths and angle measures. What special relationships exist among the interior angles of a triangle and between interior and exterior angles of a triangle?

Rip 'Em Up

Draw any triangle on a piece of patty paper. Tear off the triangle's three angles. Arrange the angles so that they are adjacent angles.

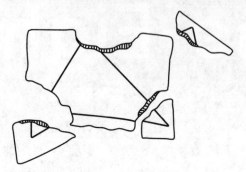

1. **What do you notice about these angles? Write a conjecture about the sum of the three angles in a triangle.**

2. **Compare your angles and your conjecture with your classmates'. What do you notice?**

In the previous activity, what you noticed about the relationship between the three angles in a triangle is called *The Triangle Sum Theorem*. The **Triangle Sum Theorem** states that the sum of the measures of the interior angles of a triangle is 180°.

Trevor is organizing a bike race called the Tri-Cities Criterium. Criteriums consist of several laps around a closed circuit. Based on the city map provided to him, Trevor designs three different triangular circuits and presents scale drawings of them to the Tri-Cities Cycling Association for consideration.

1. Classify each circuit according to the type of triangle created.

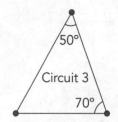

2. Use the Triangle Sum Theorem to determine the measure of the third angle in each triangular circuit. Label the triangles with the unknown angle measures.

3. Measure the length of each side of each triangular circuit. Label the side lengths in the diagram.

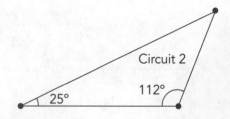

The sharper the angles on a race course, the more difficult the course is for cyclists to navigate.

4. Perform the following tasks for each circuit.

   a. List the angle measures from least to greatest.

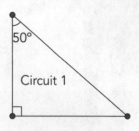

   b. List the side lengths from shortest to longest.

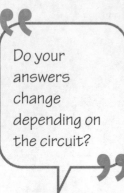

Do your answers change depending on the circuit?

c. Describe what you notice about the location of the angle with the least measure and the location of the shortest side.

d. Describe what you notice about the location of the angle with the greatest measure and the location of the longest side.

5. Traci, the president of the Tri-Cities Cycling Association, presents a fourth circuit for consideration. The measures of two of the interior angles of the triangle are 57° and 61°. Determine the measure of the third angle, and then describe the location of each side with respect to the measures of the opposite interior angles without drawing or measuring any part of the triangle.

a. measure of the third angle

Which circuit would you select for the race?

b. longest side of the triangle

c. shortest side of the triangle

6. List the side lengths from shortest to longest for each diagram.

a.
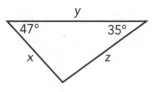

b.
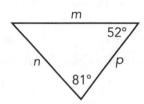

c.
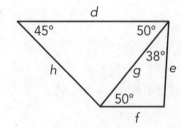

> If two angles of a triangle have equal measures, what does that mean about the relationship between the sides opposite the angles?

ACTIVITY

1.2 **Exterior Angle Theorem**

You now know about the relationships among the angles inside a triangle, the *interior angles of a triangle*, but are there special relationships between interior and *exterior angles* of a triangle?

An **exterior angle of a polygon** is an angle between a side of a polygon and the extension of its adjacent side. It is formed by extending a ray from one side of the polygon.

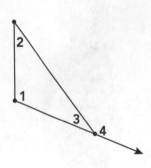

In the diagram, $\angle 1$, $\angle 2$, and $\angle 3$ are the interior angles of the triangle, and $\angle 4$ is an exterior angle of the triangle.

1. Make a conjecture about the measure of the exterior angle in relation to the measures of the other angles in the diagram.

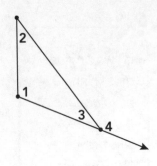

2. Let's investigate the relationships among measures of the angles in the diagram.

    a. What does $m\angle 1 + m\angle 2 + m\angle 3$ equal?
        Explain your reasoning.

    b. What does $m\angle 3 + m\angle 4$ equal? Explain your reasoning.

    c. State a relationship between the measures of $\angle 1$, $\angle 2$, and $\angle 4$. Explain your reasoning.

How have you heard the word "remote" used in other contexts?

3. In a triangle, for each exterior angle there are two "remote" interior angles.

    a. Why would $\angle 1$ and $\angle 2$ be referred to as "remote" interior angles with respect to the exterior angle, $\angle 4$?

    b. Extend another side of the triangle and label the exterior angle $\angle 5$. Then name the two remote interior angles with respect to $\angle 5$.

The **remote interior angles of a triangle** are the two angles that are non-adjacent to the specified exterior angle.

4. Rewrite $m\angle 4 = m\angle 1 + m\angle 2$ using the terms *sum, remote interior angles of a triangle,* and *exterior angle of a triangle.*

. The original diagram was drawn as an obtuse triangle with one exterior angle. If the triangle had been drawn as an acute or right triangle, would this have changed the relationship between the measure of the exterior angle and the sum of the measures of the two remote interior angles? Explain your reasoning.

Was your conjecture from Question 1 correct? If so, you have proven an important theorem in the study of geometry!

The **Exterior Angle Theorem** states that the measure of the exterior angle of a triangle is equal to the sum of the measures of the two remote interior angles of the triangle.

. Use the Exterior Angle Theorem to determine each unknown angle measure.

a.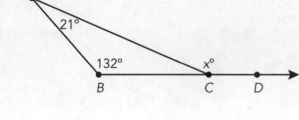

b.

c.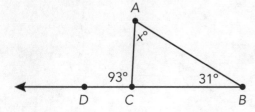

7. Write and solve an equation to determine the value of x in each diagram.

a.

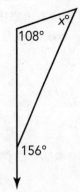

b.

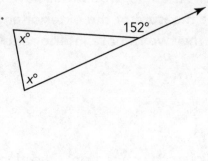

c.

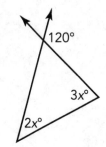

d.

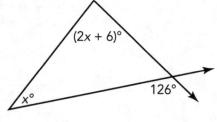

TALK the TALK

So Many Angles!

1. Consider the diagram shown.

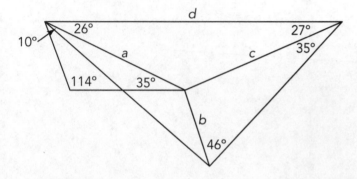

a. Determine the measures of the eight unknown angle measures inside the figure.

b. List the labeled side lengths in order from least to greatest.

NOTES

2. **Determine the unknown angle measures in the figure.**

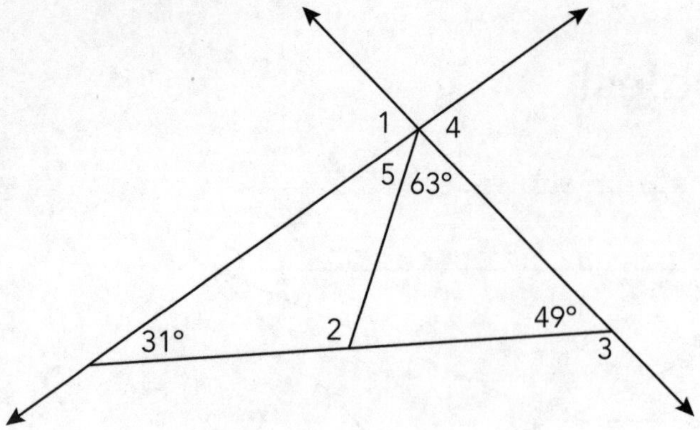

Assignment

Write

Write the term that best completes each statement.

1. The _____
   states that the sum of the measures of the interior angles of a
   triangle is 180°.

2. The _____
   states that the measure of an exterior angle of a triangle is equal
   to the sum of the measures of the remote interior angles of the
   triangle.

3. The _____
   are the two angles that are non-adjacent to the specified
   exterior angle.

4. A(n) _____ is
   formed by extending a side of a polygon.

Remember

The sum of the measures of
the interior angles of a triangle
is 180°.

The measure of the exterior
angle of a triangle is equal to
the sum of the measures of the
two remote interior angles of
the triangle.

Practice

1. Use the figure shown to answer each question.

   a. Explain how you can use the Exterior Angle Theorem to calculate
      the measure of ∠PMU.

   b. Calculate the measure of ∠PMU.

   c. Explain how you can use the Triangle Sum Theorem to calculate
      the measure of ∠UPM.

   d. Calculate the measure of ∠UPM.

   e. List the sides of △PMB in order from shortest to longest. Explain how you determined your answer.

   f. List the sides of △PUB in order from shortest to longest. Explain how you determined your answer.

2. Determine the measure of the unknown angle in each triangle.

   a.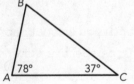

   b.

c.

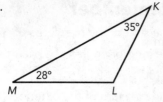

d.

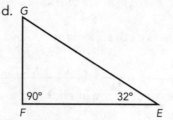

3. List the side lengths from shortest to longest for each diagram.

a.

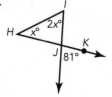

b.

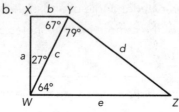

4. Determine the value of x in each diagram.

a.

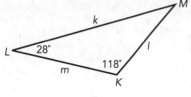

b.

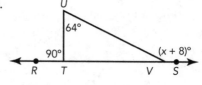

c.

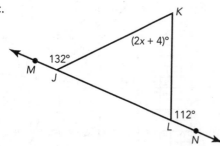

d.

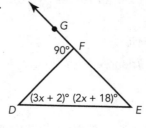

Stretch

To tessellate a plane means to cover a surface by repeated use of a single shape or design without gaps or overlaps. M.C. Escher was a Dutch graphic artist who is famous for his tessellations, perspective drawings, and impossible spaces.

Not all shapes or patterns can be tessellated. Use what you know about interior and exterior angles to show why it is possible to tessellate with a regular hexagon but not with a regular pentagon.

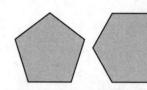

Review

1. Triangle *ABC* is similar to Triangle *DEF*. Determine a sequence of transformations that maps
△*ABC* onto △*DEF*.

a.

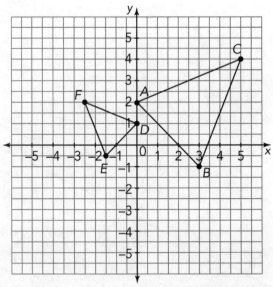

b.

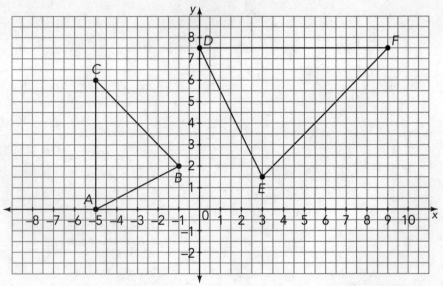

2. Dilate △XYZ by the given scale factor, using point P as the center of dilation.

   a. Dilate by a scale factor of $\frac{3}{4}$.

   b. Dilate by a scale factor of 1.5.

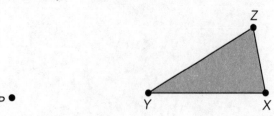

3. Calculate the measure of each angle.

   a.

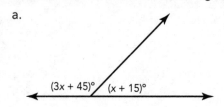

   b.

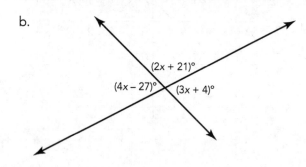

Crisscross Applesauce

Angle Relationships Formed by Lines
Intersected by a Transversal

2

WARM UP

Use the numbered angles in the diagram to answer each question.

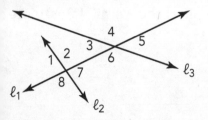

1. Which angles form vertical angles?

2. Which angles are congruent?

LEARNING GOALS

- Explore the angles determined by two lines that are intersected by a transversal.
- Use informal arguments to establish facts about the angles created when parallel lines are cut by a transversal.
- Identify corresponding angles, alternate interior angles, alternate exterior angles, same-side interior angles, and same-side exterior angles.
- Determine the measure of alternate interior angles, alternate exterior angles, same-side interior angles, same-side exterior angles, and corresponding angles.

KEY TERMS

- transversal
- alternate interior angles
- alternate exterior angles
- same-side interior angles
- same-side exterior angles

When two lines intersect, special angle pair relationships are formed. What special angle pair relationships are formed when three lines intersect?

Euclid's Fifth Postulate

Euclid is known as the father of geometry, and he stated five postulates upon which every other geometric relationship can be based. The fifth postulate is known as the *Parallel Postulate*. Consider one of the equivalent forms of this postulate:

"Given any straight line and a point not on the line, there exists one and only one straight line that passes through the point and never intersects the line."

1. Draw a picture that shows your interpretation of this statement of the postulate.

2. Why do you think this postulate is called the Parallel Postulate?

A common definition of parallel lines is co-planar lines that are always equidistant, or the same distance apart.

3. Explain what is meant by this definition and demonstrate it on your diagram.

Creating New Angles from Triangles

In the previous lesson, *Pulling a One-Eighty!* you determined measures of interior and exterior angles of triangles.

Consider the diagram shown. Lines *m* and *ℓ* are parallel. This is notated as *m* ∥ *ℓ*.

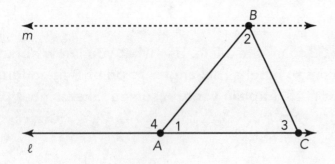

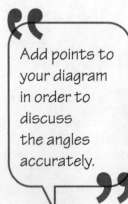

> Add points to your diagram in order to discuss the angles accurately.

1. Explain the relationships between the numbered angles in the diagram.

2. Trace the diagram onto two sheets of patty paper and extend $\overline{AB}$ to create a line that contains the side of the triangle. Align the triangles on your patty paper and translate the bottom triangle along $\overline{AB}$ until $\overline{AC}$ lies on line *m*. Trace your translated triangle on the top sheet of patty paper. Label the translated triangle *A'B'C'*.

3. Angle 1 in △*A'B'C'* is a translation of Angle 1 in △*ABC*.
   How are the measures of these angles related to each other?
   Explain your reasoning.

4. Extend $\overline{CB}$ to create a line. Use what you know about special
   angle pairs to label all six angles at point *B* as congruent to
   ∠1, ∠2, or ∠3. Explain your reasoning. Sketch your patty
   paper drawing.

Consider your diagram from the previous activity. If you remove $\overline{BC}$ and the line containing $\overline{BC}$, your diagram might look similar to the diagram shown.

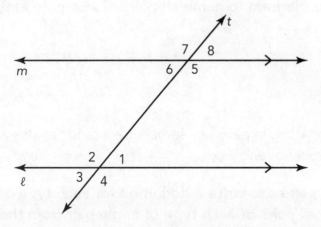

In this diagram the two parallel lines, *m* and *ℓ*, are intersected by a *transversal*, *t*. A **transversal** is a line that intersects two or more lines.

Recall that corresponding angles are angles that have the same relative positions in geometric figures. In the previous activity, when you translated △*ABC* to create △*A′B′C′* you created three sets of corresponding angles. You can also refer to corresponding angles in relation to lines intersected by a transversal.

Arrowheads in diagrams indicate parallel lines. Lines or segments with the same number of arrowheads are parallel.

The transversal, *t*, in this diagram corresponds to the line that contained side *AB* in your patty paper diagram.

1. **Use the diagram to name all pairs of corresponding angles.**

2. **Analyze each angle pair: ∠1 with ∠6 and ∠2 with ∠5.**

   a. **Are the angles between (on the *interior of*) lines *m* and *ℓ*, or are they outside (on the *exterior of*) lines *m* and *ℓ*?**

   b. **Are the angles on the same side of the transversal, or are they on opposite (*alternating*) sides of the transversal?**

There is a special relationship between angles like $\angle 1$ and $\angle 6$ or $\angle 2$ and $\angle 5$. **Alternate interior angles** are angles formed when a transversal intersects two other lines. These angle pairs are on opposite sides of the transversal and are between the two other lines.

Alternate exterior angles are also formed when a transversal intersects two lines. These angle pairs are on opposite sides of the transversal and are outside the other two lines.

3. **Use your diagram to name all pairs of alternate exterior angles.**

Two additional angle pairs are *same-side interior angles* and *same-side exterior angles*.

4. **Use the names to write a definition for each type of angle pair. Identify all pairs of each type of angle pair from the diagram.**

   a. **same-side interior angles**

   b. **same-side exterior angles**

5. In the diagram from the previous activity, each time you extended a side of the triangle, you created a transversal. Identify the angle pairs described by each statement.

a. corresponding angles if $\overleftrightarrow{BC}$ is the transversal

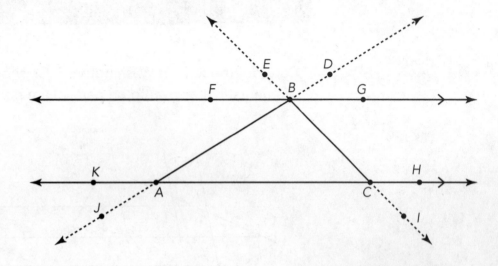

b. alternate interior angles if $\overleftrightarrow{BC}$ is the transversal

c. alternate exterior angles if $\overleftrightarrow{AB}$ is the transversal

d. same-side interior angles if $\overleftrightarrow{AB}$ is the transversal

Same-side interior angles are on the same side of the transversal and are between the other two lines.

e. same-side exterior angles if $\overleftrightarrow{AB}$ is the transversal

Same-side exterior angles are on the same side of the transversal and are outside the other two lines.

Analyzing Special Angle Pairs

Consider the map of Washington, D.C., shown. Assume that all line segments that appear to be parallel are parallel.

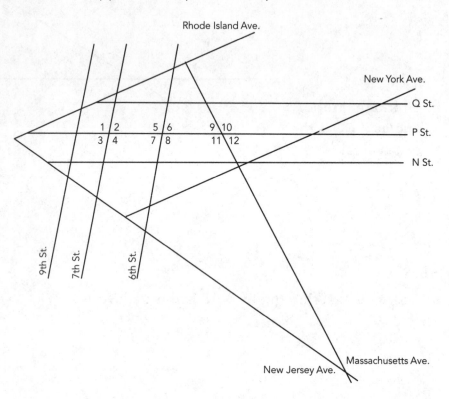

1. **Consider only P St., N St., Massachusetts Ave., and 6th St. Which of these streets, if any, are transversals? Explain your reasoning.**

Let's explore the relationships between the angles formed from lines cut by transversals.

2. **Use a protractor to measure all 12 angles labeled on the diagram.**

3. Consider only 6th St., 7th St., and P St.

a. Which of these streets, if any, are transversals? Explain your reasoning.

NOTES

b. What is the relationship between 6th St. and 7th St.?

c. Name the pairs of alternate interior angles. What do you notice about their angle measures?

d. Name the pairs of alternate exterior angles. What do you notice about their angle measures?

e. Name the pairs of corresponding angles. What do you notice about their angle measures?

f. Name the pairs of same-side interior angles. What do you notice about their angle measures?

g. Name the pairs of same-side exterior angles. What do you notice about their angle measures?

4. Consider only 6th St., Massachusetts Ave., and P St.

   a. Which of these streets, if any, are transversals?

   b. What is the relationship between 6th St. and Massachusetts Ave.?

   c. Name the pairs of alternate interior angles. What do you notice about their angle measures?

   d. Name the pairs of alternate exterior angles. What do you notice about their angle measures?

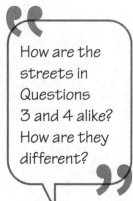

How are the streets in Questions 3 and 4 alike? How are they different?

   e. Name the pairs of corresponding angles. What do you notice about their angle measures?

   f. Name the pairs of same-side interior angles. What do you notice about their angle measures?

   g. Name the pairs of same-side exterior angles. What do you notice about their angle measures?

In the previous activity, you explored angle pairs formed by a transversal intersecting two non-parallel lines and a transversal intersecting two parallel lines.

1. Make a conjecture about the types of lines cut by a transversal and the measures of the special angle pairs.

Refer back to the measurements of the labeled angles on the diagram of Washington, D.C.

2. What do you notice about the measures of each pair of alternate interior angles when the lines are

   a. non-parallel?

   b. parallel?

3. What do you notice about the measures of each pair of alternate exterior angles when the lines are

   a. non-parallel?

   b. parallel?

4. What do you notice about the measures of each pair of corresponding angles when the lines are

   a. non-parallel?

   b. parallel?

5. What do you notice about the measures of the same-side interior angles when the lines are

   a. non-parallel?

   b. parallel?

6. What do you notice about the measures of the same-side exterior angles when the lines are

   a. non-parallel?

   b. parallel?

7. Summarize your conclusions in the table by writing the relationships of the measures of the angles. The relationships are either congruent or not congruent, supplementary or not supplementary.

Angles	Two Parallel Lines Intersected by a Transversal	Two Non-Parallel Lines Intersected by a Transversal
Alternate Interior Angles		
Alternate Exterior Angles		
Corresponding Angles		
Same-Side Interior Angles		
Same-Side Exterior Angles		

8. Use transformations to explain how to map the angle pairs that are congruent.

9. Use transformations to explain why certain angle pairs are supplementary.

Use what you know about angle pairs to answer each question.

1. Sylvia and Scott were working together to solve the problem shown.

   Given: $\overleftrightarrow{AB} \parallel \overleftrightarrow{CD}$. Solve for x. Show all your work.

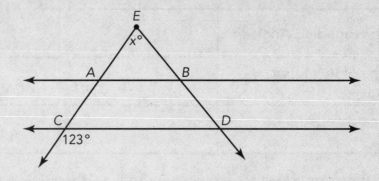

   a. Sylvia concluded that x = 66°. How did Sylvia get her answer?

   b. Scott does not agree with Sylvia's answer. He thinks there is not enough information to solve the problem. How could Scott alter the figure to show why he disagrees with Sylvia's answer?

   c. Who is correct?

2. Opposite sides of the figure shown are parallel. Suppose that the measure of angle *M* is equal to 30°. Solve for the measures of angles *G*, *E*, and *O*. Explain your reasoning.

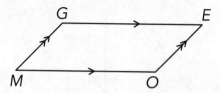

3. Determine the measure of each unknown angle.

a.

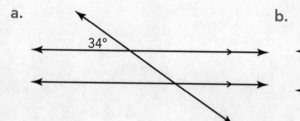

b.

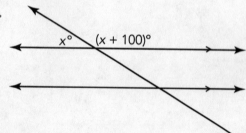

4. In this figure, $\overleftrightarrow{AB} \parallel \overleftrightarrow{CD}$ and $\overrightarrow{EC} \perp \overrightarrow{ED}$. Solve for *x*. Show all your work.

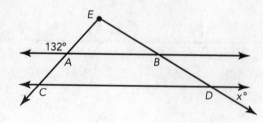

5. Determine the measure of each angle in this figure.

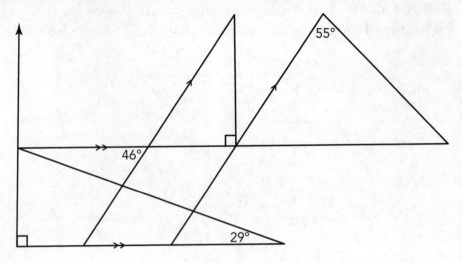

6. Solve for x. Show all your work.

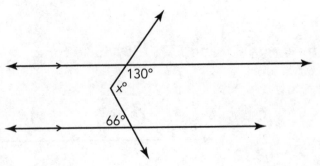

TALK the TALK 💬

What's So Special?

1. If two lines are intersected by a transversal, when are

   a. alternate interior angles congruent?

   b. alternate exterior angles congruent?

   c. vertical angles congruent?

   d. corresponding angles congruent?

   e. same-side interior angles supplementary?

   f. same-side exterior angles supplementary?

   g. linear pairs of angles supplementary?

2. Briana says that she can use what she learned about parallel lines cut by a transversal to show that the measures of the angles of a triangle sum to 180°. She drew the figure shown.

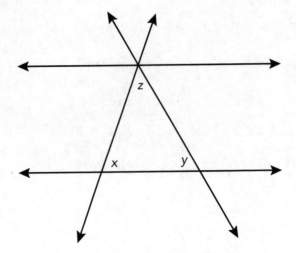

Explain what Briana discovered.

Assignment

Write

Write the term that best completes each sentence.

1. _____ are pairs of angles formed when a third line (transversal) intersects two other lines. These angles are on opposite sides of the transversal and are outside the other two lines.

2. A _____ is a line that intersects two or more lines.

3. _____ are pairs of angles formed when a third line (transversal) intersects two other lines. These angles are on the same side of the transversal and are outside the other two lines.

4. _____ are pairs of angles formed when a third line (transversal) intersects two other lines. These angles are on opposite sides of the transversal and are in between the other two lines.

5. _____ are pairs of angles formed when a third line (transversal) intersects two other lines. These angles are on the same side of the transversal and are in between the other two lines.

Remember

When two parallel lines are intersected by a transversal,

- corresponding angles are congruent,
- alternate interior angles are congruent,
- alternate exterior angles are congruent,
- same-side interior angles are supplementary, and
- same-side exterior angles are supplementary.

Practice

The figure shows part of a map of Chicago, Illinois.

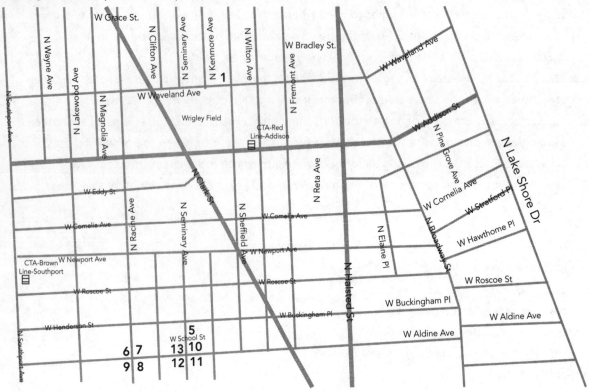

1. Use the numbered angles to identify a pair that illustrates each relationship.

   a. Name a pair of alternate interior angles.

   b. Name a pair of alternate exterior angles.

   c. Name a pair of corresponding angles.

   d. Name a pair of same-side interior angles.

   e. Name a pair of same-side exterior angles.

2. Look at the intersection of W. Waveland Ave. and N. Sheffield Ave. Notice the northwest corner is labeled ∠1. Label the other angles of this intersection in clockwise order angles 2, 3, and 4. Next, label the angles created by the intersection of W. Addison St. and N. Sheffield Ave. angles 14, 15, 16, and 17 clockwise, starting at the northwest corner.

   a. Determine the type of angle pair for ∠1 and ∠14.

   b. Determine the type of angle pair for ∠3 and ∠15.

   c. Determine the type of angle pair for ∠1 and ∠16.

   d. Determine the type of angle pair for ∠1 and ∠17.

   e. Determine the type of angle pair for ∠3 and ∠14.

3. Determine the measure of all the angles in each diagram.

a.

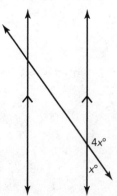

4x°

x°

b.

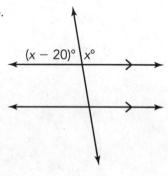

(x − 20)° x°

4. Solve for x. Show all your work.

a.

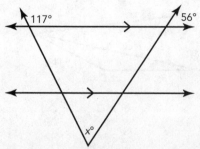

117°

56°

x°

b.

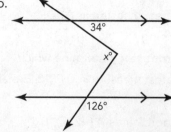

34°

x°

126°

Stretch

Given: $\ell_1 \parallel \ell_2$ and $\ell_3 \parallel \ell_4$.

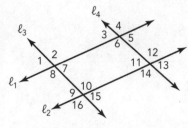

1. Explain why every angle in the diagram is congruent to ∠6 or ∠7.

2. What can you conclude about the sum of the measures of ∠6, ∠7, ∠10, and ∠11? Explain your reasoning.

3. Use what you learned in this lesson to explain what you know about the angles in any parallelogram.

Review

1. Determine the unknown angle measures.

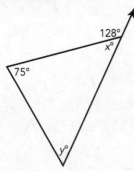

2. Use the diagram to answer each question.

   a. Without using a protractor, determine which angle has the greatest measure in △KDR. Explain your reasoning.

   b. Without using a protractor, determine which angle has the greatest measure in △PRK. Explain your reasoning.

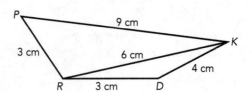

3. Triangle *ABC*, with coordinates *A* (−2, 5), *B* (0, 7), and *C* (1, 3), is dilated by a scale factor of $\frac{1}{2}$, with a center of dilation at the origin. Determine the coordinates of Triangle *A'B'C'*.

4. Dilate Quadrilateral *ABCD* by a scale factor of 2, using point *P* as the center of dilation.

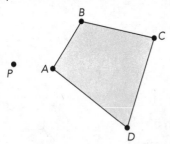

5. Factor the expression 1.5x + 6.

6. Expand the expression $4(\frac{3}{2}x + 5)$.

The Vanishing Point

The Angle-Angle Similarity Theorem

WARM UP
Suppose that $\triangle BHX$ is similar to $\triangle KRC$.

1. List the corresponding angles.

2. Write the ratios to identify the proportional side lengths.

LEARNING GOALS
- Develop the minimum criteria to show that two triangles are similar.
- Use informal arguments to establish facts about the angle-angle criterion for similarity of triangles.
- Use the Angle-Angle Similarity Theorem to identify similar triangles.

KEY TERM
- Angle-Angle Similarity Theorem

You have determined that when two triangles are similar, the corresponding angles are congruent and the corresponding sides are proportional. How can you show that two triangles are similar without measuring all the angles and side lengths?

Vanishing Point

Graphic artists use knowledge about similarity to create realistic-looking perspective drawings. Choose where the horizon should be and a vanishing point—a point where all the parallel lines in the drawing should appear to meet—and you too can create a perspective drawing.

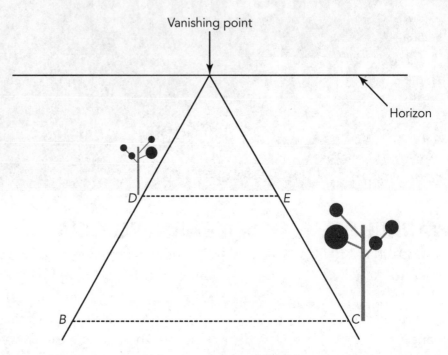

The symbol ~ means "is similar to."

1. Suppose the vanishing point is point A and that $\overline{DE} \parallel \overline{BC}$. How could you demonstrate that $\triangle ABC \sim \triangle ADE$?

2. Draw a horizontal line in the path to create another similar triangle. Then sketch a tree at that line using the appropriate scale factor.

You have determined that when two triangles are similar, the corresponding angles are congruent and the corresponding sides are proportional. To show that two triangles are similar, do you need to show that all of the corresponding sides are proportional and all of the corresponding angles are congruent?

Let's explore an efficient method to determine if two triangles are similar.

1. **If the measures of two angles of a triangle are known, is that enough information to draw a similar triangle? Let's explore this possibility.**

   a. **Use a straightedge to draw △*ABC* in the space provided.**

   b. **Use a protractor to measure ∠*A* and ∠*B* of △*ABC* and record the measurements.**

      m∠*A* = _____   m∠*B* = _____

   c. **Use the Triangle Sum Theorem to determine m∠*C*.**

d. Draw a second triangle, △DEF, in the space provided using the angle measurements from part (b).

e. Based on your knowledge, what other information is needed to determine if the two triangles are similar, and how can you acquire that information?

f. Determine the measurements to get the additional information needed and decide if the two triangles are similar.

You have just shown that given the measures of two pairs of congruent corresponding angles of two triangles, it is possible to determine that two triangles are similar. In the study of geometry, this is expressed as a theorem.

The **Angle-Angle (AA) Similarity Theorem** states that if two angles of one triangle are congruent to the corresponding angles of another triangle, then the triangles are similar.

Using the Angle-Angle Similarity Theorem

Identify the triangles that are similar by the AA Similarity Theorem. Explain how you know that the triangles are similar.

1. $\overline{CD} \parallel \overline{GH}$

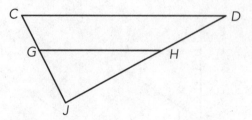

2.

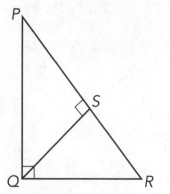

3.

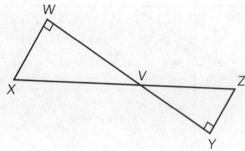

4.

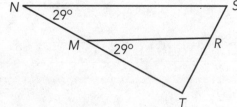

Labeling the diagram can help you visualize the given information.

Use what you have learned about triangle similarity to answer each question.

Given: $\overleftrightarrow{BD} \parallel \overleftrightarrow{HG}$, $\overleftrightarrow{AH} \parallel \overleftrightarrow{DF}$, $\overleftrightarrow{AH} \perp \overleftrightarrow{AG}$, $\overleftrightarrow{DF} \perp \overleftrightarrow{AG}$

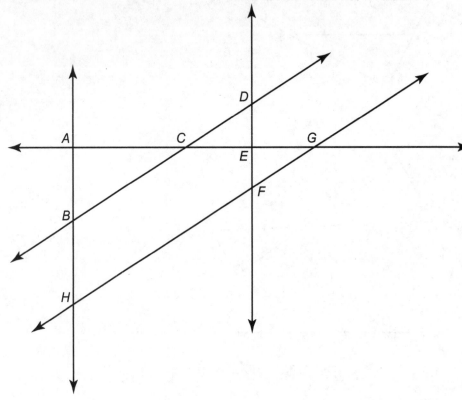

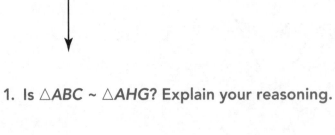

1. Is △ABC ~ △AHG? Explain your reasoning.

2. Is △ABC ~ △EDC? Explain your reasoning.

3. Is △EDC ~ △EFG? Explain your reasoning.

4. Is △ABC ~ △EFG? Explain your reasoning.

5. Is △AHG ~ △EFG? Explain your reasoning.

TALK the TALK

Bow-Tie Triangles

You can draw special triangles known as bow-tie triangles. First, draw a pair of parallel line segements. Then, connect the pairs of endpoints with line segments so that the line segments intersect, like this:

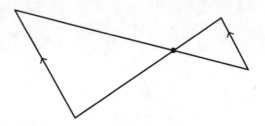

1. Are bow-tie triangles always similar? Show your work and explain your reasoning. Then, compare your work with your classmates' work.

Assignment

Write

In your own words, explain the Angle-Angle (AA) Similarity Theorem.

Remember

You can use dilations and other transformations, line and angle relationships, measurements, and/or the Angle-Angle Similarity Theorem to demonstrate that two figures are similar.

Practice

Use the AA Similarity Theorem and a protractor, if necessary, to demonstrate how the triangles in each pair are similar. Show your work.

1.

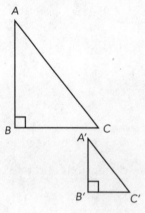

2.

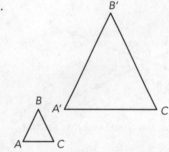

3.

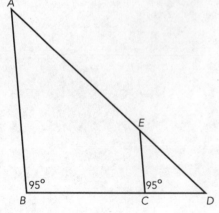

4.

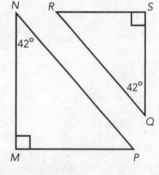

Stretch

Vicki says that any two right triangles with two congruent angles are similar. Patrick says that the triangles are similar and congruent. Who is correct? Explain how you know.

Review

1. In the figure shown, lines ℓ_1 and ℓ_2 are intersected by transversal ℓ_3. Name the corresponding angles.

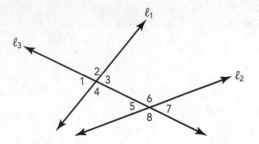

2. Sketch an example of alternate interior angles.

3. A photo has a width of 250 pixels and a height of 320 pixels. Determine the new dimensions and tell whether the enlarged or reduced photo is similar.

   a. Width: 150%, height: 200%

   b. Width: 75%, height: 75%

4. Solve each equation.

   a. $3(x + 3) = -6$

   b. $-20 = -2(4 - x)$

Line and Angle Relationships Summary

KEY TERMS

- Triangle Sum Theorem
- exterior angle of a polygon
- remote interior angles of a triangle
- Exterior Angle Theorem
- transversal
- alternate interior angles
- alternate exterior angles
- same-side interior angles
- same-side exterior angles
- Angle-Angle Similarity Theorem

LESSON 1

Pulling a One-Eighty!

The **Triangle Sum Theorem** states that the sum of the measures of the interior angles of a triangle is 180°. The longest side of a triangle is opposite the interior angle with the greatest measure and the shortest side is opposite the interior angle with the least measure.

An **exterior angle of a polygon** is an angle between a side of a polygon and the extension of its adjacent side. It is formed by extending a ray from one side of the polygon. For example, in the diagram, ∠1, ∠2, and ∠3 are the interior angles of the triangle, and ∠4 is an exterior angle of the triangle. ∠1 and ∠2 are remote interior angles. The **remote interior angles of a triangle** are the two angles that are non-adjacent to the specified exterior angle.

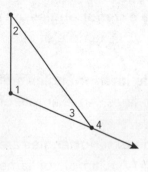

The **Exterior Angle Theorem** states that the measure of the exterior angle of a triangle is equal to the sum of the measures of the two remote interior angles of the triangle. In the diagram shown, m∠1 + m∠2 = m∠4.

Crisscross Applesauce

A **transversal** is a line that intersects two or more lines. In this diagram, two parallel lines, *m* and *l*, are intersected by a transversal, *t*.

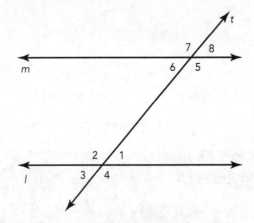

Corresponding angles have the same relative positions in geometric figures. An example of corresponding angles are ∠2 and ∠7.

Alternate interior angles are on opposite sides of the transversal and are between the two other lines. An example of alternate interior angles are ∠1 and ∠6.

Alternate exterior angles are on opposite sides of the transversal and are outside the other two lines. An example of alternate exterior angles are ∠4 and ∠7.

Same-side interior angles are on the same side of the transversal and are between the other two lines. An example of same-side interior angles are ∠2 and ∠6.

Same-side exterior angles are on the same-side of the transversal and are outside the other two lines. An example of same-side exterior angles are ∠4 and ∠ 8.

When two parallel lines are intersected by a transversal,
- Corresponding angles are congruent.
- Alternate interior angles are congruent.
- Alternate exterior angles are congruent.
- Same-side interior angles are supplementary.
- Same side exterior angles are supplementary.

The **Angle-Angle (AA) Similarity Theorem** states that if two angles of one triangle are congruent to the corresponding angles of another triangle, then the triangles are similar.

For example, in the figure shown, $\triangle XWV$ is similar to $\triangle ZYV$ by the AA Similarity Theorem. Because $\angle XWV$ and $\angle ZYV$ are right angles, they are congruent to each other. Because $\angle WVX$ and $\angle YVZ$ are vertical angles, they are congruent to each other. Thus, $\triangle XWV$ is similar to $\triangle ZYV$.

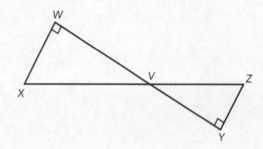

You can use dilations and other transformations, line and angle relationships, measurements, and/or the Angle-Angle Similarity Theorem to demonstrate that two figures are similar.

DEVELOPING

f(unction)

FOUNDATIONS

The lessons in this module build on your experience with proportional relationships and the work you did in *Transforming Geometric Objects*. You will analyze and represent linear relationships using tables, equations, graphs, and scenarios. You will develop an understanding of functions. Once you know how to describe functional relationships and construct linear models, you will apply these skills to analyze bivariate data. The concepts in this module will provide the basis for the majority of your high school algebra and statistics studies.

From Proportions to Linear Relationships

Where might you see the sign shown? What can you say about the triangle on the sign? What do you think 8% represents?

Module 2: Developing Function Foundations

TOPIC 1: FROM PROPORTIONS TO LINEAR RELATIONSHIPS

In this topic, students build on their knowledge of ratio and proportional relationships to develop connections between proportional relationships, lines, and linear equations. Students compare proportional relationships represented in different ways to ensure a firm understanding of the meaning of proportionality. Students then use similar triangles to explain why the slope of a line is always the same between any two points on the line.

Where have we been?

In grade 6, students developed their understanding of ratio. The next year, they determined characteristics of scenarios, tables, graphs, and equations of proportional relationships. Students review their prior knowledge of ratios and proportional relationships, including unit rate and the constant of proportionality.

Where are we going?

This topic establishes an important link from a major concept of middle school mathematics, ratios and proportional relationships, to a major focus of high school mathematics, functions. In the next topic, students will increase their familiarity and flexibility with determining slope and writing equations of linear relationships from different representations and in different forms.

Using Graphs to Show Proportional and Non-Proportional Relationships

Both of these graphs show linear relationships between time and distance. They both show speeds. The graph on the left shows a proportional linear relationship, because the graph is a straight line through the origin. The graph on the right shows a non-proportional relationship.

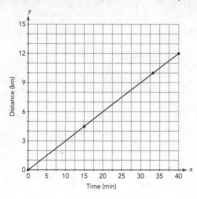
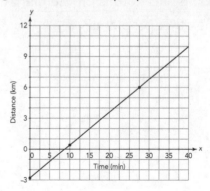

Myth: There is one right way to do math problems.

Employing multiple strategies to arrive at a single, correct solution is important in life. Suppose you are driving in a crowded downtown area. If one road is backed up, then you can always take a different route. If you know only one route, then you're out of luck.

Learning mathematics is no different. There may only be one right answer, but there are often multiple strategies to arrive at that solution. Everyone should get in the habit of saying: *Well, that's one way to do it. Is there another way? What are the pros and cons?* That way, you avoid falling into the trap of thinking there is only one right way because that strategy might not always work or there might be a more efficient strategy.

Teaching students multiple strategies is important. This helps students understand the benefits of the more efficient method. In addition, everyone has different experiences and preferences. What works for you might not work for someone else.

#mathmythbusted

Talking Points

You can further support your student's learning by asking them to take a step back and think about a different strategy when they are stuck.

Questions to Ask

• What strategy are you using?
• What is another way to solve the problem?
• Can you draw a model?
• Can you come back to this problem after doing some other problems?

Key Terms

constant of proportionality
In a proportional relationship, the ratio of all *y*-values to their corresponding *x*-values is constant. This ratio, $\frac{y}{x}$, is called the constant of proportionality.

slope
In any linear relationship, slope describes the direction and steepness of a line. In a proportional relationship, the constant of proportionality and the slope are the same.

Post-Secondary Proportions

Representations of Proportional Relationships

WARM UP
Determine each equivalent ratio.

1. $\dfrac{7}{16} = \dfrac{x}{48}$

2. $\dfrac{t}{90} = \dfrac{5}{9}$

3. $\dfrac{10}{P} = 1$

4. $250 = \dfrac{1000}{q}$

LEARNING GOALS
- Represent proportional relationships with tables, lines, and linear equations.
- Compare graphs of proportional relationships.
- Compare two different proportional relationships represented in multiple ways.

KEY TERMS
- proportional relationship
- constant of proportionality

You have studied proportional relationships in previous courses. How can you represent and compare proportional relationships using graphs, tables, and equations?

Ratio of Women to Men

Government agencies and civil rights groups monitor enrollment data at universities to ensure that different groups are fully represented. One study focused on the enrollment of women at a certain university The study found that three out of every five students enrolled were women.

Use the findings of the study to write each ratio.

1. the number of enrolled female students to the total number of students

2. the number of enrolled male students to the total number of students

3. the number of enrolled female students to the number of enrolled male students

4. the number of enrolled male students to the number of enrolled female students

ACTIVITY 1.1	Representing Proportional Relationships

Use the findings of the enrollment study to make predictions.

1. Determine the number of enrolled female students for each given total number of enrolled students. Explain your reasoning.

   a. 15 total students   b. 250 total students

   c. 4000 total students

2. Compare the total number of enrolled students to the number of enrolled male students.

   a. Complete the table.

Total Students Enrolled in a University	Male Students Enrolled in a University
0	
250	
6000	
	6000

   b. Explain how you calculated each value.

3. Determine the number of female students if 800 enrolled students are male. Show all work and explain your reasoning.

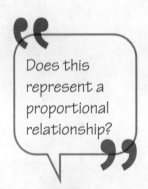

Does this represent a proportional relationship?

4. Choose the correct equation to match each description. Then compare the equations.

$y = \frac{2}{5}x$ $y = 2x + 3$ $y = \frac{2}{3}x$

$y = \frac{3}{2}x$ $y = \frac{3}{5}x$

$y = \frac{5}{2}x$ $y = 2x + 5$ $y = 3x + 2$

a. the number of female students enrolled, y, for x total number of students enrolled

b. the number of male students enrolled, y, for x total number of students enrolled

c. the number of female students enrolled, y, for x male students enrolled

d. the number of male students enrolled, y, for x female students enrolled

e. Describe the similarities and differences in each of the correct equations.

5. Create graphs that display each ratio. Then compare the graphs.

   a. the total number of female students enrolled, *y*, with respect to the total number of students enrolled, *x*

   b. the total number of male students enrolled, *y*, with respect to the total number of students enrolled, *x*

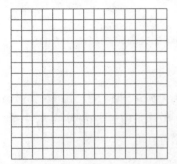

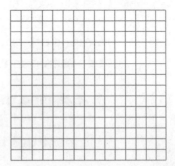

   c. Describe the similarities and differences of the two graphs.

In this lesson, you are studying relationships that are proportional. A **proportional relationship** is one in which the ratio of the inputs to the outputs is constant. For example, the ratio of women to men at a university is 3 : 2. Proportional relationships are always written in the form $y = kx$, where x represents an input value, y represents an output value, and k represents some constant that is not equal to 0. The constant k is called the **constant of proportionality**.

6. Identify the constant of proportionality for each relationship in Question 4.

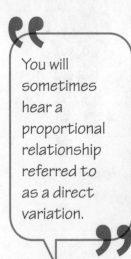

You will sometimes hear a proportional relationship referred to as a direct variation.

7. Identify the constant of proportionality, or rate of change, for each graph in Question 5. Then explain how to determine k from a graph.

ACTIVITY 1.2

Comparing Ratios and Graphs

Graphs provide a variety of information about relationships between quantities.

> Can you determine proportionality or dependence?

1. **Examine the lines graphed on the coordinate plane. What can you determine about the relationships between the quantities by inspecting the graph?**

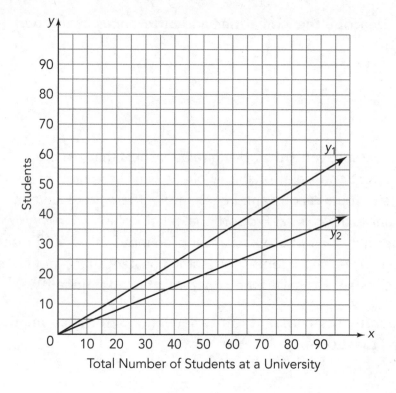

Total Number of Students at a University

The lines y_1 and y_2 each represent a proportional relationship. One line represents the proportional relationship between the number of females enrolled and the total number of students. The other line represents the proportional relationship between the number of males enrolled and the total number of students.

2. Determine which line represents each relationship. Explain your reasoning.

a. the number of females enrolled in a university

b. the number of males enrolled in a university

The ratio of the number of students who enjoy music to the total number of students is slightly more than the ratio of female students to the total number of students.

3. Draw a line on the coordinate plane that might represent the ratio of the number of students who enjoy music to the total number of students. Label this line y_3. Explain your reasoning.

In a linear relationship, any change in an independent variable will produce a corresponding change in the dependent variable.

The ratio of students who work full-time to total students is less than the ratio of male students to total students.

4. Draw a line on the coordinate plane that might represent the ratio of students at a university who work full-time to the total number of students. Label this line y_4. Explain your reasoning.

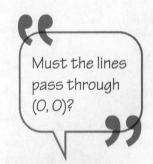

Must the lines pass through (0, 0)?

5. Of the lines on the coordinate plane, which is the steepest? How does this relate to the ratios?

Daisa attends college in another state. During summer break, she drives home from college to visit her family and friends.

Daisa's Drive Home

Time (hours)	Distance (miles)
3	180
2	120
1.5	90
2.5	150

1. Daisa decides to keep track of the time it takes her to drive home from school. She records her distance after various numbers of hours. Her data are shown in the table.

   a.   Does this table represent a proportional relationship? Explain your reasoning.

   b.   Write a ratio for distance to time.

   c.   Write the unit rate for distance per 1 hour.

Unit rate is a comparison of two quantities in which the denominator has a value of one unit.

One of Daisa's high school classmates, Tymar, attends college with Daisa. He also drives home during the summer break but takes a different route.

2. Analyze the graph of his trip.

   a. Does the graph represent a proportional relationship? Explain your reasoning.

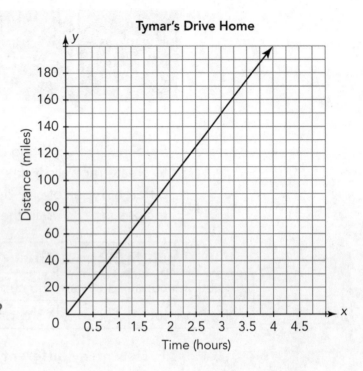

Tymar's Drive Home

   b. Who drives faster—Daisa or Tymar? Explain your reasoning.

A third friend, Alisha, offers to drive Daisa and Tymar home for spring break so that they can share the cost of gas money. When asked how fast she drives, Alisha reported that the distance traveled, y, for the time, x, can be expressed as $y = 57x$.

3. Does Alisha's equation represent a proportional relationship? Explain your reasoning.

4. Compare the representations of the three friends.

   a. Who drives the fastest? Explain your reasoning.

   b. Rank the friends in order from the slowest driver to the fastest driver.

Students in a sculpting class at a university are working in teams to create modeling clay. The students learned that they can make different types of clay by changing the ratio of flour to water. Their recipes are shown in the table.

	Group 1	Group 2	Group 3	Group 4	Group 5	Group 6	Group 7
Flour	2.5 cups	3 cups	7.5 cups	4 cups	12 cups	3.75 cups	5 cups
Water	1 cup	2 cups	3 cups	2 cups	8 cups	1.5 cups	2 cups

1. **How many different recipes for clay did the students create? Show all work and explain your reasoning.**

The art professor would like all of the projects to include the same shade of orange. The students have learned that orange paint is created by mixing red and yellow paints. Three groups presented suggestions for the shade of orange to be used for the art projects.

Avi's Group	Zander's Group		Paul's Group
$y = \frac{4}{5}x$, where x is the amount of red paint and y is the amount of yellow paint	**Red Paint (parts)**	**Yellow Paint (parts)**	Orange Recipe
	6	1.5	
	8	2	
	12	3	
	15	3.75	

Paul's Group graph: Orange Recipe, x-axis "Red Paint (parts)" from 0 to 18, y-axis "Yellow Paint (parts)" from 0 to 18. A line is drawn through the origin rising to the upper right.

2. Explain how you know that each group's proposal represents a proportional relationship.

   a. Avi's Group

   b. Zander's Group

   c. Paul's Group

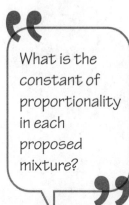

What is the constant of proportionality in each proposed mixture?

The greater the ratio of yellow to red paint used, the lighter the shade of orange paint.

3. Rate the group's proposals from lightest orange to deepest orange. Explain your reasoning.

4. Write an equation, where x is the amount of red paint and y is the amount of yellow paint, that would create a shade of orange that is between the two deepest shades. Explain your reasoning.

TALK the TALK

Proportional Relationships

All of the relationships in this lesson are examples of proportional relationships.

1. Complete the graphic organizer to summarize proportional relationships. Include characteristics, examples, and non-examples using tables, equations, and graphs.

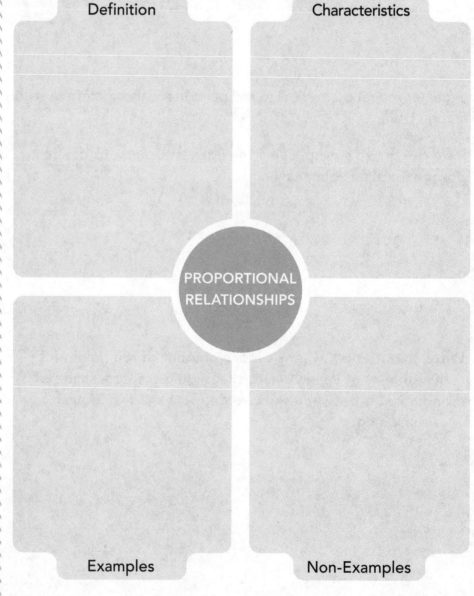

Definition

Characteristics

PROPORTIONAL
RELATIONSHIPS

Examples

Non-Examples

Assignment

Write

Explain how to compare proportional relationships represented in different forms.

Remember

Proportional relationships can be represented using tables, graphs, and equations. In a table, all the ratios of corresponding x- and y-values must be constant. On a graph, a proportional relationship is represented as a linear graph passing through the origin. The equation for a proportional relationship is written in the form $y = kx$, where k is the constant of proportionality.

Practice

1. Determine the constant of proportionality represented in each graph.

a.
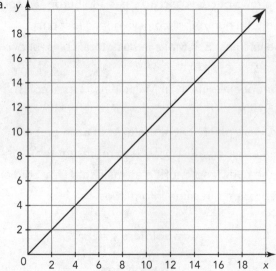

b.
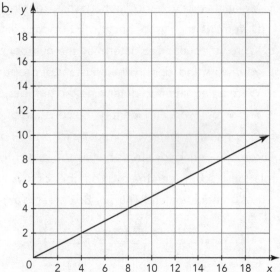

c.
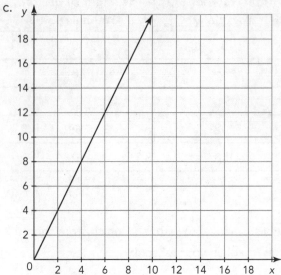

2. Determine the constant of proportionality for each proportional relationship. Assume that y represents all of the outputs and x represents all of the inputs.

   a. $2x = 10y$ b. $\left(\frac{3}{5}\right)y = 8x$

   c. $\frac{y}{10} = 10x$ d. $\left(\frac{1}{2}\right)x = y$

3. Melanie collects coins from all over the world. She is reorganizing her collection into coins from Europe and coins from other parts of the world. After sorting the coins, she comes to the conclusion that six out of every ten of the coins in her collection come from Europe.

   a. Write a ratio for the number of European coins to the total number of coins, the number of non-European coins to the total number of coins, and the number of European coins to the number of non-European coins.

   b. Melanie has 230 coins in her collection. Determine the number of European and non-European coins that she has in her collection.

   c. Melanie adds to her collection while keeping the same ratio of coins and now has 180 European coins. Determine the number of non-European coins and the total number of coins in her collection.

   d. Write an equation to determine the number of European coins, E, if Melanie has t total coins. Show your work and identify the constant of proportionality.

   e. Write an equation to determine the number of non-European coins, N, if Melanie has t total coins. Show your work and identify the constant of proportionality.

   f. Graph your equations from parts (d) and (e) on a coordinate plane. Label the axes of each graph.

4. Three competing toy stores review their inventory. FunTimeToys creates a graph to represent the relationship between the total number of toys sold and the number of stuffed animals sold. Toy Soldiers writes an equation and The Toy Box creates a table to represent the same information.

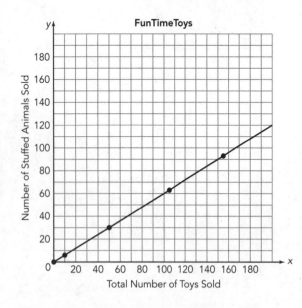

FunTimeToys

Toy Soldiers $y = \frac{1}{2}x$

The Toy Box

Total Number of Toys Sold	Number of Stuffed Animals Sold
0	0
12	8
54	36
102	68
156	104

Fluffy Stuffy Stuffed Animals wants to sell their stuffed animals in a local toy store. In which store should they sell their products if they hope to make the most money? Explain your reasoning.

5. Analyze each scenario and graph.

A voice instructor notices that only one out of every ten of her students can sing soprano.

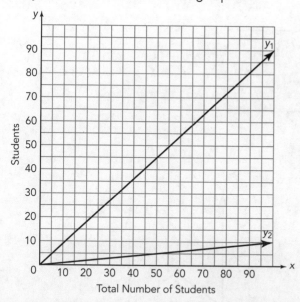

Total Number of Students

A store owner notices that in his parking lot, two out of every six vehicles are trucks.

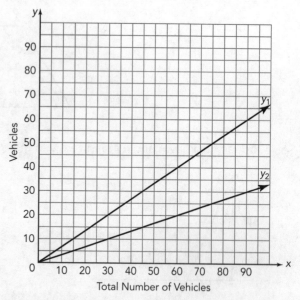

Total Number of Vehicles

a. Identify the proportional relationship represented by each line as it relates to the scenario. Explain your reasoning.

b. Write an equation that has a constant of proportionality between those represented on the graph. Explain what relationship is represented by your equation.

Stretch

Consider the relationship between the side length of a square and the area of the square. Does this represent a proportional relationship? Use a table of values, equation, and graph to justify your answer.

Review

1. In the diagram, $\triangle ABC \sim \triangle XYZ$. State the corresponding sides and angles.

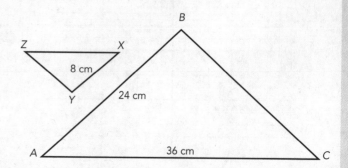

2. In the diagram, $\overline{BD} \parallel \overline{AE}$.
   a. Explain why $\triangle BDC \sim \triangle AEC$.
   b. Determine the length of $\overline{DE}$.

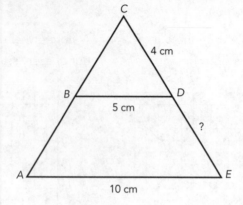

3. Solve for each unknown angle measure given that $\ell_1 \parallel \ell_2$.

   a.

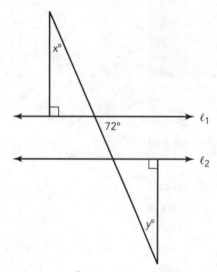

   b.

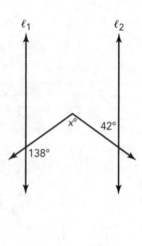

4. Describe a transformation or sequence of transformations to generate line segment $A'B'$ from original line segment AB.

   a.

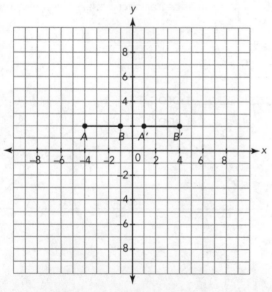

   b.

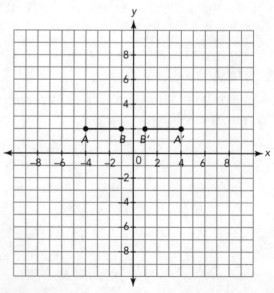

Jack and Jill Went Up the Hill

2

Using Similar Triangles to Describe the Steepness of a Line

WARM UP

Identify the coefficients and constants in each equation.

1. $64x + 24$

2. $36 - 8z$

3. $-3a^2 + 18a$

4. $42mn + 27m - 1$

LEARNING GOALS

- Analyze the rate of change between any two points on a line.
- Use similar triangles to explore the steepness of a line.
- Derive the equations $y = mx$ and $y = mx + b$, representing linear relationships.
- Graph proportional relationships, interpreting the unit rate as the slope of the graph.

KEY TERMS

- rate of change
- slope

You have learned about rates, unit rates, and the constant of proportionality. How can you connect all of those concepts to describe the steepness of a line?

Let It Steep

Examine each triangle shown.

Figure A

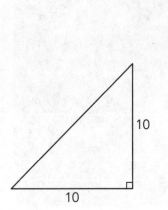

10

10

Figure B

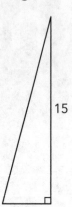

15

4

Figure C

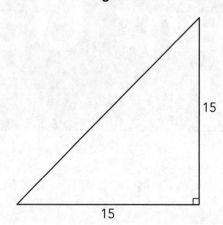

15

15

Figure D

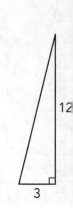

12

3

1. For each triangle, write a ratio that represents the relationship between the height and the base of each triangle.

2. Write each ratio as a unit rate.

3. How can you use these rates to compare the steepness of the triangles?

Constant of Proportionality as Rate of Change

On Monday, Jack and Jill walked from their home up a hill to get to the bus stop. They walked 4 yards every 3 seconds.

1. Write an equation to represent the distance, *d*, Jack and Jill walked over time, *t*.

2. Does this situation represent a proportional relationship? If so, identify the constant of proportionality.

3. Complete the table. Then graph the points. Finally, draw a line to represent the relationship between the time Jack and Jill walked and their distance from home.

Time Spent Walking (seconds)	Distance from Home (yards)
	0
1	
3	
	8
7.5	
9	

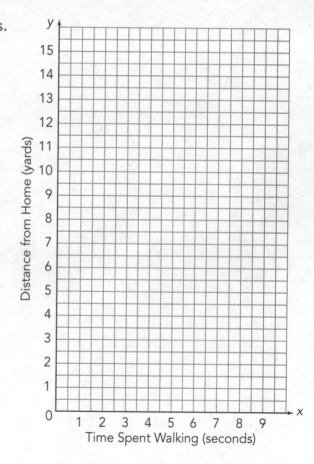

4. What is the unit rate? Explain what the unit rate means in terms of this situation.

5. Explain why Tanner's reasoning is incorrect. Then explain why the graph goes up as you move from left to right.

> **Tanner**
>
> This graph goes up from left to right because Jack and Jill were walking up a hill.

The **rate of change** for a situation describes the amount that the dependent variable changes compared with amount that the independent variable changes.

6. Consider the Jack and Jill situation.

   a. Identify the independent and dependent variables. Explain your reasoning.

   b. Identify the rate of change.

7. Consider the rate of change, the constant of proportionality, and the unit rate for this situation. What do you notice?

8. How would the rate of change and the graph of the relationship change if Jack and Jill walked faster? How would they change if Jack and Jill walked more slowly?

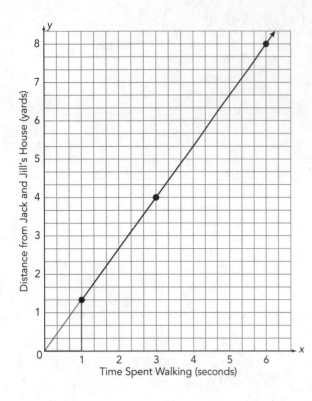

The graph shown represents the relationship between the time Jack and Jill walk and the distance they walk from their home.

Let's analyze three different moments in time during Jack and Jill's walk to the bus stop.

$$t = 1 \quad t = 3 \quad t = 6$$

The graph shows a right triangle drawn to represent $t = 1$.

1. Trace the triangle on a piece of patty paper. Label the horizontal and vertical sides of the right triangle with their respective lengths.

2. Draw right triangles to model $t = 3$ and $t = 6$ on the coordinate plane. Then trace each triangle on a separate piece of patty paper. Label the horizontal and vertical sides of the right triangle with their respective lengths.

3. Determine the steepness of each triangle by writing a ratio of the vertical side length to the horizontal side length. How do these ratios compare?

4. What is the relationship among the three right triangles? Justify your reasoning.

5. Identify and label the triangle that represents the unit rate. Explain how you know.

6. Slide the unit rate triangle along the graph of the line. What do you notice?

7. Slide the other two triangles along the graph of the line. What do you notice?

Keep your patty paper drawings. You will need those in the next lesson.

In the last two activities you investigated a relationship using a rate of change of $\frac{4}{3}$ to represent Jack and Jill walking 4 yards away from their home in 3 seconds, or as a unit rate of $\frac{4}{3}$ yards per second. Because this situation is a proportional relationship, the rate of change can specifically be called the constant of proportionality, represented by the variable k.

In this activity, you created three similar triangles each using two points from the line to explore the steepness of the line. By sliding the similar triangles along the line you noticed the steepness of the line remained constant between any two points on the line. In any linear relationship, **slope** describes the direction and steepness of a line and is usually represented by the variable m. Slope is another name for rate of change. It represents the ratio of the change in vertical distance to the change in horizontal distance between any two points on the line. The slope of a line is constant between any two points on the line.

You wrote the equation $d = \frac{4}{3}t$ to represent the distance, d, Jack and Jill walked from home with respect to time, t. Let's generalize this linear relationship.

The sign of the slope indicates the direction of a line. If the slope of a line is positive, then the graph will increase from left to right. If the slope of a line is negative, then the graph will decrease from left to right.

8. Let y represent the dependent variable, x represent the independent variable, and m represent the slope of the line.

   a. Write a general equation to relate these quantities.

   b. How is this equation similar to the equation for the constant of proportionality?

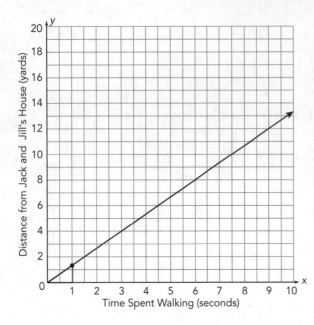

Jack and Jill's Aunt Mary lives 10 yards from their home closer to the bus stop. After spending Monday night at Aunt Mary's house, they leave for the bus stop from there Tuesday morning. They walk at the same rate from either house, 4 yards every 3 seconds.

The graph shows the line $y = \frac{4}{3}x$, which represents the relationship between the time Jack and Jill walk and their distance from their house.

1. Compare the two situations.

a. How do the slopes compare?

b. How do the starting points compare?

2. Let's graph the line to represent their walk to the bus stop from Aunt Mary's house.

a. On a piece of patty paper, trace the line $y = \frac{4}{3}x$ that represents Jack and Jill's walk to the bus stop from their house. Be sure to include the triangle representing the unit rate in your trace.

b. Translate this line to represent their walk from Aunt Mary's house and then transfer this line onto the graph.

3. Analyze the translated line.

a. Does your new line represent a proportional or non-proportional relationship? Explain how you know.

b. How does this translation affect the coordinates of the line? Complete the table to show how the translation affects the coordinates of your new line.

Time Spent Walking (seconds)	Distance from Jack and Jill's House on Monday (yards)	Distance from Jack and Jill's House on Tuesday (yards)
x	y_1	y_2
0	0	
1	$\frac{4}{3}$	
3	4	
6	8	
7.5	10	
9	12	

c. How does this translation affect the unit rate?

d. Write an equation to represent the translated line. Let y_2 represent the distance from Jack and Jill's house and let x represent their time spent walking. Explain how this line is the same and different from the line $y_1 = \frac{4}{3}x$.

You have written a general equation, $y = mx$, to relate the independent and dependent variables and the slope in a proportional linear relationship. How does this general equation change when the line is translated vertically by b units?

4. Write a general equation to represent the relationship $y = mx$ after it is vertically translated b units.

ACTIVITY 2.4

A Negative Unit Rate

Jack and Jill are walking back home from the bus stop which is 30 yards from their house. They walk at the same rate, 4 yards every 3 seconds.

Consider the two graphs shown.

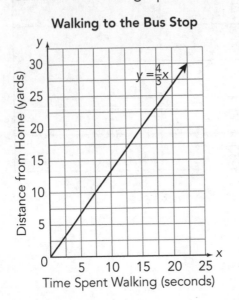

Walking to the Bus Stop

$y = \frac{4}{3}x$

Distance from Home (yards)

Time Spent Walking (seconds)

Walking Home from the Bus Stop

Distance from Home (yards)

Time Spent Walking (seconds)

1. Analyze the graph of Jack and Jill walking home from the bus stop.

   a. Does this situation represent a proportional or non-proportional relationship? Explain your reasoning.

   b. Is the slope of the line positive or negative? Explain how you know.

2. Compare and contrast the rate of change, or slope, of each line.

a. Use patty paper to trace and create any right triangle that represents the rate of change, or slope, from the Walking to the Bus Stop graph.

b. Place your patty paper on the Walking Home from the Bus Stop graph. How can you transform the right triangle you drew from the Walking to the Bus Stop graph to the Walking Home from the Bus Stop graph?

c. Slide the right triangle along the line of the Walking Home from the Bus Stop graph. What do you notice?

d. What is the slope of line in the Walking Home from the Bus Stop graph? Explain your reasoning.

> Remember the slope of a line represents steepness and direction.

3. Write an equation to represent Jack and Jill's walk home from the bus stop. Let y represent the distance from home and x represent the time spent walking.

4. How does the equation you wrote to represent Jack and Jill's walk home from the bus stop compare to the equation that represents their walk to the bus stop?

ACTIVITY 2.5 — Describing Linear Equations

You have discovered that the equation $y = mx$ represents a proportional relationship. The equation represents every point (x, y) on the graph of a line with slope m that passes through the origin $(0, 0)$.

An equation of the form $y = mx + b$, where b is not equal to zero, represents a non-proportional relationship. This equation represents every point (x, y) on the graph of a line with slope m that passes through the point $(0, b)$.

1. Consider each graph shown.

   • Determine whether the graph represents a proportional or non-proportional relationship.

   • Write an equation in the form $y = mx$ or $y = mx + b$ to represent the relationship between the independent and dependent quantities.

a.

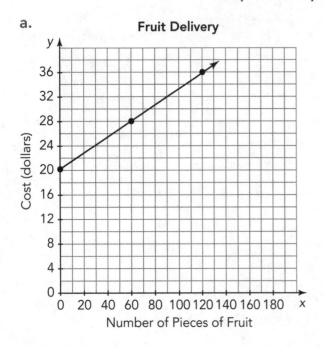

b.

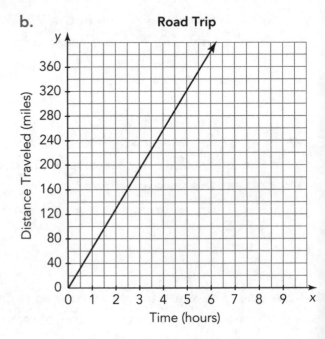

c.

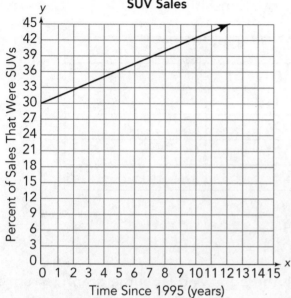

SUV Sales

2. Determine the slope of this graph and write an equation to represent it. Describe a situation that could be modeled by this graph.

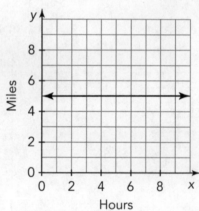

3. Complete the table of values to represent the linear relationship specified. Then, write an equation to represent the relationship.

a. proportional relationship

x	y
0	
1	
2	12
3	
4	

b. non-proportional relationship

x	y
0	
1	
2	12
3	
4	

4. Draw a line through the point and label the graph to represent the linear relationship specified. Then, write an equation.

a. proportional relationship

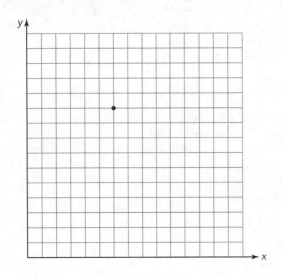

b. non-proportional relationship

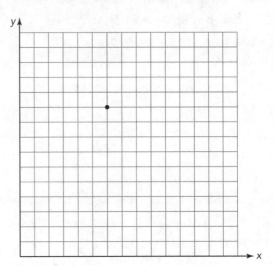

TALK the TALK

A Web of Connections

In this lesson, you learned that the steepness of a line can be described by its slope, which is a concept that is connected to many other concepts you have learned previously.

1. Complete the graphic organizer to describe how steepness is related to slope, rate of change, unit rate, and the constant of proportionality. Include definitions, graphs, and equations. Be sure to address both proportional and non-proportional relationships.

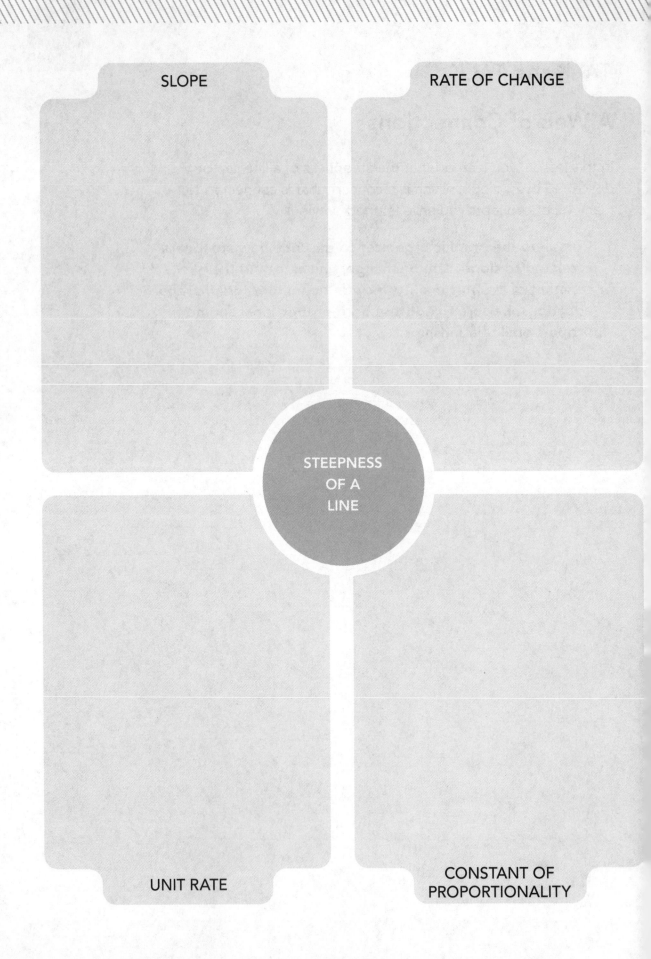

SLOPE

RATE OF CHANGE

STEEPNESS
OF A
LINE

UNIT RATE

CONSTANT OF
PROPORTIONALITY

Assignment

Write

In your own words, explain how slope is related to the right triangles formed along the line. Use examples to illustrate your explanation.

Remember

- Slope is another name for the rate of change of a linear relationship graphed as a line.
- The equation for a proportional linear relationship is $y = mx$, where m is the slope. The equation represents all of the points (x, y) on the line.
- An equation for a non-proportional linear relationship is $y = mx + b$, where m is the slope and b is the y-coordinate of the point where the graph crosses the y-axis. The equation represents all of the points (x, y) on the line.

Practice

1. Maximilian is cleaning shrimp. He cleans 4 shrimp every minute. Use time in minutes as the independent quantity and the number of shrimp as the dependent quantity.

    a. Is the relationship proportional or non-proportional? Explain how you can determine this using a graph and the equation.

    b. Identify the unit rate of this relationship. Explain what the unit rate means in terms of the situation.

    c. Write an equation that determines the number of shrimp cleaned given any time.

    d. Create a graph of the relationship.

2. Consider each graph shown.
    - Determine whether the graph represents a proportional or non-proportional relationship.
    - Write an equation in the form $y = mx$ or $y = mx + b$ to represent the relationship between the independent and dependent quantities.

    a.

    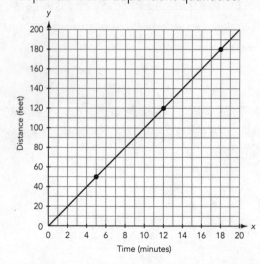

    b.

    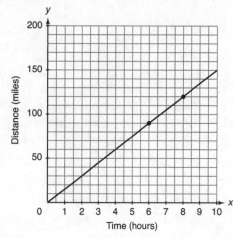

c.

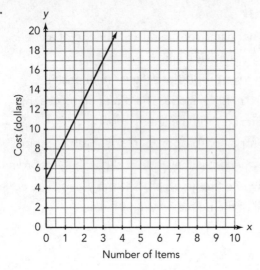

d.

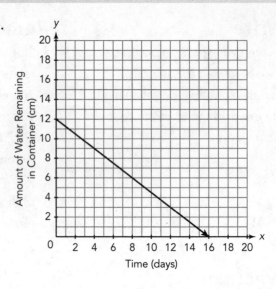

Stretch

Write an equation that determines where the graph crosses the y-axis, given the slope and the coordinates of one point.

Review

1. Determine whether each equation represents a proportional relationship.
   a. $y = 2.5x$
   b. $y = x - 4$

2. Examine the figure shown.

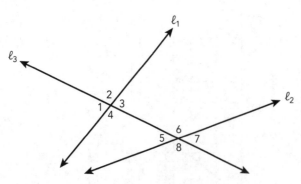

   a. Name 2 pairs of same-side interior angles.
   b. Name 2 pairs of congruent angles.
   c. Name 2 pairs of supplementary angles.

3. In the diagram shown, line s and line t are parallel. Determine the measures of all the angles.

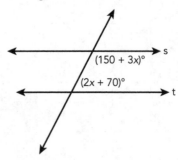

Slippery Slopes

3

Exploring Slopes Using Similar Triangles

WARM UP

For each diagram, describe how you can show that the triangles are similar.

1.

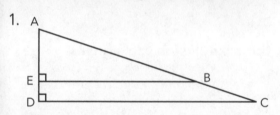

2. Given: *PQ* ‖ *MR*.

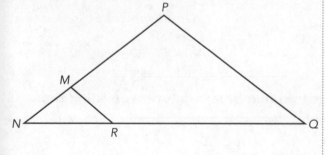

LEARNING GOALS

- Use similar triangles to show that the slope is the same between any two distinct points on a non-vertical line in a coordinate plane.
- Use right triangles to identify the slope of a line from a graph.

You have used similar triangles to describe the steepness of a line. How can you use similar triangles to explain why the slope is the same between any two distinct points on a non-vertical line?

Steep Grade

Consider the three street signs shown.

Discuss each question with your partner.

1. Where might you see each of the signs?

2. What do you know about the triangles on the signs?

3. For the signs that include numbers, what do you think those numbers represent?

Triangles and the Equation $y = mx$

In the previous lesson, *Jack and Jill Went Up the Hill,* you used patty paper to analyze the slope of the line $y = \frac{4}{3}x$ using similar triangles formed at $x = 1$, $x = 3$, and $x = 6$.

Now, let's investigate if the slope of a line is always the same between any two points on a line.

Consider the graph of $y = \frac{3}{2}x$.

_____

Remember, slope describes the direction and steepness of a line.

_____

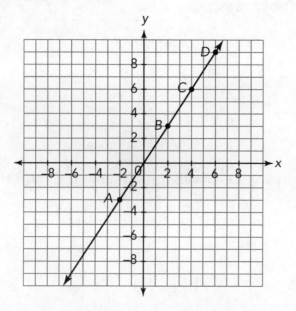

1. Is the slope of the line positive or negative? Explain your reasoning.

2. Examine the slope between points A and B.

   a. Create a right triangle using points A and B and trace onto patty paper.

   b. Label the triangle with the vertical and horizontal distances.

   c. Label the patty paper with the slope of the line between points A and B.

3. Does the orientation of the right triangle matter? Place your patty paper on the graph, use point *A* as the center of rotation, and rotate your triangle 180°.

   a. Compare and contrast these two triangles. How are they the same? How are they different?

   b. Does the new triangle give you the same slope? Explain your reasoning.

4. Create right triangles using points *B* and *C*, and then *B* and *D*.

   a. Label the horizontal and vertical distances.

   b. Label the patty paper with the slope of the line.

5. Compare the triangles created on the line. How can you verify that all of the triangles are similar?

6. What is the slope of the line?

7. Cooper claims that all right triangles formed on a given line are similar. Is Cooper correct? Explain your reasoning.

ACTIVITY 3.2 Triangles, Slope, and the Equation $y = mx + b$

Consider the graph shown.

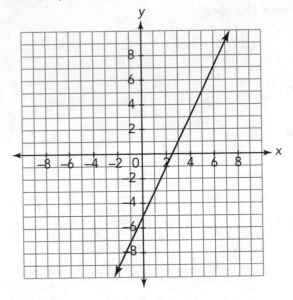

1. Is the slope of the line positive or negative? Explain your reasoning.

2. Create at least three similar triangles using points on the line.

   a. Use any method to justify that these triangles are similar.

   b. Determine the slope of the line.

3. How many similar triangles can be formed on the graph of a line? How do you know?

4. Consider each graph shown. Determine the slope of each line and then use similar triangles to justify that the slope is the same between any two points.

a.

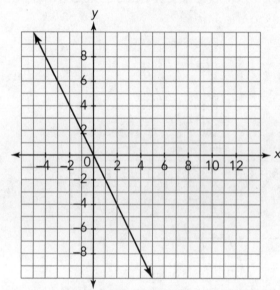

b.

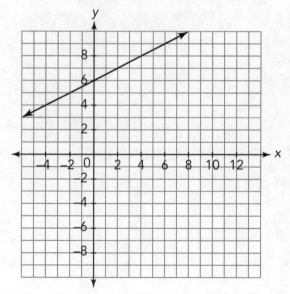

TALK the TALK

Connecting Similar Triangles and Slope of a Line

Audra was absent for this lesson on the connection between similar triangles and the slope of a line. Write an explanation of what you learned in this lesson. Be sure to include how you can use a graph to determine the slope of a non-vertical line, and how you can use similar triangles to show the slope is the same between any two points on the line.

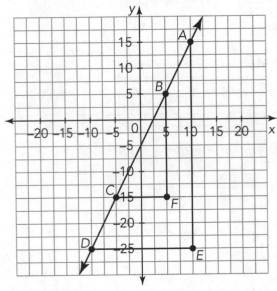

Assignment

Write

Explain why the slope between any two points on a line is always the same.

Remember

The properties of similar triangles can be used to explain why the slope m is the same between any two distinct points on a non-vertical line in the coordinate plane.

Practice

1. Consider the graph of the equation $y = 2x + 3$.

   a. The points on the line were used to create triangles. Describe the relationship between the two triangles.

   b. How can transformations be used to verify the relationship between the triangles?

   c. Use the similar triangles to determine the slope between any two points on the line.

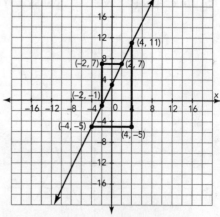

2. Consider each graph shown. Determine the slope of each line and then use similar triangles to justify that the slope is the same between any two points.

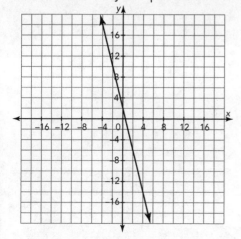

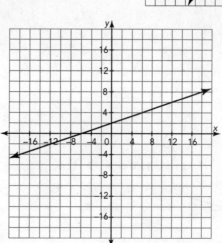

Stretch

Create a table of values for the equation $y = x^2$. Use the points with x-values of 0, 1, 2, and 3 to create triangles with the length of each base equal to 1 unit.

- Describe the relationship between the heights of the resulting triangles.
- Are the triangles similar? Explain your reasoning.

Review

1. Determine the unknown angle measure for each triangle.

    a. $m\angle A = 46°$, $m\angle B = 90°$, $m\angle C = ?$

    b. $m\angle P = ?$, $m\angle Q$: 10°, $m\angle R = 110°$

2. Consider the graph of lines a, b, c, and d.

    a. Which line(s) have positive slope?

    b. Which line(s) have negative slope?

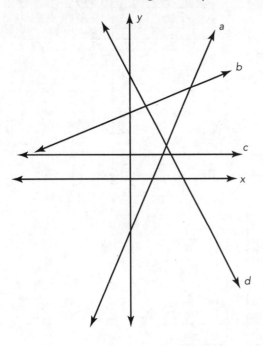

3. Solve for the unknown angle measure given that $f \parallel g$.

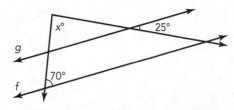

Up, Down, and All Around

Transformations of Lines

WARM UP

Identify whether the equation represents a proportional or non-proportional relationship. Then state whether the graph of the line will increase or decrease from left to right.

1. $y = -2x - 9$

2. $y = 2x - 3$

3. $y = \frac{2}{3}x$

LEARNING GOALS

- Translate linear graphs horizontally and vertically.
- Use transformations to graph linear relationships.
- Determine the slopes of parallel lines.
- Identify parallel lines.
- Explore transformations of parallel lines.

You have learned how the coordinates of an image are affected when a pre-image is translated, reflected, rotated, or dilated. How can you use knowledge about geometric transformations to transform the graphs and equations of linear relationships?

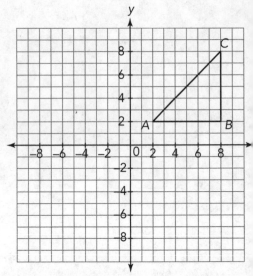

Transformation Station

Consider △ABC with coordinates A (2, 2), B (8, 2), and C (8, 8) shown on the coordinate plane.

1. Suppose the triangle is translated in a single direction. In general, how does this affect the coordinates of the figure?

(x, y)	4 Units Up	4 Units Down	4 Units Left	4 Units Right
New Coordinates				

2. Suppose the triangle is reflected across an axis. How does this affect the coordinates of the figure?

(x, y)	x-Axis	y-Axis
New Coordinates		

3. Suppose the triangle is rotated through an angle with the origin as the center of rotation. How does this affect the coordinates of the figure?

(x, y)	90° Counterclockwise	180°	270° Counterclockwise
New Coordinates			

4. Suppose the triangle is dilated by a factor of *m* with a center of dilation at the origin. How does this affect the coordinates of the figure?

(x, y)	Dilation
New Coordinates	

5. How do you think translations, reflections, rotations, and dilations affect lines?

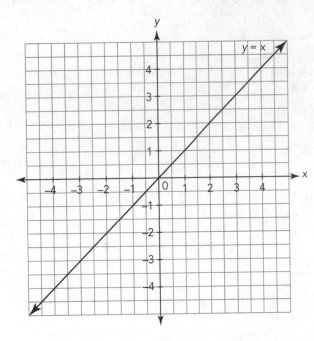

In this activity, you will investigate how the equation of a line changes as you translate the line up and down the y-axis.

Consider the graph of the basic linear equation $y = x$, which is of the form $y = mx$. The line represents a proportional relationship with a rate of change, or slope, of 1.

1. Trace the axes and the line $y = x$ on a sheet of patty paper.

2. Keep the y-axis on your patty paper on top of the corresponding y-axis of the coordinate plane. Slide the line $y = x$ up and down the y-axis.

   a. How does the slope of the line change as you move it up and down the y-axis?

   b. How do the coordinates of the line change as you move it up and down the y-axis?

3. Translate the line $y = x$ up 4 units.

a. Graph and label the line with its equation.

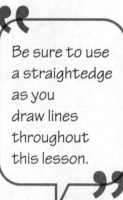

b. Compare the equation of $y = x$ to the equation of its translation up 4 units. What do you notice?

4. Translate the line $y = x$ down 4 units.

a. Graph and label the line with its equation.

b. Compare the graph and equation of $y = x$ to the graph and equation of its translation down 4 units. What do you notice?

5. For any x-value, how does the y-value change when you translate $y = x$ up or down?

6. Are the translated lines proportional or non-proportional relationships? Explain your reasoning.

7. The lines on the graph are translations of the line represented by $y = x$.

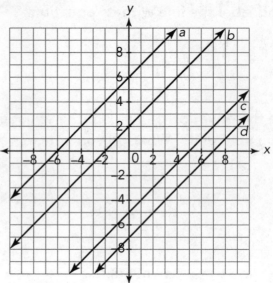

a. Describe each translation in terms of a translation up or down. Then write the equation.

b. Identify the slope of each line.

The lines drawn on the coordinate plane in Question 7 represent parallel lines. Remember that parallel lines are lines that lie in the same plane and do not intersect no matter how far they extend. Parallel lines are always equidistant.

8. Analyze the graph of each line and its corresponding equation.

a. How can you verify that the lines graphed are equidistant?

b. How can you tell by looking at the set of equations that the lines are parallel?

9. Based on your investigation, complete the sentence:

The line $y = x + b$ is a _____ of the line $y = x$

that maps the point (0, 0) onto the point _____ and maps the

point (1, 1) onto the point (1, _____).

The graph of the basic linear equation $y = x$ is shown on the coordinate plane.

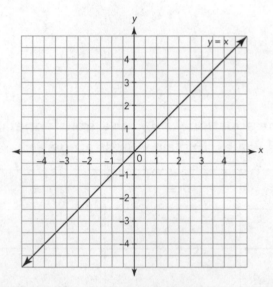

Let's investigate how the line $y = x$ changes when the rate of change, or slope, changes.

1. Use a thin piece of pasta to explore how the characteristics of the line change as you dilate the line $y = x$ to create the lines with equation $y = 2x$ and $y = \frac{1}{2}x$. Then complete the table based on your investigation.

x	$y = x$	$y = 2x$	$y = \frac{1}{2}x$	$y = mx$
−2				
0				
1				
2				
4				

2. Based on your investigation, complete the sentence:

The line $y = mx$ is a _____ of the line

$y = x$ that maps the point (0, 0) onto the point _____

and maps the point (1, 1) onto the point (1, ___).

3. Consider the equation $y = \frac{3}{4}x$. Use transformations to complete the table of values. Explain your strategy.

x	$y = x$	$y = \frac{3}{4}x$
−2		
−1		
0		
1		
2		

4. The equation $y = -x$ is a transformation of $y = x$.

   a. How are the equations similar? How are they different?

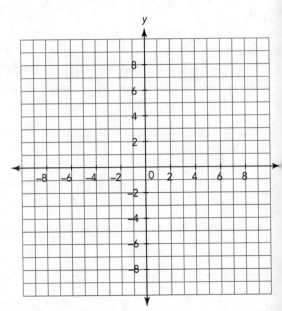

b. Graph both equations to determine the transformation.

c. Based on your investigation, complete the sentence:

The line $y = -x$ is a _____ of the line $y = x$ that

maps the point (0, 0) onto the point _____ and maps

the point (1, 1) onto the point (1, _____).

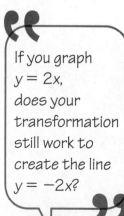

If you graph
$y = 2x$,
does your
transformation
still work to
create the line
$y = -2x$?

Using Transformations to Graph Lines

You have explored how the basic linear equation $y = x$ is translated to create the equation $y = x + b$ or dilated to create the equation $y = mx$. In this activity, you will combine both dilations and translations to graph equations of the form $y = mx + b$.

1. Consider the set of equations.

   - $y = 2x$

   - $y = 2x + 3$

   - $y = 2x - 5$

   - $y = 2x + 5$

   a. What do all of the equations have in common?

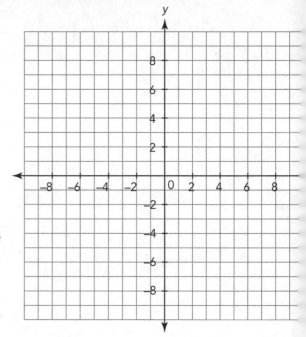

   b. Use transformations to graph each equation on the coordinate plane.

   c. Describe the relationship among the lines.

2. Consider the set of equations.

- $y = -3x$

- $y = -3x - 2$

- $y = -3x + 5$

- $y = -3x - 8$

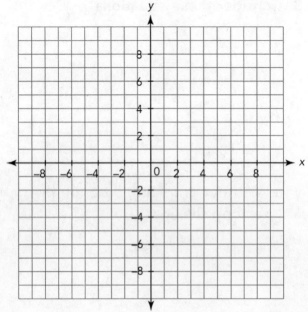

Conventionally, $y = -x$ is considered a reflection of $y = x$ across the x-axis.

a. What do all of the equations have in common?

b. Use transformations to graph each equation on the coordinate plane.

c. Describe the relationship among the lines.

d. Describe and use a strategy for verifying the relationship among the lines.

3. Consider these equations.

- $y = \frac{1}{2}x$

- $y = \frac{1}{2}x + 6$

- $y = \frac{1}{2}x - 3$

- $y = \frac{1}{2}x - 2$

a. Without graphing, describe the graphical relationship among the lines.

b. Explain how you determined the relationship.

4. Determine if the quadrilateral formed by joining the points A (3, 1), B (8, 1), C (10, 5), and D (5, 5) in alphabetical order is a parallelogram.

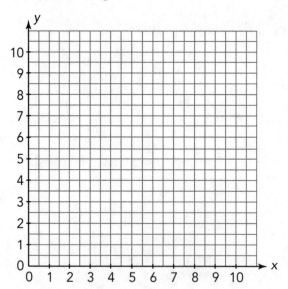

Now that you understand linear equations in terms of transformations, you can use transformations to graph lines.

WORKED EXAMPLE

Graph $y = 3x - 4$ using transformations of the basic linear equation $y = x$.

First, graph the basic equation, $y = x$, and consider at least 2 sets of ordered pairs on the line, for example (0, 0), (1, 1), and (2, 2).

Then dilate the y-values by 3.

Finally, translate all y-values down 4 units.

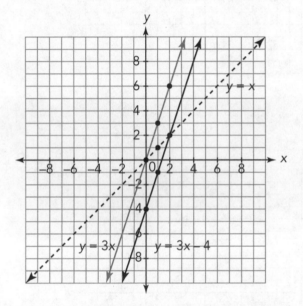

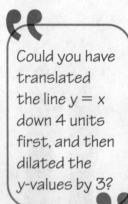

Could you have translated the line $y = x$ down 4 units first, and then dilated the y-values by 3?

Try using even numbers for the x-values.

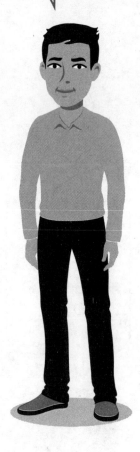

5. Graph each equation using transformations. Specify which transformations you use.

a. $y = \frac{1}{2}x + 5$

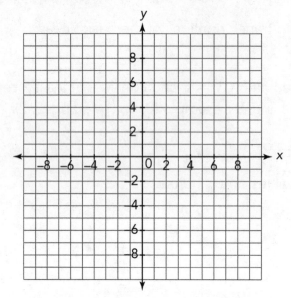

b. $y = \frac{3}{2}x - 3$

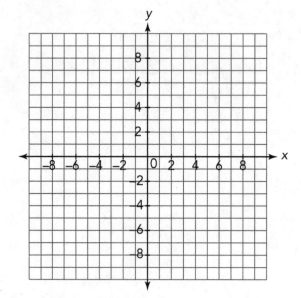

ACTIVITY 4.4

Reflecting and Rotating Parallel Lines

You have learned what happens when a line or figure is reflected across the *y*-axis. What happens if you reflect a pair of lines across the *y*-axis?

1. Line segment *AB* and line segment *CD* are shown on the coordinate plane.

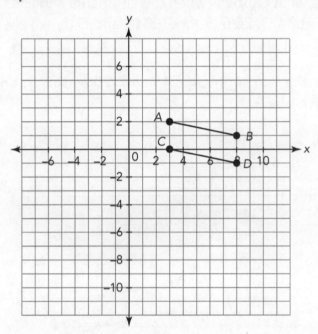

> Patty paper might be helpful when reflecting across the *y*-axis.

a. What is the relationship between segments *AB* and *CD*? Justify your reasoning.

b. Trace line segments *AB* and *CD* onto a sheet of patty paper. Reflect the line segments across the *y*-axis to create segments *A'B'* and *C'D'*.

c. What are the coordinates of points *A'*, *B'*, *C'*, and *D'*?

d. What is the relationship between segments *A'B'* and *C'D'*? Justify your reasoning.

e. Extend segments *AB*, *CD*, *A′B′*, and *C′D′* to create lines *AB*, *CD*, *A′B′*, and *C′D′*. Draw the lines on your graph. What do you notice about the relationship between the lines?

f. Reflecting parallel lines across the same line of reflection results in lines that are _____.

Let's explore what happens when the segments and lines created from the points *A* (3, 2), *B* (8, 1), *C* (3, 0), and *D* (8, −1) are rotated.

2. Consider the line segments *AB* and *CD* as shown on the coordinate plane.

You learned that when you rotate a point (*x*, *y*) 90 degrees counterclockwise about the origin, the image of the point is (−*y*, *x*). However, what happens when you rotate two parallel lines?

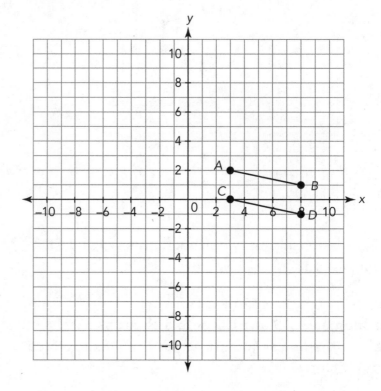

a. Rotate each point 90° counterclockwise to create segments *A′B′* and *C′D′*. What are the coordinates of points *A′*, *B′*, *C′*, and *D′*?

b. What is the relationship between line segments $A'B'$ and $C'D'$? Justify your reasoning.

c. Rotate each original point 180° to create a new set of segments. What are the coordinates of the new points?

d. What is the relationship between the segments created by rotating the original points 180°? Justify your reasoning.

e. Extend line segments AB, CD, $A'B'$, and $C'D'$ to create lines AB, CD, $A'B'$, and $C'D'$. Draw the lines on graph. What do you notice about the relationship between the lines?

f. Rotating parallel lines results in lines that are _____.

TALK the TALK

Are They Parallel?

1. Which transformations of linear graphs result in parallel lines? Explain each response.

   a. dilation by a non-zero factor other than 1

   b. translation up or down

   c. reflection across an axis

   d. rotation 90° counterclockwise

2. Create and graph four linear equations that represent lines with the same slope. Label each line with its corresponding equation.

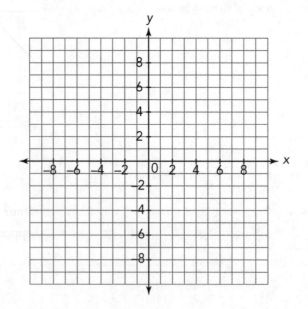

Assignment

Write

Explain how to use transformations of the basic equation $y = x$ to graph the equation $y = mx + b$.

Remember

Translations, reflections, and rotations map parallel lines and line segments to corresponding parallel lines and line segments.

Practice

1. Write an equation for each linear relationship after transforming $y = x$.
   a. dilation by a factor of $\frac{5}{6}$
   b. dilation by a factor of 8
   c. reflection across the x-axis
   d. translation down 6 units
   e. dilation by a factor of 2, then a translation up 3 units
   f. reflection across the x-axis, dilation by a factor of 3, and then a translation down 9 units

2. Use the graph of the linear relationship shown to complete each task.
   a. Write the equation of the line.
   b. Write the equation of the line after a translation down 8 units. Graph the line.
   c. Write the equation of the line after a translation up 8 units. Graph the line.

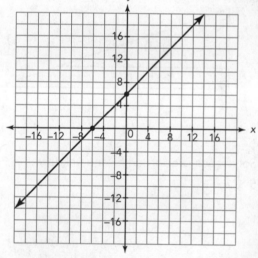

Stretch

Graph each given sequence of transformations. Are the equations the same? Explain why the equations must be the same or why they are not the same. Use transformations to support your answer.

1. Translate $y = x$ up 4 units, and then dilate by a factor of 2.
2. Dilate $y = x$ by a factor of 2, and then translate up 4 units.

Review

Draw similar triangles on the graph to determine each slope.

1.
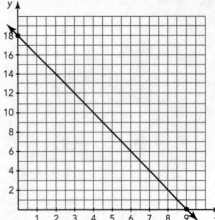

2.
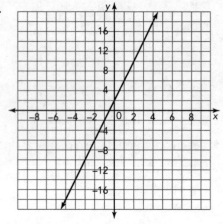

Identify the similar triangles and explain how the triangles are similar by the Angle-Angle Similarity Theorem.

3.
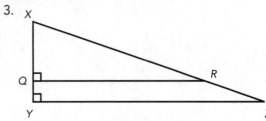

4.
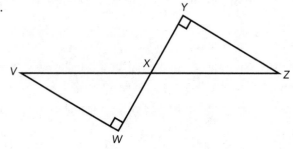

Solve each proportion for the unknown.

5. $\frac{2}{3} = \frac{x}{3.5}$

6. $\frac{0.6}{m} = \frac{4}{30}$

From Proportions to Linear Relationships Summary

KEY TERMS

- proportional relationship
- constant of proportionality

- rate of change
- slope

LESSON 1	Post-Secondary Proportions

A **proportional relationship** is one in which the ratio of the inputs to the outputs is constant. For example, the ratio of women to men at a certain university is 3 : 2.

Proportional relationships can be represented using tables, graphs, and equations.

In a table, the values in a proportional relationship increase or decrease at a constant rate beginning or ending at (0, 0). The 3 : 2 ratio of women to men at a university is represented by this table.

Female Students Enrolled in a University	Male Students Enrolled in a University
0	0
600	400
1500	1000

On a graph, a proportional relationship is represented as a linear graph passing through the origin. The given graph shows the same proportional relationship as represented by the table.

The equation for a proportional relationship is written in the form $y = kx$, where x represents an input value, y represents an output value, and k represents some constant that is not equal to 0. The constant k is called the **constant of proportionality.** The 3 : 2 ratio of women to men at a university is represented by the equation $y = \frac{2}{3}x$. The constant of proportionality is $\frac{2}{3}$.

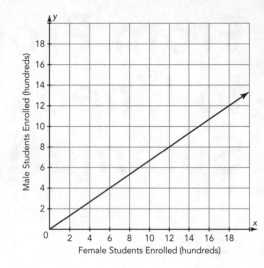

Jack and Jill Went Up the Hill

The **rate of change** for a situation is the amount that the dependent quantity changes compared with the amount that the independent quantity changes.

In any linear relationship, **slope** describes the direction and steepness of a line and is usually represented by the variable m. Slope is another name for the rate of change of a linear relationship graphed as a line. The slope of the line is constant between any two points on the line. The sign of the slope indicates the direction of a line. If the slope of a line is positive, then the graph will increase from left to right. If the slope of a line is negative, then the graph will decrease from left to right.

The equation $y = mx$ represents a proportional relationship. The equation represents every point (x, y) on the graph of a line with slope m that passes through the origin $(0, 0)$.

An equation of the form $y = mx + b$, where b is not equal to 0, represents a non-proportional relationship. This equation represents every point (x, y) on the graph of a line with slope m that passes through the point $(0, b)$. For example, the graph shown represents a non-proportional relationship where $m = 2$ and $b = 4$.

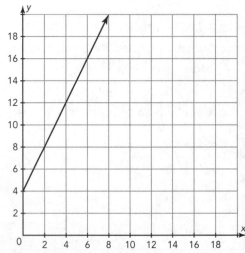

A line with a negative slope goes in the opposite direction. It decreases from left to right.

For example, consider the two graphs. The first represents a tank being filled at $\frac{2}{3}$ gallon per second. The second represents the tank being emptied at $\frac{2}{3}$ gallon per second, starting at 12 gallons.

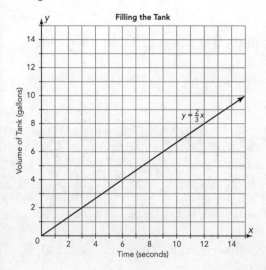

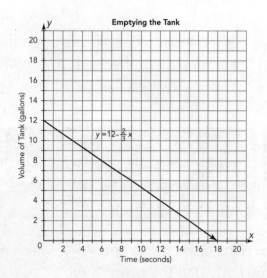

The slope of the line representing the tank being filled is $\frac{2}{3}$. You can draw a triangle to represent the slope of this line and then horizontally reflect it onto the line representing the tank being emptied. This shows that the slope of this line is $-\frac{2}{3}$.

LESSON
3

Slippery Slopes

The properties of similar triangles can be used to explain why the slope m is the same between any two distinct points on a non-vertical line on the coordinate plane.

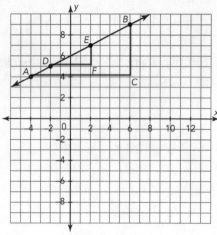

For example, Points A, B, D, and E along the graphed line can be used to create two right triangles in the coordinate plane.

Because $\angle BAC$ and $\angle EDF$ are corresponding angles on parallel lines cut by a transversal, you know that $\angle BAC \cong \angle EDF$. Likewise, because $\angle ABC$ and $\angle DEF$ are corresponding angles on parallel lines cut by a transversal, you know that $\angle ABC \cong \angle DEF$. Therefore, by the AA Similarity Theorem, $\triangle ABC$ is similar to $\triangle DEF$.

In both triangles, the ratio of the vertical distance and the horizontal distance is $\frac{1}{2}$. The slope of the line is the same between points A and B and between points D and E.

Translations, reflections, and rotations map parallel lines and line segments to corresponding parallel lines and line segments.

The line $y = x + b$ is a translation of the line $y = x$ that maps the point $(0, 0)$ to the point $(0, b)$ and maps the point $(1, 1)$ to the point $(1, 1 + b)$.

LESSON 4

Up, Down, All Around

The line $y = mx$ is a dilation of the line $y = x$, which maps the point $(0, 0)$ to the point $(0, 0)$ and maps the point $(1, 1)$ to the point $(1, m)$.

The line $y = -x$ is a reflection of the line $y = x$, which maps the point $(0, 0)$ to the point $(0, 0)$ and maps the point $(1, 1)$ to the point $(1, -1)$.

For example, you can graph $y = 3x - 4$ using transformations of the basic linear equation $y = x$.

First, graph the basic equation $y = x$, and consider at least two sets of ordered pairs on the line, for example $(0, 0)$, $(1, 1)$, and $(2, 2)$.

Then dilate the y-values by 3.

Finally, translate all y-values down 4 units.

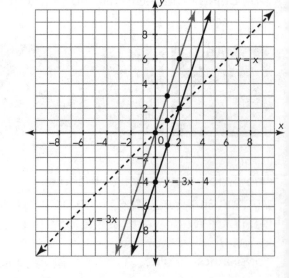

TOPIC 2
Linear Relationships

The elevation of these planes increases over time. The paths formed by these relationships are straight lines.

Module 2: Developing Function Foundations

TOPIC 2: LINEAR RELATIONSHIPS

In this topic, students develop fluency with analyzing linear relationships, writing equations of lines, and graphing lines. Students use intuition and prior knowledge about writing equations, creating tables of values, and graphing equations to compare two linear relationships. Students determine the *y*-intercept of linear relationships from tables, two points, graphs, and contexts. Students graph lines presented in slope-intercept form and in point-slope form and learn about standard form.

Where have we been?

Students come into this topic with an understanding of slope as a unit rate of change and as a ratio of vertical change to horizontal change. They have experiences in representing proportional relationships with tables, graphs, and equations.

Where are we going?

This topic provides the foundation for students' algebraic fluency with determining and using equations of linear relationships. The skills developed in this topic will be used in the next two topics as students develop equations for linear functions, interpret those functions, and compare functions represented in different ways. Beyond grade 8, students should understand that different forms of an equation can shed light on the problem situation.

Using Numberless Graphs to Compare Linear Relationships

Numberless graphs are graphs which do not show *x*-axis or *y*-axis intervals or labels. These graphs are used to show the important information about linear relationships: the steepness of the graph, whether it increases or decreases from left to right, and whether it goes through the origin or not.

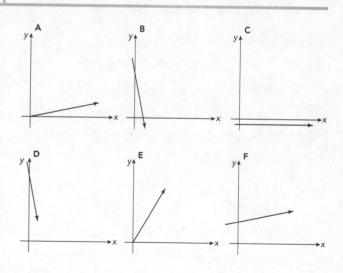

Myth: Students only use 10% of their brains.

Hollywood is in love with the idea that humans only use a small portion of their brains. This notion formed the basis of the movies *Lucy* (2014) and *Limitless* (2011). Both films ask the audience: Imagine what you could accomplish if you could use 100% of your brain!

Well, this isn't Hollywood, and you're stuck with an ordinary brain. The good news is that you **do** use 100% of your brain. As you look around the room, your visual cortex is busy assembling images; your motor cortex is busy moving your neck; and all of the associative areas recognize the objects that you see. Meanwhile, the corpus callosum, which is a thick band of neurons that connect the two hemispheres, ensures that all of this information is kept coordinated. Moreover, the brain does this automatically, which frees up space to ponder deep, abstract concepts...like mathematics!

#mathmythbusted

Talking Points

You can further support your student's learning by asking questions about the work they do in class or at home. Your student is learning to think about linear relationships as objects that can be analyzed, graphed, and compared.

Questions to Ask

- How does this problem look like something you did in class?
- Can you show me the strategy you used to solve this problem? Do you know another way to solve it?
- Does your answer make sense? How do you know?
- Is there anything you don't understand? How can you use today's lesson to help?

Key Terms

first differences
First differences are the values determined by subtracting consecutive *y*-values in a table when the *x*-values are consecutive integers.

y-intercept
The *y*-intercept is the *y*-coordinate of the point where a graph crosses the *y*-axis.

slope-intercept form
The slope-intercept form of a linear equation is $y = mx + b$, where *m* is the slope of the line and $(0, b)$ is the *y*-intercept.

point-slope form
The point-slope form of a linear equation is $y - y_1 = m(x - x_1)$, where *m* is the slope of the line and (x_1, y_1) is any point on the line.

U.S. Shirts

Using Tables, Graphs, and Equations

1

WARM UP

Determine the value of y in each equation for the given value of x.

1. $y = -2x + 4$, $x = 3.5$

2. $y = \frac{1}{2}x + 11$, $x = -1$

3. $x + y = 1$, $x = 0$

4. $2x - y = 5$, $x = 4$

LEARNING GOALS

- Construct a table of (x, y) values and a graph to model a linear relationship between two quantities.
- Use different representations to model a problem situation.
- Analyze the characteristics of different linear representations.
- Compare linear representations using tables, graphs, and equations.

You have analyzed linear relationships by considering points on the line and rate of change. How can you compare two linear relationships in a problem situation?

Cost Analysis

This past summer you were hired to work at a custom T-shirt shop, U.S. Shirts. One of your responsibilities is to calculate the total cost of customers' orders. The shop charges $8 per shirt plus a one-time charge of $15 to set up a T-shirt design.

1. Describe the problem situation and your responsibility in your own words.

2. Is the relationship between the number of shirts ordered and the total cost of an order proportional or non-proportional? Explain how you know.

Modeling a Linear Relationship

Let's analyze various customer orders with U.S. Shirts.

1. What is the total cost of an order for:

   a. 3 shirts?   b. 10 shirts?

If the order doubles, does the total cost double?

   c. 100 shirts?

   d. Explain how you calculated each total cost.

2. How many shirts can a customer buy if they have:

   a. $50 to spend?   b. $60 to spend?

   c. $220 to spend?

   d. Explain how you calculated the number of shirts
      that the customer can buy.

3. Identify the variable quantities and constant quantities in this problem situation. Include each quantity's units.

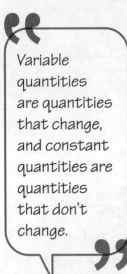

Variable quantities are quantities that change, and constant quantities are quantities that don't change.

4. Identify the independent and dependent variables in the situation. Explain your reasoning.

5. Complete the table of values for U.S. Shirts. Round to the nearest penny.

Number of Shirts Ordered	Total Cost (dollars)

6. Create a graph of the data from your table on the grid shown. First, choose your bounds and intervals by completing the table shown. Remember to label your graph clearly and provide a title for your graph.

Variable Quantity	Lower Bound	Upper Bound	Interval
Number of shirts			
Total cost			

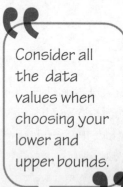

> Consider all the data values when choosing your lower and upper bounds.

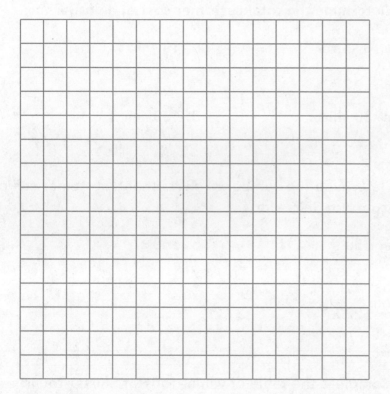

7. Define the variables and write an algebraic equation for this problem situation.

Remember, you can draw a line through your points to model the relationship. You then need to decide whether or not all points on your line make sense in terms of the problem situation.

In your own words, describe this problem situation and how it will affect the business at U.S. Shirts.

Previously, you explored a job at U.S. Shirts. One of U.S. Shirts' competitors, Hot Shirts, advertises that it makes custom T-shirts for $5.50 each with a one-time setup fee of $49.95. Your boss brings you the advertisement from Hot Shirts and asks you to figure out how the competition might affect business.

1. Determine the total customer cost of an order for:

   a. 3 shirts.

   b. 10 shirts.

   c. 50 shirts.

   d. 100 shirts.

2. Determine the number of shirts that a customer can purchase from Hot Shirts for:

   a. $50.

   b. $60.

   c. $220.

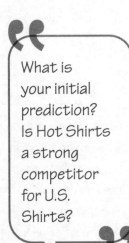

What is your initial prediction? Is Hot Shirts a strong competitor for U.S. Shirts?

3. Complete the table of values for Hot Shirts. Round to the nearest penny.

Number of Shirts Ordered	Total Cost (dollars)

4. Create a graph of the data from the table on the grid shown. First, choose your bounds and intervals by completing the table shown. Remember to label your graph clearly and provide a title for your graph.

Variable Quantity	Lower Bound	Upper Bound	Interval
Number of shirts			
Total cost			

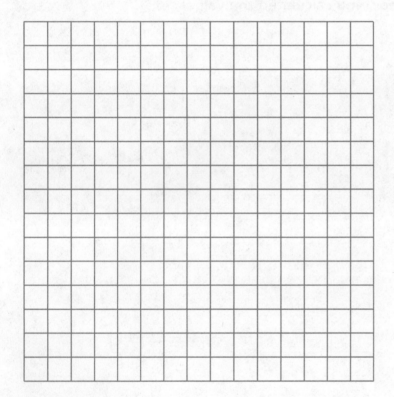

5. Define the variables and write an algebraic equation for this problem situation.

ACTIVITY
1.3

Comparing Linear Relationships

You have explored the costs of ordering T-shirts from two companies, U.S. Shirts and Hot Shirts. Your boss has asked you to determine which company has the better price for T-shirts in different situations.

1. Compare the two businesses for orders of 5 or fewer shirts, 18 shirts, and 80 shirts. Is U.S. Shirts or Hot Shirts the better buy for each? What would each company charge? Describe how you calculated the values.

2. Create graphs for the total cost for U.S. Shirts and Hot Shirts on the grid shown. Use the bounds and intervals for the grid in the table shown. Label each graph and provide a title.

Variable Quantity	Lower Bound	Upper Bound	Interval
Number of shirts	0	100	5
Total cost	0	1000	50

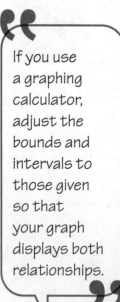

If you use a graphing calculator, adjust the bounds and intervals to those given so that your graph displays both relationships.

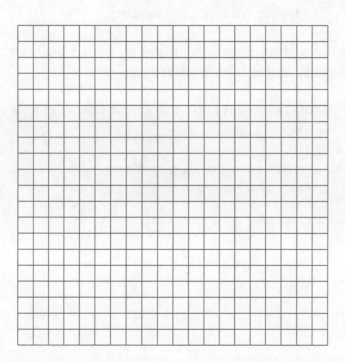

3. Estimate the number of shirts for which the total cost is the same. Explain how you determined the number of shirts.

TALK the TALK 💬

Business Report Presentation

Consider the graphs for U.S. Shirts and Hot Shirts. Notice that the graphs intersect at about (14, 127). This point of intersection indicates where the total cost for each company is the same. Therefore, when U.S. Shirts sells 14 shirts, the total cost is $127, and when Hot Shirts sells 14 shirts, the total cost is $127.

1. Prepare a presentation for your boss that compares the costs of ordering from each company.

   • Include a statement describing when it's better to buy from U.S. Shirts than from Hot Shirts.

   • Include a statement listing the cost per shirt and startup fee for each business.

   • Try to answer your boss's question: "Will Hot Shirts' prices affect the business at U.S. Shirts?"

Assignment

Write

Describe how tables, graphs, and equations are related. Then describe the advantages of each representation.

Remember

In mathematics, when representing quantities in a table it is important to include a row to identify the quantities and units of measure. Typically, the independent quantity is represented in the left column and the dependent quantity is represented in the right column.

When graphing a relationship, the convention is to represent the independent quantity on the horizontal axis of a graph and the dependent quantity on the vertical axis. You should include labels on each axis.

When writing an equation in the form of $y = mx + b$, the x-value represents the independent quantity and the y-value represents the dependent value. It is important to define the variables you choose.

Practice

1. Great Freights, a local shipping company, bases its charges on the weight of the items being shipped. In addition to charging $0.40 per pound, Great Freights also charges a one-time fee of $10 to set up a customer's account.

   a. How much does Great Freights charge a new customer to ship a package that weighs 20 pounds?

   b. How much does Great Freights charge a new customer to ship a package that weighs 50 pounds?

   c. Estimate the weight of a package if Great Freights charges a new customer $45 to ship the package.

   d. Write an equation for the problem situation.

2. Twin brothers, Mike and Mark, are looking for week-long winter break jobs. They are both offered jobs at grocery stores. Mike is offered a job at Fresh Foods making $10 per hour. Mark is offered a job at Groovy Groceries making $8 an hour, plus a one-time hiring bonus of $100. Each twin believes that he has been offered the better job.

   a. How much does Mike earn at Fresh Foods if he works 20 hours? 40 hours? 60 hours? Show your work.

   b. Explain how you determined Mike's earnings in part (a).

   c. How much does Mark earn at Groovy Groceries if he works 20 hours? 40 hours? 60 hours? Show your work.

   d. Explain how you determined Mark's earnings in part (c).

   e. Create a table using the data and your answers from parts (a) and (c).

   f. Create a graph of the data in the table in part (e). First, choose your bounds and intervals. Remember to label your graph clearly and name your graph.

   g. After how many hours will the twins earn the same amount of money? Explain your reasoning.

   h. Whose job is better, Mike's or Mark's? Explain your reasoning.

Stretch

Two catering companies have different one-time fixed fees. Company A charges a fixed fee of $75, and Company B charges a fixed fee of $100. Each company also has a cost per person.

Suppose the independent quantity is the number of people and the dependent quantity is the cost. The graphs for the two companies never intersect. What does this tell you about how much each company charges?

Review

1. Draw a line through the point and label the graph to represent each linear relationship. Then, write an equation to represent the relationship.

   a. linear proportional relationship

   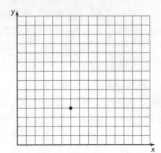

   b. linear non-proportional relationship

   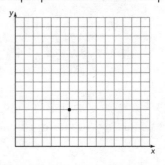

2. Use the equation $y = -3x$ to complete the table of values. Graph the equation. Then use the points on the graph to sketch similar triangles that may be used to show the rate of change of the line is the same between any two points.

x	y
−2	
−1	
0	
1	
2	

3. Solve for each unknown angle measure given that $\ell_1 \| \ell_2$.

   a.

   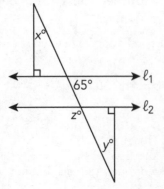

   b.

   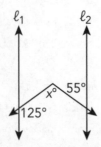

At the Arcade

Linear Relationships in Tables

WARM UP

Use similar right triangles to determine the slope of each line.

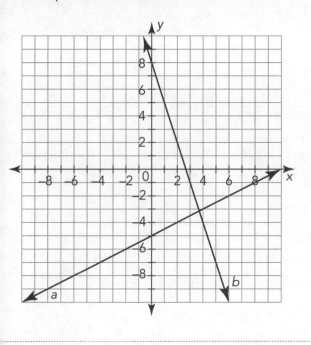

LEARNING GOALS

- Determine the rate of change of a linear relationship by reading (x, y) values from a table.
- Develop a formula to calculate the slope of a line given a table of values.
- Use the slope formula to calculate the rate of change from a table of values or two coordinate pairs.
- Determine whether a table of values represents a linear proportional or linear non-proportional relationship.

KEY TERM

- first differences

You have used graphs to analyze and compare linear relationships. You have used similar right triangles to determine slopes of lines graphed on a coordinate plane. How can you calculate the slope of a linear relationship given a table of values without creating a graph?

Slope Matching

You have used slope to describe the steepness and direction of a line. Consider each graph shown.

1. **Identify the graph(s) whose line may have the given slope. Then, describe your strategy for matching the graphs to the given slopes.**

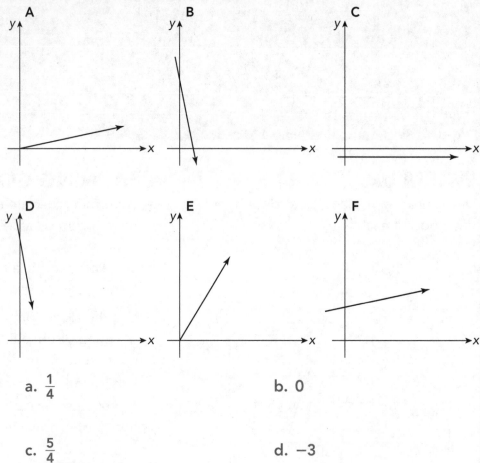

   a. $\frac{1}{4}$

   b. 0

   c. $\frac{5}{4}$

   d. −3

2. **How did you use the graphs to estimate their slope?**

Ron has a player's card for the arcade at the mall. His player's card keeps track of the number of credits he earns as he wins games. Each winning game earns the same number of credits, and those credits can be redeemed for various prizes. Ron has been saving his credits to collect a prize worth 500 credits.

The table and graph show the number of credits Ron had on his game card at various times today when he checked his balance at the arcade.

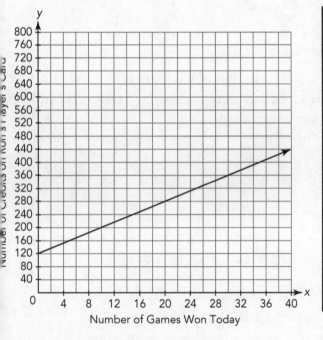

Number of Games Ron Won Today	Number of Credits on Ron's Player's Card
0	120
12	216
18	264
25	320
40	440

1. Is this relationship proportional or non-proportional? Explain how you know.

2. Explain the meaning of the ordered pair (0, 120) listed in the table.

3. Use the graph to determine the slope of the line. Then explain the meaning of the slope in terms of this problem situation.

4. Analyze Rhonda's reasoning. Explain why her reasoning is incorrect.

> Rhonda
>
> $$\frac{440 \text{ credits}}{40 \text{ games won}} = \frac{11 \text{ credits}}{1 \text{ game won}}$$
>
> The slope is 11.

5. Before Ron started winning games today, how many games had he won for which he had saved the credits on his player's card? Show your work.

6. After Ron won his fortieth game today, how many more games does he need to win to collect a prize worth 500 credits? Show your work and explain your reasoning.

7. Summarize what you know about this scenario based on your analysis. Be sure to include each item listed.

   • the initial values of the independent and dependent variables in the context of the problem

   • a sentence explaining the rate of change in terms of the context of the problem

   • the final values of the independent and dependent variables in the context of the problem

ACTIVITY 2.2	Calculating Rate of Change from a Table

So far, you have determined the rate of change from a graph using similar triangles and writing a ratio of the vertical distance to the horizontal distance. However, you can also determine the rate of change, or slope, from a table.

1. Complete the steps to determine the slope from a table.

Number of Games Ron Won Today	Number of Credits on Ron's Player's Card
0	120
12	216
18	264
25	320
40	440

a. Choose any two values of the independent variable. Calculate their difference.

b. Calculate the difference between the corresponding values of the dependent variable. It is important that the order of values you used for determining the difference of the independent variables be followed for the dependent variables.

c. Write a rate to compare the change in the dependent variable to the change in the independent variable.

d. Rewrite the rate as a unit rate.

2. Examine each example. Follow the arrows to calculate the slope. Was the slope calculated correctly in each case? Explain any errors that may have occurred when the arrows were drawn.

Example 1

Number of Games Ron Won Today	Number of Credits on Ron's Player's Card
0	120
12	216
18	264
25	320
40	440

Example 2

Number of Games Ron Won Today	Number of Credits on Ron's Player's Card
0	120
12	216
18	264
25	320
40	440

Example 3

Number of Games Ron Won Today	Number of Credits on Ron's Player's Card
0	120
12	216
18	264
25	320
40	440

There is a formal mathematical process that can be used to calculate the slope of a linear relationship from a table of values with at least two coordinate pairs.

The slope can be calculated using two ordered pairs and the formula:

$$m = \frac{y_2 - y_1}{x_2 - x_1},$$

where the first point is (x_1, y_1) and the second point is (x_2, y_2).

You can calculate the slope of a linear relationship from a table of values. Consider the table showing the number of credits Ron had on his game card at various times at the arcade.

Number of Games Ron Won Today	Number of Credits on Ron's Player's Card
0	120
12	216
18	264
25	320
40	440

Step 1: From the table of values, use (12, 216) as the first point and (25, 320) as the second point.

Step 2: Label the points with the variables.

(12, 216)   (25, 320)
↓ ↓   ↓ ↓
(x_1, y_1) (x_2, y_2)

Step 3: Use the slope formula.

$$m = \frac{y_2 - y_1}{x_2 - x_1} = \frac{320 - 216}{25 - 12}$$
$$= \frac{104}{13}$$
$$= 8$$

The slope is $\frac{8 \text{ credits}}{1 \text{ game}}$ or 8 credits per game.

Does it make a difference which points you choose?

3. Repeat the process to calculate the slope using two different values from the table. Show your work.

4. How is using the slope formula given a table related to using similar triangles given a graph?

ACTIVITY 2.3

Practice with Linear Relationships in Tables

> Analyze the values in the table before you start calculating the rate of change. Do you think the rate of change will be positive or negative?

You can now use the slope formula to calculate the slope of a line given a table of values.

1. Calculate the slope of each linear relationship using the formula. Show all your work.

a.

Number of Carnival Ride Tickets	Cost (dollars)
4	9
8	12
16	18
32	30

b.

x	y
−1	13
0	−2
4	−62
10	−152

c.

Days Passed	Vitamins Remaining in Bottle
7	25
8	23
9	21
10	19

d.

x	y
7	9
18	9
29	9
40	9

e. (10, 25) and (55, 40)

f. (4, 19) and (24, 3)

. Which relationships in Question 1 are proportional relationships? Explain your reasoning.

. Complete each sentence to describe how you can tell whether the slope of a line is positive or negative by analyzing given points.

   a. If the slope of a line is positive, then as the value of x increases the value of y _____.

   b. If the slope of a line is negative, then as the value of x increases the value of y _____.

. Consider the relationship represented in each table shown.

x = 1	
x	y
1	−5
1	10
1	15
1	30

y = 2	
x	y
5	2
6	2
7	2
8	2

   a. Sketch a graph of each relationship. Which relationship is represented by a horizontal line? a vertical line?

   b. What can you conjecture about the slopes of these lines?

ACTIVITY 2.4 — Determining If a Relationship Is Linear

You previously used similar right triangles to show that if you are given a line on a graph, then the slope is the same between any two points on that line. The converse is also true. If the slope between every ordered pair in a table of values is constant, then the ordered pairs will form a straight line.

So, in order to determine if a table of values represents a linear relationship, show that the slope is the same between every set of ordered pairs.

A conditional statement uses the words "if" and "then" to show assumptions and conclusions. For example, if today is Monday, then tomorrow is Tuesday. A converse statement switches the order. For example, if tomorrow is Tuesday, then today is Monday. For any conditional statement the converse may or may not be true.

1. Calculate the slope between the given ordered pairs to determine if they form a straight line. Show your work.

x	y
4	13
9	28
11	34
16	47

a. (4, 13) and (9, 28)

b. (9, 28) and (11, 34)

c. (11, 34) and (16, 47)

d. Will the ordered pairs listed in the table form a straight line when plotted? Explain your reasoning.

2. Determine whether the ordered pairs listed in each table will form a straight line when plotted. Show your work. Explain your reasoning.

a.

x	y
2	7
6	13
8	16
20	34

b.

x	y
1	33
2	40
3	47
4	54
5	61

How is the table in part (b) different from part (a)? How does this difference affect your calculations?

Consecutive means one right after the other, such as 12, 13, and 14.

When the values for the independent variable in a table are consecutive integers, you can examine only the column with the dependent variable and calculate the differences between consecutive values. If the differences are the same each time, then you know that the rate of change is the same each time. The relationship is a linear relationship.

WORKED EXAMPLE

The differences have been calculated for the table shown.

x	y
1	99
2	86
3	73
4	60
5	47

$86 - 99 = -13$

$73 - 86 = -13$

$60 - 73 = -13$

$47 - 60 = -13$

The differences between consecutive values for the dependent variable are the same each time. Therefore the rate of change is the same each time as well. The ordered pairs in this table will therefore form a straight line when plotted.

In this process, you are calculating *first differences*. **First differences** are the values determined by subtracting consecutive *y*-values in a table when the *x*-values are consecutive integers. The first differences in a linear relationship are constant.

3. Use first differences to determine whether the ordered pairs in each table represent a linear relationship. Show your work and explain your reasoning.

a.

x	y
1	25
2	34
3	45
4	52
5	61

b.

x	y
1	12
2	8
3	4
4	0
5	−4

Looking at the first differences identifies whether or not there is a constant rate of change in the table values.

c.

x	y
1	1
2	4
3	9
4	16
5	25

d.

x	y
1	15
2	18
3	21
4	24
5	27

TALK the TALK

Walk the Walk

The table shows the distance Angel walked compared to the number of steps she took.

Number of Steps	Distance Walked (ft)
16	50
40	120
110	300

1. Calculate the slope between each set of ordered pairs. Show your work.

2. Is the graph of the relationship linear? What does this mean in terms of the problem situation?

3. The ordered pairs from the table are represented on the given graph. Show how to use the graph to verify the slope you calculated from the table.

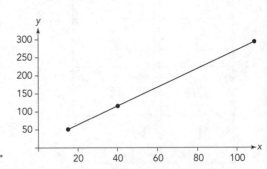

4. How is calculating the slope from a table similar to calculating the slope of a linear relationship from a graph?

Assignment

Write

Define the term *first differences* in your own words.

Remember

You can use the slope formula, $m = \frac{y_2 - y_1}{x_2 - x_1}$, to determine the rate of change between two points represented in a table of values. If the rate is constant, this formula gives the rate of change for the relationship, or slope. The slope of a horizontal line is 0. The slope of a vertical line is undefined.

Practice

1. Each table represents a linear relationship. Which table(s) represent a slope of 2?

Table 1

x	y
0	32
3	26
5	22
9	14

Table 2

x	y
1	3
2	5
3	7
4	9

Table 3

x	y
0	8
3	14
7	22
9	26

2. Calculate the rate of change between the points listed in each table. Determine if the table represents a proportional relationship.

a.

x	y
2	14
5	35
7	49
10	70

b.

x	y
−10	50
−2	10
4	−20
14	−70

c.

x	y
−1	−24
2	48
4	90
8	192

d.

x	y
−6	12
−3	6
3	−6
6	−10

e.

x	y
2	13.5
5	33.75
10	67.5
15	101.25

f.

x	y
−4	−38
−1	−9.5
2	19
3	27

Stretch

Is the relationship described by the equation $y = x^2$ linear? Is it proportional? Describe how you determined your answers.

Review

1. Determine the slope of each linear relationship.

a.

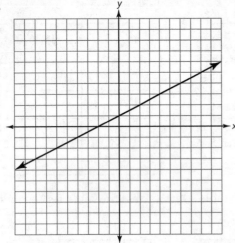

b.

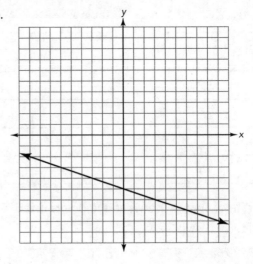

c. $y = 2x$

d. $\frac{5}{6} = \frac{y}{x}$

2. Consider the graph shown.

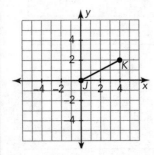

a. Segment *JK* is rotated 90° clockwise resulting in segment *J′K′*. What are the coordinates of *K′*?

b. Segment *JK* is reflected across the line $x = -1$ resulting in segment *J′K′*. What are the coordinates of *K′*?

Dining, Dancing, Driving

3

Linear Relationships in Contexts

WARM UP

The lunch special at the pizza shop is two slices of pizza for $5.00.

1. Express the cost of the pizza as a unit rate.

2. Create a table to represent this context.

Number of Slices of Pizza	Cost (dollars)

3. Write an equation to represent this situation. Define your variables.

LEARNING GOALS

- Determine the slope from a context.
- Connect the rate of change represented in a context to the rate of change in other representations.
- Interpret the rate of change of a linear relationship in terms of the situation it models.
- Generate the values of two coordinate pairs from information given in context.
- Determine the independent and dependent quantities from contexts.

You have analyzed linear relationships in graphs and tables. How can you determine rates of change from word problems alone?

Dependent on Your Point of View

Identify the dependent quantity and the independent quantity in each problem situation.

1. Terrence is purchasing canned vegetables at his local grocery store to donate to the local food pantry. Each can costs $0.59.

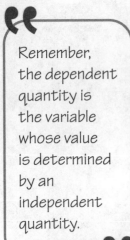

Remember, the dependent quantity is the variable whose value is determined by an independent quantity.

2. The amount of electricity used by a light changes as the knob on the dimmer switch is turned.

3. Stephanie is selling Girl Scout cookies to raise money for her local troop. For each box of cookies she sells, the troop receives $2.00.

4. How would each problem situation change if you switched the independent and dependent quantities? Would each problem still make sense?

You can choose different independent and dependent quantities to model the same information, depending on what you want to know. Once you have determined the independent and dependent quantities, you need just two points to determine the slope, or unit rate.

Josh took a road trip with his family to visit Yosemite National Park in California. Some information about their trip is shown in the table.

Total Miles	Total Cost for Gas ($)	Total Gallons
2600	200	80

1. After they arrived, Josh was curious about how many miles per gallon their car got on the trip.

   a. Given this question, what are the independent and dependent quantities?

   b. Write the ordered pairs of two points you can use to answer the question. Explain what each of your ordered pairs means in terms of the situation.

   c. Determine the rate. Explain what this means in terms of the problem situation.

   d. How many miles per gallon did their car get on the road trip?

2. The family wants to know about how many gallons of gas on average they used for each mile of the trip.

   a. Given this question, what are the independent and dependent quantities?

   b. Write the ordered pairs of two points you can use to answer the question. Explain what each of your ordered pairs means in terms of the situation.

   c. Determine the rate. Round to the nearest hundredth. Explain what this means in terms of the problem situation.

   d. What was the family's average gallons per mile for the trip?

3. If the family had flown, they would have traveled 2100 miles and spent $3250 for tickets alone. Compare the costs per mile for flying and driving. Determine the independent and dependent quantities and rates for each relationship. Show your work.

For each context, complete each task.

- Identify the independent and dependent quantities.
- Write the ordered pairs of two points you can use to answer the question. Explain what each of your ordered pairs means in terms of the situation.
- Then, determine the rate described.

1. Bella's Pizza Shop charges $4.50 for a small pizza, $7.00 for a medium pizza, and $9.00 for a large pizza. Toppings cost extra, depending on the size of the pizza ordered. Bruce ordered a large pizza with three toppings that cost a total of $12.60. What is the cost per number of toppings for a large pizza?

2. A maintenance crew is paving a road in 7-hour shifts. After 10 shifts, 1.25 miles of road have been paved. After 45 shifts, 5.625 miles of road have been paved. At what rate is the maintenance crew paving the road in miles per shift?

3. Melanie is baking breakfast rolls for a band camp fundraiser. She bakes 15 dozen breakfast rolls in 3 hours. After 8 hours, she has baked 40 dozen breakfast rolls. At what rate does Melanie bake breakfast rolls each hour?

4. Aleesa's dog, Bull, has been put on a diet by his veterinarian. He weighs 149 pounds after 8 weeks on his diet. By Week 13, he weighs 134 pounds. What is his average weight loss per week?

Solve each problem.

5. Kathy is working after school to finish assembling the 82 favors needed for the school dance. When she starts at 3:15 PM, she counts the 67 favors that are already assembled. She works until 4:30 PM to finish the job.

   a. How many favors can Kathy assemble each minute?

   b. How many minutes does it take Kathy to assemble one favor?

   c. Which rate is more meaningful in this situation? Explain your reasoning.

6. Eddie rented a moving van to travel across the country. The odometer registered 34,567 miles after he drove for 4 hours. After 7 hours of driving, the odometer read 34,741 miles. What was Eddie's driving rate in miles per hour?

7. Julie used her gift card for the local coffee shop to buy iced teas for herself and five friends. After she and one friend placed their orders, the balance on Julie's gift card was $14.85. After all six members of the group got their iced teas, she had a balance of $3.97 on her gift card. Determine the cost for one glass of iced tea.

TALK the TALK

And Stamps and Tickets

1. A book of 20 postage stamps costs $8.80. What is the cost of one postage stamp?

2. Ticket sales for a local concert totaled $101,244 yesterday. After the ticket window closed today, the cashiers counted 968 tickets sold with a two-day total of $143,836. What is the cost of one concert ticket?

Number of Tickets Sold Today	Total Amount of Sales (dollars)

3. List two similarities between Questions 1 and 2.

4. List two differences between Questions 1 and 2.

Assignment

Write

Describe how to use the independent and dependent quantities in a word problem to determine the rate of change, or slope.

Remember

Two ordered pairs are needed to determine a unit rate given a real-world problem situation.

Practice

1. Lashawna is making jewelry to sell at a craft fair. On Monday, she makes 12 bracelets. On Tuesday, she works an additional 2.5 hours and has a total of 22 bracelets. Determine the time it takes Lashawna to make one bracelet.

2. Nina and her friends are going to the downtown rib festival. The festival organizers expect 10,000 people to attend the four-day festival. At the end of the festival, the organizers say that they have exceeded their expected attendance by 2000 people. Determine the average number of people that attended the festival per day.

3. Aiko spends 2.5 hours baking croissants for a community center bake sale. She bakes the 90 croissants in 5 batches. Determine the number of batches Aiko baked per hour.

4. Nelson is selling his photographs at an art festival. The festival is open for 6 hours each day for 3 days. At the conclusion of the festival, Nelson has sold 54 photographs. Determine the number of photographs Nelson sold per hour.

5. Clayton wants to purchase tickets for the rides at a carnival. He can choose to purchase tickets individually, or he can purchase a ticket package. The package includes 25 tickets for $18.75. Determine the cost per ticket if he purchases the package.

6. Tameca is planning a hiking trip. The trail she would like to follow is 7.5 miles long. She plans to start her hike at 10:00 am. She hopes to reach the end of the trail at 3:00 pm. Determine the number of miles per hour that Tameca plans to hike.

Stretch

Create a situation that can be represented by a linear relationship whose unit rate value doesn't change when you switch the independent and dependent quantities.

Review

Determine whether the relationships represented in the tables are linear. If so, calculate the rate of change.

1.

Number of Bull's-Eyes Made	Points Displayed
0	12,000
3	36,000
5	52,000
9	84,000

2.

x	y
6	12
−4	7
−12	−3
−22	−8

Determine whether the slope of the line represented by each equation is positive, negative, zero, or undefined.

3. $y = -x + 5$

4. $x = 0$

In the figure, parallel lines r and s are cut by transversal w.

5. List all pairs of corresponding angles.

6. List all pairs of alternate interior angles.

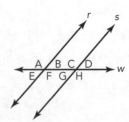

Derby Day

Slope-Intercept Form of a Line

4

WARM UP

Solve each equation for y.

1. $4 = \dfrac{y - 5}{3}$

2. $\dfrac{1}{2} = \dfrac{y + 3}{7}$

3. $-\dfrac{3}{4} = \dfrac{y - 17}{25}$

4. $-\dfrac{9}{5} = \dfrac{y + 31}{-8}$

LEARNING GOALS

- Write the y-intercept as an ordered pair.
- Determine the y-intercept of a linear equation from a context, a table, a graph, or an equation.
- Explain the meaning of the y-intercept, or initial value, when given the context of a linear equation.
- Use the slope formula to derive the slope-intercept form of a linear equation.
- Write equations of lines in slope-intercept form.
- Analyze linear relationships using slopes and initial values.

KEY TERMS

- y-intercept
- slope-intercept form

You have learned how to calculate the slope of a line given a graph, table, or context. How can you determine the initial value in a linear relationship from a table, equation, or graph?

Introducing the y-Intercept!

The slope is one important feature of a linear equation. Another important feature is the *y-intercept*. The **y-intercept** is the y-coordinate of the point where a graph crosses the y-axis. It is the value of the dependent quantity when the independent quantity is 0. The y-intercept can be written as the ordered pair (0, *y*).

For each graph, determine the y-intercept, write it as an ordered pair, and explain its meaning.

> How can you use the slope to think about where each graph would cross the y-axis?

1.

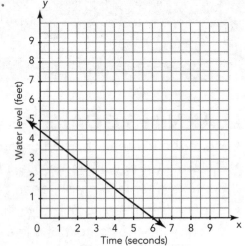

2.

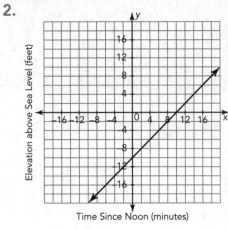

3.

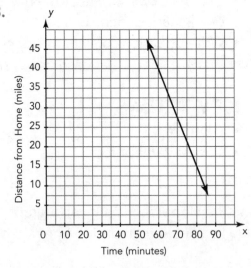

ACTIVITY 4.1 — Determining the *y*-Intercept

Just as you can determine the slope of a linear equation from a table of values or a problem situation, you can also determine the *y*-intercept. Let's start with what you already know: the slope formula.

The table of values represents a linear relationship between the variables *x* and *y*.

x	y
2	7
3	10
4	13

WORKED EXAMPLE

You can use the slope formula to determine the *y*-intercept $(0, y)$ for the graph of a linear relationship.

- First, determine the slope.

$$m = \frac{y_2 - y_1}{x_2 - x_1}$$

$$= \frac{10 - 7}{3 - 2} = \frac{3}{1} = 3$$

- Next, choose any point from the table.

$$(4, 13)$$

- Now, substitute what you know into the slope formula: $m = 3$, $(4, 13)$, and $(0, y)$.

$$m = \frac{y_2 - y_1}{x_2 - x_1}$$

$$3 = \frac{y - 13}{0 - 4}$$

- Finally, solve for the value of the *y*-coordinate.

$$3 = \frac{y - 13}{-4}$$

$$-12 = y - 13$$

$$1 = y$$

The *y*-intercept is $(0, 1)$.

1. How would the worked example change if different points were chosen to calculate the slope? Explain your reasoning.

2. Use a different point from the table to calculate the *y*-intercept. Do you get the same *y*-intercept?

Each table represents a linear relationship. Determine the y-intercept using the slope formula. Write the y-intercept in coordinate form.

3.

x	y
200	14
225	16
250	18
275	20
300	22

4.

x	y
16	90
19	91
22	92
25	93
28	94

How did you calculate the slope when given a context?

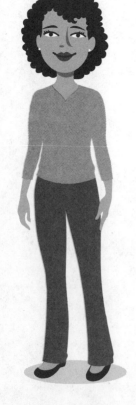

Each context represents a linear relationship. Determine the y-intercept using the slope formula. Write the y-intercept in coordinate form. Explain what the y-intercept represents in each problem situation.

5. **Kim spent $18 to purchase a ride-all-day pass for the amusement park and to play 8 games. After playing a total of 20 games, she realized she'd spent $24.**

6. **Mitch saved money he received as gifts and put it toward buying a bike. When he added one week's allowance to his savings, he had $125. After 3 more weeks of saving his allowance, he had $161 toward the cost of his bike.**

ACTIVITY 4.2 Writing Equations in Slope-Intercept Form

Now that you know how to determine the slope and y-intercept for a linear relationship from a table, graph, or context, you can use this information to write the equation of a line.

Let's use the slope and the y-intercept to determine the equation of the linear relationship represented in the table.

x	y
0	1
2	7
3	10
4	13

WORKED EXAMPLE

Just as you used the slope formula to determine the y-intercept. You can use the slope formula with an unknown point (x, y) to write an equation of the line.

- First, determine the slope and the y-intercept.

  $m = 3$

  y-intercept: (0, 1)

- Next, substitute the slope, y-intercept, and the unknown point (x, y) into the slope formula.

  $m = \frac{y_2 - y_1}{x_2 - x_1}$

  $3 = \frac{y - 1}{x - 0}$

- Finally, solve the equation for y.

  $3 = \frac{y - 1}{x - 0}$

  $3(x - 0) = y - 1$

  $3x = y - 1$

  $3x + 1 = y$

The equation is $y = 3x + 1$.

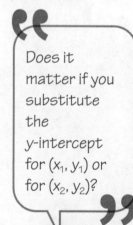

Does it matter if you substitute the y-intercept for (x_1, y_1) or for (x_2, y_2)?

This linear equation is written in *slope-intercept form*. The **slope-intercept form** of a linear equation is $y = mx + b$, where m is the slope of the line and (0, b) is the y-intercept. You can use this form to write linear equations when you know the slope and the y-intercept.

x	y
100	10
105	6
110	2
115	−2
120	−6

By convention, the slope-intercept form is written as $y = mx + b$, but $y = b + mx$ is also correct.

---

1. Determine the slope, y-intercept, and the slope-intercept form of the linear equation for the relationship represented in the table.

2. Write the equation for each linear relationship in slope-intercept form.

   a. $m = -\frac{5}{3}$
      y-intercept: (0, 8)

   b. slope: 6.2
      y-intercept: (0, −2.5)

   c. The line containing points (6, 19) and (0, −35)

   d. Javi regularly checks the balance on his bus pass. Friday afternoon, his balance was $26.25. Monday morning, his balance was $1.50.

3. Consider the equations that you wrote in Question 2.

   a. Write an equation that represents a line with the same y-intercept as part (a) but a steeper slope.

   b. Write an equation that represents a line with the same y-intercept as part (b) but a steeper slope.

| ACTIVITY 4.3 | Analyzing Linear Relationships | |

Each year, your class sponsors a go-kart derby to raise money for a local food bank. Jamie, a member of your class, has claimed the first-place trophy each year for the last four years. Everyone in the class is determined to capture the trophy this year.

Today is Derby Day! You and each member of your group are derby drivers competing against Jamie and Liza. Who is going to win? Your teacher will distribute Derby Day cards to your group. These cards contain the information your group needs to determine the winner.

Rules:

- The members of your group must work cooperatively to answer all the questions on the cards.

- Each member of your group will be assigned Driver A, B, C, or D.

- When you get your Driver card, do not show your card to your group members. You may only communicate the information contained on the card.

- Liza's and Jamie's cards will be shared by the entire group.

- Be sure everyone in your group discusses the entire problem and its solution.

1. **Use the graph paper located at the end of the lesson and your clue cards to help you determine the outcome of the derby.**

Explain the rules to a partner at your table to make sure that everyone understands them.

2. Use the table to organize the information from your graphs
   and to write equations for the drivers in slope-intercept form.

Driver	Slope	y-Intercept	Equation
A:			
B:			
C:			
D:			
Liza			
Jamie			

3. What was the speed of the driver who won the race?
   Explain your reasoning.

4. In what order did the drivers finish the derby? List their names
   or letters and the time it took them to finish.

5. After eight seconds, which driver had traveled the shortest
   distance from the starting line? Who had traveled the
   longest distance? Explain your reasoning.

6. Locate and label a point when one driver passed another driver. Describe this point and explain your reasoning.

7. Is there a point when three drivers are tied? If so, describe the point.

8. If the derby were only 20 meters long, would the order of the winners change? List their names or letters and the time it would take them to finish.

9. After 16 seconds, how far had each driver traveled from the starting line?

10. How long would the derby have to be for Driver C to win?

TALK the TALK 💬

More or Less

Write an equation in slope-intercept form for a line with each of the given characteristics.

1. The line is decreasing from left to right and has a positive *y*-intercept.

2. The line is decreasing from left to right. The line is steeper than the line represented by the equation $y = -3x + 8$.

3. The line is increasing from left to right. The line is less steep than the line represented by the equation $y = 7x - 85$.

4. Create a context that represents a linear relationship, with (0, 22) as its *y*-intercept and a positive slope. Then write the equation of the line in slope-intercept form.

Derby Day

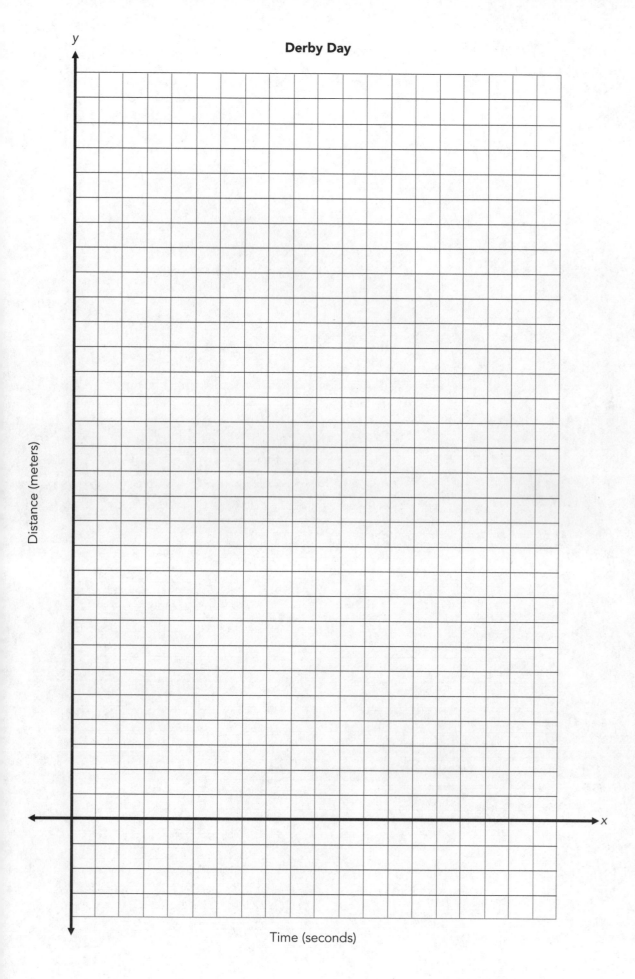

Distance (meters)

Time (seconds)

Assignment

Practice

1. Examine the linear graph. Determine the y-intercept and write the y-intercept in coordinate form. Then write the equation of the line in slope-intercept form.

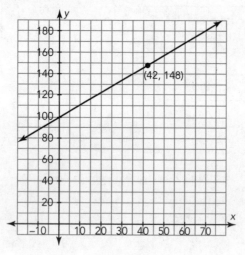

2. The table represents a linear relation. Use the table to identify the y-intercept. Write the y-intercept in coordinate form. Then write the equation in slope-intercept form.

x	y
20	144
24	172
28	200
32	228
36	256

3. Each context represents a linear relation. Read each and determine the y-intercept. Write the y-intercept in coordinate form. Explain what the y-intercept represents in the problem situation. Then write the equation in slope-intercept form.

   a. The water level of a river is 34 feet, and it is receding at a rate of 0.5 foot per day.

   b. Betty worked at a golf course during the summer after eighth grade. After working for two weeks, she added her earnings to the gifts she got for graduation and found she had $570. After four more weeks of work, she had a total of $870.

4. Define the variables and write a linear equation in slope-intercept form for each problem situation. Explain the meaning of the y-intercept.

   a. A catering company charges a fixed fee and an additional charge per person.

   b. A line has a constant rate of change of $\frac{3}{7}$ and passes through the point $(0, -8)$.

   c. A group bike tour costs $75 plus $12 per bike rental.

   d. A salesperson receives a base salary and a percentage of the total sales for the year.

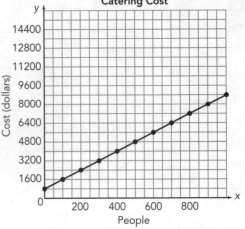

Total Sales (dollars)	Total Income (dollars)
25,000	41,250
30,000	41,500
35,000	41,750
40,000	42,000

5. The graph shows three lines. The equations of the lines are as follows.

$$p: 2y = -x + 10$$
$$q: y = x + 2$$
$$r: 7x - 2y = 14$$

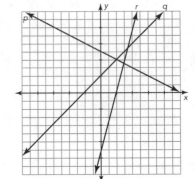

   a. Determine the slope of each line.

   b. Write the lines in order from least steep to most steep.

   c. Write the equation of a line that is steeper than line r.

   d. Write the equation of a line with a negative slope that is steeper than line p.

   e. Write the equation of a line with a positive slope that is less steep than line q.

   f. Write a possible context for each of the lines.

6. Draw a linear graph that is decreasing and has a y-intercept of $(0, 4)$. Write the equation in slope-intercept form.

7. Create a table that represents a linear relation with four values, a y-intercept of $(0, 6)$, and a slope of 3.

Stretch

Determine the equation for a vertical line and the equation for a horizontal line. What are the slope and y-intercept for each type of line?

Review

Determine the rate of change for each situation.

1. Rosa is ordering a submarine sandwich from the corner deli. The deli charges $6.25 for a 7-inch sub. Additional toppings cost extra. Rosa's sandwich with two extra toppings costs $7.75. What is the cost per additional topping?

2. Carmen is selling pies at the cherry festival to raise money for her local volunteer fire department. She sells 85 pies for $12 each. The supplies to make the pies cost Carmen $340. What is the unit rate of the profit made for each pie?

For each graph, determine the slope and explain what the slope means in terms of the independent and dependent quantities. Then write an equation in the form $y = mx$ or $y = mx + b$ to represent the relationship between the independent and dependent quantities.

3. Kodiak is riding her skateboard down a hill, as shown in the graph.

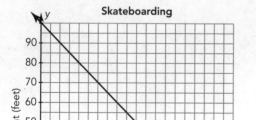

Skateboarding

4. Andy needs a specific amount of flour to bake rolls, as shown in the graph.

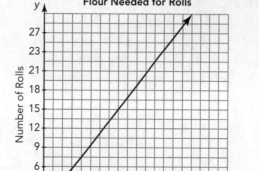

Flour Needed for Rolls

Determine the measure of each unknown angle.

5.

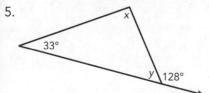

6.

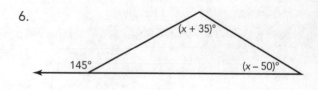

What's the Point?

Point-Slope Form of a Line

5

WARM UP

Write an equation for each linear relationship.

1. The contestant at a game show had already won a total of $2750 when the game show was continued today. He earns an additional $250 for each question he answers correctly today.

2.

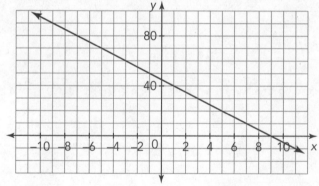

LEARNING GOALS

- Use the slope formula to derive the point-slope form of a linear equation.
- Construct an equation in point-slope form to model a linear relationship between two quantities.
- Write equations for vertical and horizontal lines.

KEY TERM

- point-slope form

You have used the slope-intercept form to represent linear relationships. Are there other forms of a linear equation that you can use? How do you write equations for horizontal and vertical lines?

Draining the Pool

Cyrus and Ava are pool cleaners who have been hired to drain the community diving pools at the end of the summer. They are comparing the rate at which the two pools drain.

1. For each pool, write an equation to represent the linear relationship.

   a. Cityscape Diving Pool is at a water level of 14 feet and drains at a rate of 3 feet per hour.

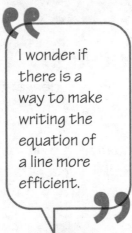

> I wonder if there is a way to make writing the equation of a line more efficient.

   b. Bayside Diving Pool is at a water level of 15 feet after draining for 2 hours and at 12 feet after draining for 4 hours.

2. Compare your process for writing each equation. How are the processes different?

Writing Equations in Point-Slope Form

In the previous lesson, you used the slope, the y-intercept, and the slope formula to write a linear equation. You can also determine the equation of a line without knowing the y-intercept.

WORKED EXAMPLE

x	y
2	6
4	5
6	4

To write an equation of a line from a table of values, you can use the slope formula.

- First, calculate the slope.

$$m = \frac{y_2 - y_1}{x_2 - x_1} = \frac{6 - 5}{2 - 4}$$

$$= \frac{1}{-2} = -\frac{1}{2}$$

- Next, choose any point from the table.

$$(2, 6)$$

- Then, substitute what you know into the slope formula: $m = -\frac{1}{2}$, $(2, 6)$, and the unknown point (x, y).

$$m = \frac{y_2 - y_1}{x_2 - x_1}$$

$$-\frac{1}{2} = \frac{y - 6}{x - 2}$$

- Finally, rewrite the equation with no variables in a denominator.

$$-\frac{1}{2} = \frac{y - 6}{x - 2}$$

$$-\frac{1}{2}(x - 2) = y - 6$$

The equation is $y - 6 = -\frac{1}{2}(x - 2)$.

This linear equation in the worked example is written in *point-slope form*. The **point-slope form** of a linear equation is $y - y_1 = m(x - x_1)$, where m is the slope of the line and (x_1, y_1) is any point on the line.

1. Solve the equation in the worked example for y so that the linear equation is in slope-intercept form. What unique information does each form of the linear equation provide? How are they similar?

Write the equation for each linear relationship in point-slope form.

2. The slope is −8. The point (3, 12) lies on the line.

3. (429, 956) and (249, 836)

Use the given information to write an equation to represent each linear relationship in either slope-intercept form or in point-slope form. Describe your process.

4. The cost to ship a package in the mail includes a basic shipping charge plus an additional cost per number of pounds the package weighs. A three-pound package costs $6.30 to ship. A ten-pound package costs $14 to ship.

5. $m = -\frac{3}{8}$; (50, 7)

6.

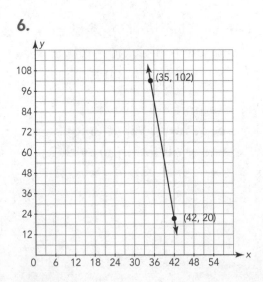

7. (7, 15) and (−39, −8)

8.

x	y
−5	−6
1	−6
2	−6

9. Examine each detail about a linear relationship that you may be provided. Which form of the equation do you prefer to use in each case? Explain your reasoning.

   a. slope and y-intercept

   b. two points

   c. slope and a point other than the y-intercept

Horizontal and vertical lines represent linear relationships, but their equations are different from the equations of lines that are not horizontal or vertical.

x	y
−5	−6
1	−6
2	−6

1. Consider the equation, $y = -6$, that you wrote for the table shown in the previous activity.

   a. How is this equation different from the other equations? What is its slope?

What is the y-intercept?

   b. Describe the graph of the coordinate pairs in this table. Why does the value of its slope make sense?

   c. Explain why the equation makes sense in terms of the graph and the table.

2. Write an equation for each linear relationship. Describe the graph of the linear relationship. State the slope and y-intercept.

   a.

x	y
−7	11
−2	11
0	11

   b. A line that passes through (−15, −3.75) and (89, −3.75)

3. Consider a new table of values representing a linear relationship.

x	y
−2	5
−2	14
−2	29

a. Explain how this table is similar to and different from the tables in Questions 1 and 2.

b. Write an equation for the linear relationship in the table.

c. Describe the graph of this linear relationship.

d. Use the slope formula to calculate the slope between two points in the table. What do you notice?

e. What is the y-intercept of this linear relationship? Explain why this makes sense.

4. Write an equation for each linear relationship. Describe the graph of the linear relationship.

a.

x	y
$\frac{17}{2}$	−18
$\frac{17}{2}$	23
$\frac{17}{2}$	267

b. A line that passes through (−7, −973) and (−7, 542)

c. Create an additional table of values and write the equation for a vertical line.

In a horizontal line there is no change in the y-values as the x-values change. Therefore, the slope is 0. A horizontal line has zero steepness. In a vertical line there is no change in the x-values as the y-values change. Therefore, the slope is undefined. A vertical line has an undefined steepness.

1. Carefully cut out the graphs, tables, contexts, and equations located the end of the lesson. Match each equation with its correct graph, table, or context. Explain how you matched the equations with the representations.

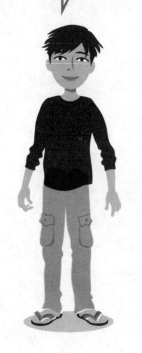

Take out your scissors. It's time to cut and sort!

2. Compare the graphs.

   a. How are they different? How are these differences reflected in the slope-intercept form of their equation?

   b. Identify the y-intercept for each graph. How can you determine this point in the slope-intercept form of the equation for each graph?

   c. Identify the slope for each graph. How is the slope represented in the slope-intercept form of each equation?

3. Analyze the equation for each table.

   a. Determine the coefficient of x for each linear relationship using the slope formula.

Can you remember the ways to determine the rate of change from a table?

   b. How can the number that is added in each equation written in slope-intercept form be determined from the table?

4. Analyze the equation for each context. Explain what each term of the equation means in each context.

TALK the TALK

Say What?

You have learned about two forms of a linear equation: the slope-intercept form, $y = mx + b$, and the point-slope form, $y - y_1 = m(x - x_1)$.

1. **What information can you determine about each line by looking at the structure of the equation?**

   a. $y = \frac{3}{5}x - 4$ b. $y - 6 = 2(x + 1)$

   c. $y + 4 = 2x$ d. $y = -\frac{2}{7}x$

   e. $y + 5 = -(x - 4)$ f. $y = 19$

2. **Create a context that represents a linear relationship that passes through the point (2, 56) and has an increasing slope. Then write the equation of the line in point-slope form and slope-intercept form.**

A

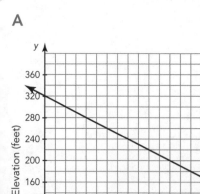

B

Michele read the first 40 pages of a mystery novel before she fell asleep. The next day, she read one page every two minutes until she finished the book, which was a total of 325 pages.

C

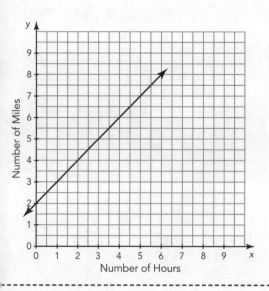

D

Time (hours)	Water Level (feet)
x	y
2	15
4	13.5
8	10.5
10	9

E

Number of Games Ron Won Today	Number of Credits on Ron's Player's Card
x	y
12	216
18	264
25	320
40	440

F

Bella's Pizza Shop charges $4.50 for a small pizza, $7.00 for a medium pizza, and $9.00 for a large pizza. Additional toppings cost extra depending on the size of the pizza ordered. Bruce ordered a large pizza with three toppings that cost a total of $12.60.

$$y = 1.2x + 9$$

$$y = -\frac{3}{4}x + \frac{33}{2}$$

$$y = \frac{1}{2}x + 40$$

$$y - x = 2$$

$$y - 200 = -5(x - 24)$$

$$y = 8x + 120$$

Assignment

Write

Compare the slope-intercept and point-slope forms of a linear equation.

Remember

The point-slope form of a linear equation is $y - y_1 = m(x - x_1)$, where m is the slope of the line and (x_1, y_1) is a point on the line. The slope of a horizontal line is 0. The slope of a vertical line is undefined.

Practice

Write an equation in point-slope form.

1. $m = 2$; (5, 6)

2. $m = -9.2$; (−17, 10)

3. (−2, −3) and (8, −8)

4. (79, 52) and (−87, 550)

5. A photography studio charges $50 for a sitting fee and 6 prints. Luigi increased his order to 11 prints and paid $65.

6. Zellie is taking the stairs in her building from her floor to the top of the building. After 2 minutes, she was 100 steps from the bottom floor. After 5 minutes, she was 196 steps from the bottom floor.

Write an equation in any form.

7. A newspaper charges a flat fee plus a charge per day to place a classified ad.

Number of Days	Total Charge ($)
2	8.00
4	13.00
6	18.00

8.

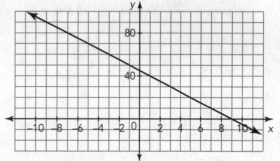

9.

x	y
−10	50
−2	10
4	−20
14	−70

10.

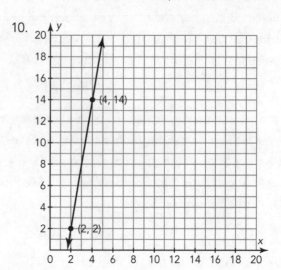

11. Pedro is traveling on a toll road. He plans to exit the road 5 miles ahead at First Avenue and pay $1.75. He changes his plans and travels 9 miles to Butler Street and pays $2.75.

12.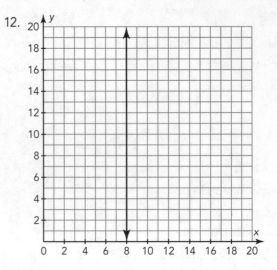

Stretch

To convert an equation from point-slope to slope-intercept form, you can solve the equation for y. How do you convert from slope-intercept to point-slope form? Rewrite each equation in point-slope form using only algebraic properties. What is special about the ordered pair now visible in the equation?

1. $y = 2x - 7$
2. $y = -5x + 15$

Review

1. Write an equation in slope-intercept form with the given characteristics.
   a. The line is increasing and passes through the point $(0, -10)$. The slope of the line is less steep than the slope of the line represented by the equation $y = x + 8$.
   b. The line is decreasing and passes through the point $(0, 5)$. The slope of the line is more steep than the slope of the line represented by the equation $y = -\frac{1}{4}x - 4$.

2. For the linear equation $x = 4y - 5$, complete each task.
   a. Use a table of values to graph the linear equation.
   b. Use the points on the graph to sketch similar triangles that may be used to show that the slope of a non-vertical line is the same between any two points on the line.
   c. Verify that the slopes are the same.

3. Solve each problem.
   a. What is a 15% tip for a restaurant bill of $24?
   b. A $50 item was marked up 20%. What is the total increased cost of the item?

The Arts Are Alive 6

Using Linear Equations

WARM UP

Solve each equation for y.

1. $-2y = -x + 7$

2. $\frac{3}{4}y = x - 6$

3. $2x + 3y = 6$

4. $\frac{1}{2}x - 4y = 8$

LEARNING GOALS

- Construct linear equations to model relationships between two quantities.
- Graph lines using the slope-intercept form of a linear equation.
- Graph lines using the point-slope form of a linear equation.
- Graph lines using the standard form of a linear equation.
- Convert equations from point-slope or standard form to slope-intercept form.
- Discuss the advantages and disadvantages of slope-intercept, point-slope, and standard form.

KEY TERM

- standard form

You have graphed equations using tables of values. Is there a more efficient method to graphing a linear relationship? Can you use the equation of a linear relationship to create a graphical representation?

Jump In the Line

Describe what you know about the graph of each relationship by analyzing each equation. Then, explain how you might graph each line given its equation.

1. $y = \frac{2}{3}x + 7$

2. $y - 3 = 5(x + 1)$

3. $x = -4$

4. $-3x + 8y = 10$

Using Slope-Intercept Form to Graph a Line

As you learned previously, the slope-intercept form of a linear equation is $y = mx + b$, where m is the slope of the line and $(0, b)$ is the y-intercept. You can use the equation to graph the relationship without first creating a table of values using the y-intercept and the slope.

Douglas is giving away tickets to a concert that he won from a radio station contest. Currently, he has 10 tickets remaining. He gives a pair of tickets to each person who asks for them.

This situation can be modeled by the equation $y = -2x + 10$, where x represents the number of people who request tickets and y represents the number of tickets available.

To graph the equation $y = -2x + 10$, you will first plot the y-intercept, $(0, 10)$, and then use the slope, -2, to plot two more points. Remember, slope describes the steepness and direction of a line. Slope is the ratio of the change in y-values to the change in x-values, commonly referred to as rise over run. In this equation, you can think of $m = -2$ as two different ratios: $\frac{-2}{1}$ or $\frac{2}{-1}$. The sign of the number tells you the direction to go to plot a new point. The ratio $\frac{-2}{1}$ has a negative rise and a positive run. It is interpreted as down 2 units and to the right 1 unit. The ratio $\frac{2}{-1}$ has a positive rise and a negative run. It is interpreted as up 2 units and to the left 1 unit.

The rule of thumb when graphing a line is to plot at least three points.

WORKED EXAMPLE

Graph $y = -2x + 10$.

Begin by plotting the y-intercept, $(0, 10)$.

Use the slope and count from the y-intercept to graph two more points on the line.

- For $m = \frac{-2}{1}$, go down 2 units and to the right 1 unit.

- For $m = \frac{2}{-1}$, go up 2 units and to the left 1 unit.

Connect the points to form a straight line.

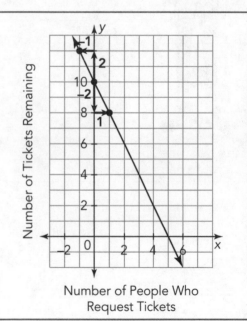

Number of People Who Request Tickets

Use the equations to graph each line.

1. $y = \frac{3}{2}x - 1$

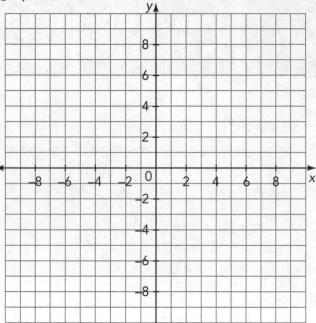

Think about the direction of the line before you start graphing.

2. $y = -\frac{5}{2}x + 3$

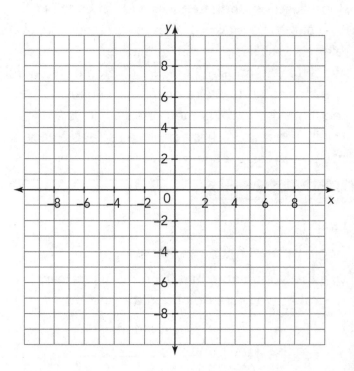

3. $y = 10x + 25$

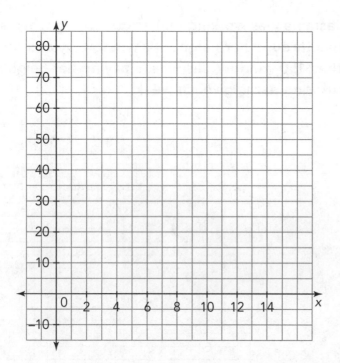

Use a straightedge to draw your lines.

Write an equation for each problem situation. Then graph each equation.

4. Avery wants to buy a virtual reality headset. He already has $30 saved and plans to mow lawns for $15 each.

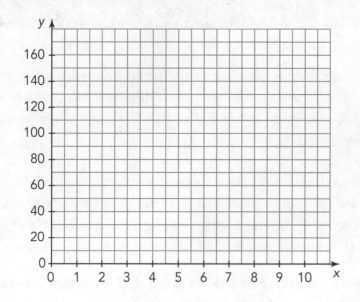

Remember to label the axes with the appropriate variable quantities.

5. Jasmine was working on her golf swing when she hit a golf ball through her neighbor's window by accident. To replace the $150 window, Jasmine is paying her neighbor $10 of her tutoring earnings each week.

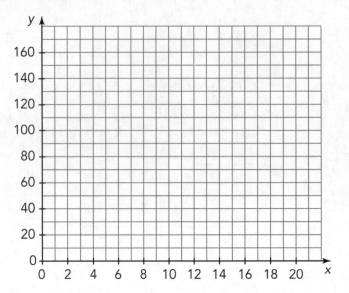

| ACTIVITY 6.2 | Using Point-Slope Form to Graph a Line |

In the previous lesson, you learned that the point-slope form of a linear equation is $y - y_1 = m(x - x_1)$, where m is the slope of the line and (x_1, y_1) is a point on the line. Use this form of a linear equation for the next problem situation.

The jazz band is selling tickets to raise money for new music stands. They already had some money in their account when they started selling tickets at $5.00 each. After selling 3 tickets, the band had a total of $50 in their account.

1. Let x = the number of tickets sold, and let y = the total amount of money in the jazz band's account.

   a. Write an equation in point-slope form.

b. Use the point-slope form to graph the equation.

- Write the coordinates for the known point. Plot the point on the coordinate plane.
- Write the slope as a ratio. Then use the slope and count from the point. To identify another point on the graph, start at the point and count either down (negative) or up (positive) for the rise. Then, count either left (negative) or right (positive) for the run.

  Continue the counting process to plot at least two more points.

- Connect the points to form a straight line.

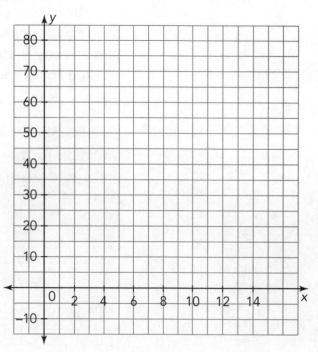

2. Identify the slope and a point on the line from the given equation. Then graph each line. Be careful to take into account the scales on the axes and the signs of the points given in the equation.

a. $y - 5 = -\frac{3}{4}(x - 14)$

b. $y + 8 = \frac{1}{2}(x + 6)$

Remember, start with the given point and then use the slope to plot two more points.

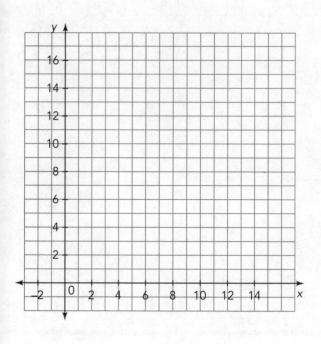

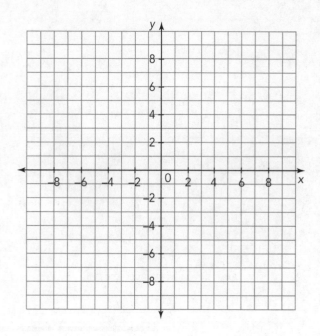

3. Vivian and her friends are spending their Saturday making friendship bracelets to donate to the local children's hospital. The group makes 7 friendship bracelets each half-hour. Vivian had already made some bracelets Friday. After the group worked for 3 hours on Saturday, they had a total of 45 bracelets.

Define your variables and units. Then write and graph an equation for the number of bracelets Vivian and her friends make to donate.

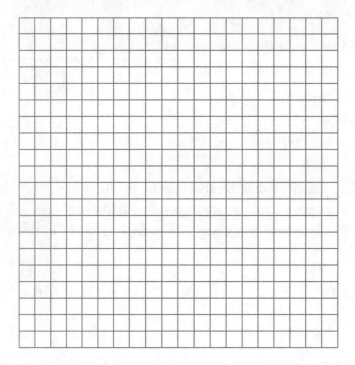

Tickets for a school play cost $5.00 for students and $8.00 for adults. On opening night, $1600 is collected in ticket sales.

This situation can be modeled by the equation $5x + 8y = 1600$. You can define the variables as shown.

x = number of student tickets sold
y = number of adult tickets sold

This equation is not written in slope-intercept form or in point-slope form. It is written in *standard form*. The **standard form** of a linear equation is $Ax + By = C$, where A, B, and C are constants and A and B are not both zero.

1. **Explain what each term of the equation represents in the problem situation.**

   a. 5x   b. 8y

   c. 1600

2. **What is the independent variable? What is the dependent variable? Explain your reasoning.**

Remember, the *y*-intercept, (0, *y*) is where a line crosses the *y*-axis, so the value of *x* is 0. To calculate a *y*-intercept, substitute 0 for *x* and solve the equation for *y*.

The *x*-intercept, (*x*, 0), is where the line crosses the *x*-axis, so the value of *y* is 0. To calculate an *x*-intercept, substitute 0 for *y* and solve the equation for *x*.

3. **Calculate and interpret the meanings of the *x*-intercept and *y*-intercept for this equation.**

4. **Use the *x*-intercept and *y*-intercept to graph the equation of the line.**

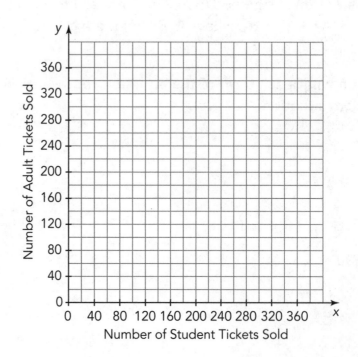

5. **Determine the slope of this line. Interpret the meaning of the slope in this problem situation.**

6. For each equation, determine the x-intercept, the y-intercept, and the slope. Record your results in the table. Leave your answers in fractional form.

Equation	x-Intercept	y-Intercept	Slope
$5x + 2y = 6$			
$3x + 4y = 7$			
$2x - 3y = 9$			
$-5x + 7y = 11$			

7. What do you notice about the relationship between the constants A, B, and C from the standard form and

a. the x-intercepts?

b. the y-intercepts?

c. the slope?

8. Match each graph with the correct equation written in standard form. Explain your reasoning.

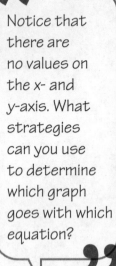

Notice that there are no values on the x- and y-axis. What strategies can you use to determine which graph goes with which equation?

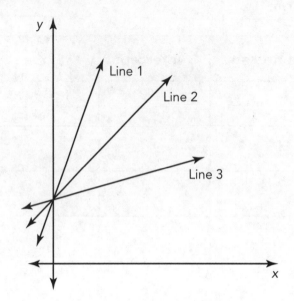

a. $3x - 12y = -60$

b. $6x - 2y = -10$

c. $9x - 9y = -45$

Define variables for each problem situation. Then write an equation in standard form and use the intercepts to graph the linear relationship.

9. Ashley burns 20 calories for every 5 minutes she jumps rope and 50 calories for every 5 minutes she runs. On Tuesday, Ashley burned a total of 500 calories.

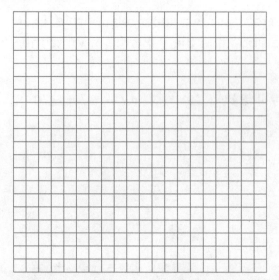

10. For the show choir's holiday performance, they are selling tickets for $4.50 per student and $6.00 per adult. On the night of their final performance, they collect $270 in ticket sales.

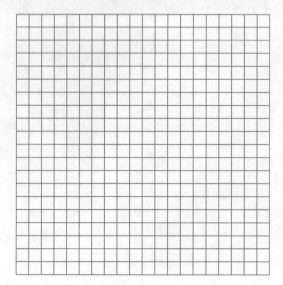

Identifying Slope and y-Intercept

Each equation represents a linear relationship. Examine each and determine the slope and the y-intercept. Write the y-intercept as an ordered pair.

Use what you know about the different forms of a line as you examine each equation.

1. $y = 3x - 9 + 8x$

2. $4x + 6y = 270$

3. $y = 5(2x - 9)$

4. $8y = -6x + 24$

5. $y + 9 = 6(x - 3)$

6. $y = 9$

7. $4x - 12y = 48$

8. $x = 10$

TALK the TALK

Choose Your Medium

For each context, complete each task:
- Write an equation in slope-intercept, point-slope, or standard form.
- State the form of the equation you used and your reason for using it.
- Graph the line using any method.
- Explain the graphing method you used and your reason for using it.

1. On a math quiz, students earned 2 points for every correct multiple-choice question and 3 points for every correct short answer question. Miguel earned a total of 36 points on the quiz.

   Let x = number of correct multiple-choice questions
   Let y = number of correct short answer questions
   Equation: Reasoning:

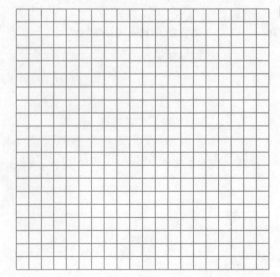

Reasoning:

2. Mario has $20, and he plans to save an additional $10 every two weeks.

   Let *x* = number of weeks
   Let *y* = Mario's total savings
   Equation: Reasoning:

Reasoning:

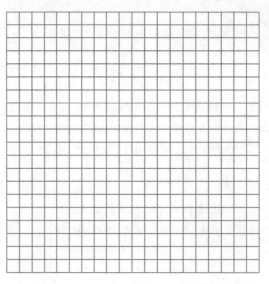

3. What are the advantages and disadvantages of using each form of a linear equation?

   a. slope-intercept form   b. point-slope form

   c. standard form

Assignment

Write

Explain how to graph a line when the equation is written in slope-intercept form, point-slope form, or standard form.

Remember

The standard form of a linear equation is $Ax + By = C$, where A, B, and C are constants and A and B are not both zero.

Practice

1. Graph each equation using its given form.
   a. $y = 4x + 2$
   b. $y = -\frac{1}{3}x - 5$
   c. $y + 1 = \frac{3}{4}(x - 8)$
   d. $y - 4 = -\frac{2}{3}(x - 6)$

2. Graph each equation using its intercepts.
   a. $4x + 6y = 48$
   b. $-2x + 8y = 56$

3. Eugenie bought magazines for $6 each and paperback books for $3 each for a total of $54.
   a. Define your variables and write an equation in standard form to represent the situation.
   b. Calculate and interpret the x-intercept and the y-intercept for this equation.
   c. Graph the equation of the line using the intercepts.
   d. Calculate and interpret the slope of this line.

4. Each equation represents a linear relation. State the slope and y-intercept for each.
   a. $-9x + 2y = -36$
   b. $y + 5 = -7(x + 3)$
   c. $y = 2$
   d. $y = \frac{5}{2}x - 9$

Stretch

You learned how to generalize the x- and y-intercepts and the slope from the standard form of an equation. Write the point-slope and slope-intercept form of a linear equation in terms of the constants from the standard form.

Review

1. Write an equation in point-slope form for each problem.
   a. $m = -8$ and passes through the point (3, 12)
   b. passes through the points (9, −18) and (−3, −26)

2. Determine if each table represents a proportional relationship.

a.

x	Y
−1	−24
2	48
4	90
8	192

b.

x	Y
2	13.5
5	33.75
10	67.5
15	101.25

3. Solve each inequality.
   a. $10 + 5x \geq -25$
   b. $-4x + 26 < 14$

Linear Relationships Summary

KEY TERMS

- first differences
- *y*-intercept
- slope-intercept form
- point-slope form
- standard form

LESSON 1 | **U.S. Shirts**

In mathematics, when representing quantities in a table it is important to include a row to identify the quantities and units of measure. Typically, the independent quantity is represented in the left column and the dependent quantity is represented in the right column.

When graphing a relationship, the convention is to represent the independent quantity on the horizontal axis of a graph and the dependent quantity on the vertical axis. You should include labels on each axis.

When writing an equation in the form $y = mx + b$, the *x*-value is the independent variable and the *y*-value is the dependent variable. It is important to define the variables you choose.

For example, the table and graph shown represent the equation $y = 5x + 5$.

Independent Quantity	Dependent Quantity
0	5
1	10
2	15
3	20

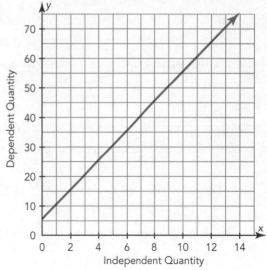

You can use the slope formula, $m = \frac{y_2 - y_1}{x_2 - x_1}$, to determine the rate of change between two points represented in a table of values. If the rate is constant, this formula gives the rate of change for the relationship, or slope.

For example, the table shows a linear relationship with a slope of 5.

Independent Quantity	Dependent Quantity
0	5
1	10
2	15
3	20

$$m = \frac{20 - 10}{3 - 1} = \frac{10}{2} = 5$$

When the values for the independent variable in a table are consecutive integers, you can examine only the column with the dependent variable and calculate the differences between consecutive values. In this process, you are calculating first differences. **First differences** are the values determined by subtracting consecutive y-values in a table when the x-values are consecutive integers. The first differences in a linear relationship are constant.

You can choose different independent and dependent quantities to model the same information, depending on what you want to know. Once you have determined the independent and dependent quantities, you need just two points to determine the slope, or unit rate.

Time Miles	Total Cost for Gas ($)	Total Gallons
2600	200	80

For example, using the information in this table, you can model the number of miles per gallon or the number of gallons per mile.

Number of miles per gallon = $\frac{2600}{60}$ = 32.5 miles per gallon

Number of gallons per mile = $\frac{80}{2600}$ ≈ 0.03 gallons per mile

Derby Day

The **y-intercept** is the y-coordinate of the point where a graph crosses the y-axis. It is the value of the dependent quantity when the independent quantity is 0. The y-intercept can be written as the ordered pair (0, y).

x	y
2	7
3	10
4	13

You can use the slope formula, $m = \frac{y_2 - y_1}{x_2 - x_1}$, to determine the y-intercept for the graph of a linear relationship from a table of values.

For example, you can determine the y-intercept of a linear equation from the table of values shown.

- First, determine the slope.

$$m = \frac{y_2 - y_1}{x_2 - x_1}$$
$$= \frac{10 - 7}{3 - 2} = \frac{3}{1} = 3$$

- Next, choose any point from the table.

(4, 13)

- Now, substitute what you know into the slope formula: $m = 3$, (4, 13), and (0, y).

$$m = \frac{y_2 - y_1}{x_2 - x_1}$$
$$3 = \frac{y - 13}{0 - 4}$$

- Finally, solve for the value of the y-coordinate.

$$3 = \frac{y - 13}{-4}$$
$$-12 = y - 13$$
$$1 = y$$

The y-intercept is (0, 1).

When you know the slope and the y-intercept, you can use this information to write a linear equation in slope-intercept form. The **slope-intercept form** of a linear equation is $y = mx + b$, where m is the slope of the line and (0, b) is the y-intercept.

What's the Point?

You can determine the equation of a line from a table of values without knowing the y-intercept using the slope formula, $m = \frac{y_2 - y_1}{x_2 - x_1}$.

For example, to write an equation of a line from a table of values, you can use the slope formula.

- First, calculate the slope.

$$m = \frac{y_2 - y_1}{x_2 - x_1} = \frac{6 - 5}{2 - 4}$$

$$= \frac{1}{-2} = -\frac{1}{2}$$

x	y
2	6
4	5
6	4

- Next, choose any point from the table.

$(2, 6)$

- Then, substitute what you know into the slope formula: $m = -\frac{1}{2}$, $(2, 6)$, and the unknown point (x, y).

$$m = \frac{y_2 - y_1}{x_2 - x_1}$$

$$-\frac{1}{2} = \frac{y - 6}{x - 2}$$

- Finally, rewrite the equation with no variables in a denominator.

$$-\frac{1}{2} = \frac{y - 6}{x - 2}$$

$$-\frac{1}{2}(x - 2) = y - 6$$

The equation is $y - 6 = -\frac{1}{2}(x - 2)$.

The linear equation you write is written in point-slope form. The **point-slope form** of a linear equation is $y - y_1 = m(x - x_1)$, where m is the slope of the line and (x_1, y_1) is any point on the line.

The slope of a horizontal line is 0. The slope of a vertical line is undefined.

You can use an equation in slope-intercept form to graph a relationship without first creating a table of values using the y-intercept and the slope.

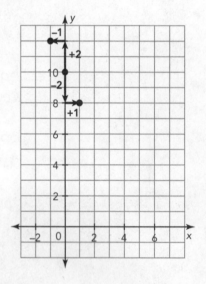

For example, graph the equation $y = -2x + 10$. Begin by plotting the y-intercept, (0, 10). Use the slope and count from the y-intercept to graph two more points on the line.

- For $m = \frac{-2}{1}$, go down 2 units and to the right 1 unit.

- For $m = \frac{2}{-1}$, go up 2 units and to the left 1 unit.

Connect the points to form a straight line.

Another way to write a linear equation is in standard form. The **standard form** of a linear equation is $Ax + By = C$, where A, B, and C are constants, and A and B are not both zero.

When an equation is in standard form, you can calculate a y-intercept, where a line crosses the y-axis, by substituting 0 for x and solving the equation for y. To calculate an x-intercept, where the line crosses the x-axis, substitute 0 for y and solve the equation for x.

TOPIC 3

Introduction to Functions

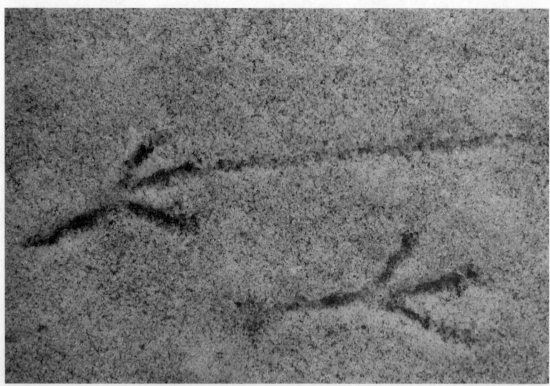

These footprints tell a story. Can you guess what animal made these tracks?

Module 2: Developing Function Foundations

TOPIC 3: INTRODUCTION TO FUNCTIONS

In this topic, students explore functions in terms of sequences, mappings, sets of ordered pairs, graphs, tables, verbal descriptions, and equations. Because students have a strong foundation in writing equations of lines, they can construct equations for linear functions. Students learn the formal definition of a function and analyze functions and relations represented in a wide variety of ways. Finally, students further investigate the focus function: the linear function.

Where have we been?

Throughout elementary school, students described patterns and explained features of the pattern. They have also formed ordered pairs with terms of two sequences and compared the terms. Therefore, sequences are used as the entry point for this topic.

Where are we going?

The study of functions is a predominant topic in high school mathematics. As students move into high school, they will develop and use formal notation (e.g., $f(x)$) to denote and operate with functions. In high school, students will use sequences as a launching point for linear and exponential functions.

Using the Vertical Line Test to Determine if a Relation Is a Function

A standard test to determine whether a graphed relation is a function is called the vertical line test. If you draw a vertical line anywhere on the graph and cross more than one point, the relation is not a function. The graph shown illustrates a relation that is not a function.

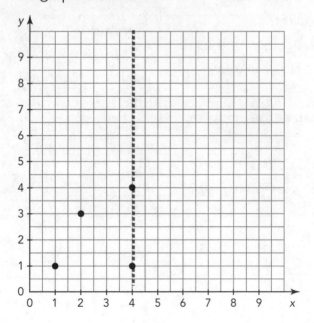

Myth: Just watch a video, and you will understand it.

Has this ever happened to you? Someone explains something, and it all makes sense at the time. You feel like you get it. But then, a day later when you try to do it on your own, you suddenly feel like something's missing? If that feeling is familiar, don't worry. It happens to us all. It's called the illusion of explanatory depth, and it frequently happens after watching a video.

How do you break this illusion? The first step is to try to make the video interactive. Don't treat it like a TV show. Instead, pause the video and try to explain it to yourself or to a friend. Alternatively, attempt the steps in the video on your own and rewatch it if you hit a wall. Remember, it's easy to confuse familiarity with understanding.

#mathmythbusted

Talking Points

You can further support your student's learning by asking questions about the work they do in class or at home. Your student is learning to think about functions for the first time.

Questions to Ask

- How does this problem look like something you did in class?
- Can you show me the strategy you used to solve this problem? Do you know another way to solve it?
- Does your answer make sense? How do you know?
- Is there anything you don't understand? How can you use today's lesson to help?

Key Terms

sequence
A sequence is a pattern involving an ordered arrangement of numbers, geometric figures, letters, or other objects.

discrete
A discrete graph is a graph of isolated points.

function
A function maps each input to one and only one output. In other words, a function has no input with more than one output. The domain of a function is the set of all inputs of the function. The range of a function is the set of all outputs of the function.

Patterns, Sequences, Rules . . .

Analyzing Sequences as Rules

WARM UP

1. List six consecutive numbers.

2. List six consecutive even numbers.

3. List six consecutive multiples of seven.

4. List six consecutive multiples of five that are decreasing.

5. List six consecutive prime numbers.

LEARNING GOALS

- Write sequences of numbers generated from the creation of diagrams and written contexts.
- State varying growth patterns of sequences.

KEY TERMS

- sequence
- term
- ellipsis

You are surrounded by patterns every day, and you have examined many mathematical patterns in school. How are patterns of numbers related to the linear relationships you have studied?

Sequences of Events

A **sequence** is a pattern involving an ordered arrangement of numbers, geometric figures, letters, or other objects. A **term** in a sequence is an individual number, figure, or letter in the sequence.

Here are some example sequences.

Sequence A:
2, 4, 6, 8, 10, 12, . . .

Sequence B:

 , , , , . . .

Sequence C:
3, 9, 27, 81, . . .

Often, only the first few terms of a sequence are listed, followed by an *ellipsis*. An **ellipsis** is a set of three periods, which stands for "and so on."

1. Identify the next term in each sequence. Explain how you determined each answer.

2. Generate a sequence, given this information:

   Starting term: 1
   Rule: Multiply each term by 3 and then subtract 1 to get the next term

Analyzing a Variety of Different Sequences

Taking Apart a Card Trick

Matthew is performing a card trick. It is important that he collect the cards shown in a particular order. Each turn, he collects all of the cards in the right-most column, and all the cards in the bottom row.

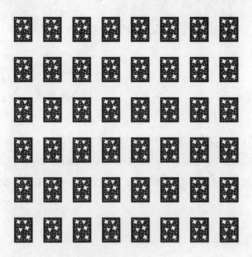

1. Write a sequence to show the number of cards removed during each of the first five turns.

2. Write a sequence to show the number of cards remaining after each of the first five turns.

3. What pattern is shown in each sequence?

Arranging Pennies

Lenny is making arrangements with pennies. He has made three penny arrangements, and now he wants to make five more arrangements. Each time he adds another arrangement, he needs to add one more row to the base, and the row needs to have one more penny than the last row in the previous arrangement.

4. **Write the first eight terms in the sequence that represents this situation. Each term should indicate the total number of pennies in each arrangement. Explain your reasoning.**

5. **Explain why the pattern does not increase by the same amount each time.**

Arranging Classroom Tables

Some schools purchase classroom tables that have trapezoid-shaped tops rather than rectangular tops. The tables fit together nicely to arrange the classroom in a variety of ways. The number of students that can fit around a table is shown in the first diagram. The second diagram shows how the tables can be joined at the sides to make one longer table.

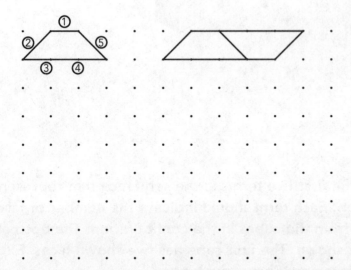

5. Write the first five terms in the sequence that represents this situation. Each term should indicate the total number of students that can sit around one, two, three, four, and five tables. Assume that the tables are joined at the sides, as shown in the second diagram above. Explain your reasoning.

7. The first trapezoid table seats five students. Explain why each additional table does not have seats for five students.

Building Stairs

Dawson is stacking cubes in configurations that look like stairs. Each new configuration has one additional step.

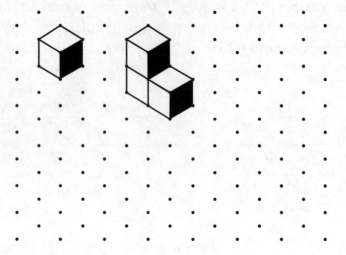

8. Write the first five terms in the sequence that represents this situation. Each term should indicate the number of faces shown from the cubes in the configuration. The bottom faces are not shown. The first cube has five shown faces. Explain your reasoning. Show your work.

9. Predict the number of shown faces in a stair configuration that is seven cubes high. Show your work.

Babysitting

Every Friday, Sarah earns $14 for babysitting. Every Saturday, Sarah spends $10 going out with her friends.

10. Write a sequence to show the amounts of money Sarah has every Friday after babysitting and every Saturday after going out with her friends for five consecutive weeks. The sequence should have 10 terms. Explain your reasoning.

Recycling

The first week of school, Ms. Sinopoli asked her class to begin collecting cans for recycling. The students started bringing in cans the second week of school. They collected 120 cans per week.

11. Write a sequence to show the running total number of cans collected through the first nine weeks of school. Explain your reasoning.

TALK the TALK

Looking Back

There are many different patterns that can generate a sequence. Some possible patterns are:

- adding or subtracting the same number each time,
- multiplying or dividing by the same number each time,
- adding a different number each time, with the numbers being part of a pattern, and
- alternating between adding and subtracting.

The next term in a sequence is calculated by determining the pattern of the sequence and then using that pattern on the last known term of the sequence.

1. **Look back at the sequences you analyzed in this lesson. Describe the pattern of each sequence by completing the table shown.**

Sequence Name	Increases or Decreases	Describe the Pattern
Taking Apart a Card Trick		
Arranging Pennies		
Arranging Classroom Tables		
Building Stairs		
Babysitting		
Recycling		

2. **Which sequences are similar? Explain your reasoning.**

Write

Define each term in your own words.

1. sequence
2. term
3. ellipsis

Remember

There are many different patterns that can generate a sequence. The next term in a sequence is calculated by determining the pattern of the sequence and then using that pattern on the last known term of the sequence.

Practice

1. Amanda is training to run a marathon. She must follow a strict schedule to make sure she is ready for the race. She will start her training by running two miles the first week. She wants to run one fewer mile the next week, and then three more miles the week after that. She will continue this pattern during her entire training regimen.

   a. Write a sequence for the number of miles that Amanda will run the first 10 weeks of her training. Explain your reasoning.

   b. In which week of training will Amanda run seven miles?

   c. Amanda needs to run 26 miles in the final week of her training. In which week will Amanda reach her goal? Explain your answer.

   d. Amanda is considering changing her regimen by running two miles the first week and then running an additional two miles each subsequent week. Write a sequence for the number of miles that Amanda would run the first 10 weeks of her training if she followed the new regimen. Explain your reasoning.

   e. In which week would Amanda reach her goal of 26 miles, if she followed the new regimen? Explain your reasoning.

2. Amanda chooses to continue with the first training regimen. Because it will take a long time to train, Amanda decides that during her periods of rest, she will sew a quilt to have as a remembrance of her achievement. She will add squares to the quilt every two weeks using the pattern shown (added squares are shaded).

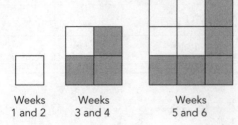

Weeks 1 and 2   Weeks 3 and 4   Weeks 5 and 6

   a. Write a sequence for the first 10 terms generated by this situation. Each term should represent the number of squares that the quilt will have. The first term has one square. Explain your reasoning.

   b. By the end of her training regimen, how many squares will the quilt have? Explain your reasoning.

Stretch

Consider the sequence 6, 11, 16, 21 . . . . What is the 50th term in this sequence?

Review

Sketch a graph of each equation. Identify the slope and y-intercept.

1. $y = 4x - 1$
2. $y = 4x$
3. $y = x + 4$
4. $y = x - 4$

Solve for x.

5.

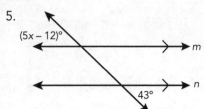

6.

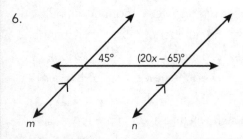

Once Upon a Graph

2

Analyzing the Characteristics of Graphs of Relationships

WARM UP

Consider the sequence 4, 6, 8, 10.

1. Use the table to list each term of the sequence.

Term Number				
Term				

2. Use the chart to write each of the terms as an ordered pair.
3. Graph the sequence on the coordinate plane.

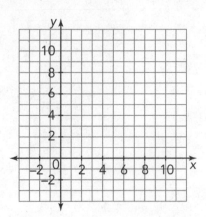

LEARNING GOALS

- Describe qualitatively the relationship between two quantities by analyzing a graph.
- Describe characteristics of graphs using mathematical terminology.
- Describe a real-world situation that could be represented by a given graph.
- Sketch a graph of a relationship between quantities given a verbal description.

KEY TERMS

- discrete
- continuous
- collinear points
- non-linear

You have analyzed the graphs of linear relationships. What other ways are there to describe the relationship between two quantities? How can you analyze non-linear graphs?

Graph Sort

1. Cut out the 12 graphs at the end of the lesson. Sort the graphs in any way you want. Explain how you sorted the graphs.

Identifying Characteristics of Graphs

A **discrete** graph is a graph of isolated points. The values between each point on a discrete graph are not a part of the relationship. A **continuous** graph is a graph with no breaks in it. All the points in a continuous graph can be a part of the relationship.

1. **Are the graphs of sequences discrete or continuous? Explain your reasoning.**

2. **Sort the graphs you cut out into two groups: those graphs that are discrete and those graphs that are continuous. Use the letter of each graph to record your findings.**

Discrete Graphs	Continuous Graphs

3. **Sort the graphs into four groups: those that are increasing, those that are decreasing, those that are both increasing and decreasing, and those that are neither increasing nor decreasing. Use the letter of each graph to record your findings.**

Remember that when you are determining whether a graph is increasing or decreasing, you analyze the graph from left to right.

Increasing	Decreasing	Both Increasing and Decreasing	Neither Increasing nor Decreasing

A linear graph is a graph that is a line or a series of *collinear points*. A **non-linear** graph is a graph that is not a line and therefore not a series of collinear points.

4. **Sort the graphs into two groups: those that are linear and those that are non-linear. Use the letter of each graph to record your findings.**

Linear Graph	Non-linear Graph

Keep your graphs. You will use them again in the next lesson.

Interpreting Graphs

> How can you tell by looking at the graph when Greg was traveling the fastest?

The graph shown represents Greg's distance from home after driving for x hours.

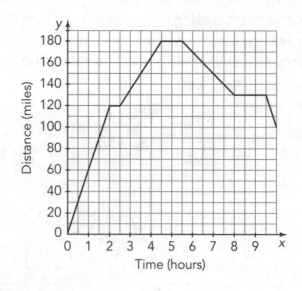

. Analyze the graph between 0 and 2 hours.

   a. How far from home was Greg after driving for 2 hours?

   b. How fast did Greg drive during this time? Explain
      your reasoning.

   c. How do you know that Greg traveled at the same rate
      for the first two hours? Describe in terms of the graph.

2. Analyze the graph between 2 and 2.5 hours.

   a. How far did Greg travel from home between 2 and
      2.5 hours?

   b. How fast did he travel during this time? Explain
      your reasoning.

   c. Describe the shape of the graph between 2 and 2.5 hours.

3. Label each segment of the graph with letters *A* through *G*, beginning from the left. Record in the table the time interval for each segment. Then, describe the distance Greg traveled, in what direction, and at what rate.

Segment	Time Interval (hours)	Description of Greg's Trip
A	0 to 2	Greg traveled 120 miles from home at a rate of 60 mph.
B	2 to 2.5	Greg took a half-hour break when he was 120 miles from home.
C		
D		
E		
F		
G		

4. The crew at the community swimming pool prepared the pool for opening day. The graph shows the depth of water in the swimming pool after *x* hours.

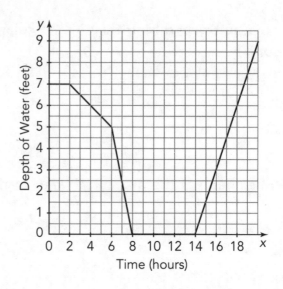

a. Why do you think the pool was emptied and then refilled?

b. Label each segment of the graph with letters A through E, beginning from the left. Record in the table the time interval for each segment. Then, describe how fast the water level in the pool changed and whether it was being drained or filled.

Segment	Time Interval (hours)	Description of the Water in the Pool
A		
B		
C		
D		
E		

c. Was the pool being emptied at the same rate the entire time? Explain using mathematics and the graph.

d. Why does it make sense for the graph of this situation to be continuous rather than discrete?

Students at East High School are designing ceramic drinking cups
for an art project. The students chose a variety of different shapes
for their cups. Six of these shapes are shown.

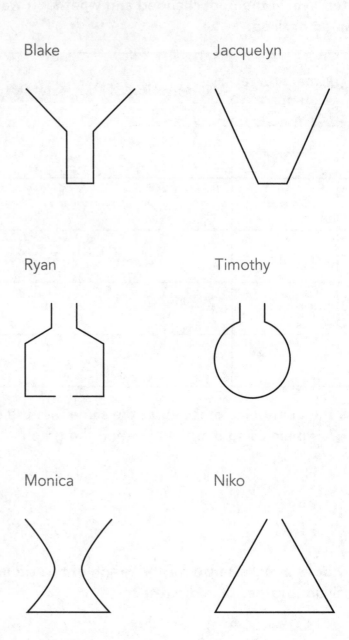

Blake

Jacquelyn

Ryan

Timothy

Monica

Niko

To test the cups, hot water is poured into each at a constant rate. The graphs shown represent the height of the liquid in each cup as the volume changes.

1. Match each cup to its graph. Explain the strategy or strategies you used to match each cup correctly to its graph.

Graph A

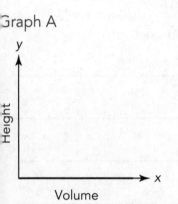

Graph B

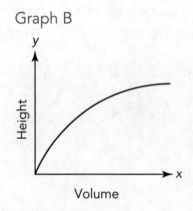

Graph C

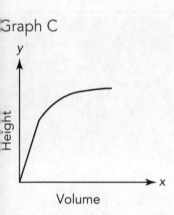

Graph D

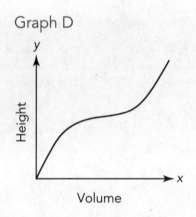

Graph E

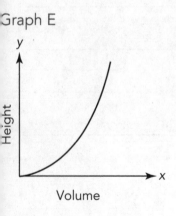

Graph F

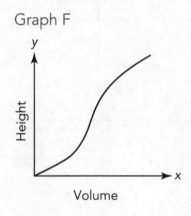

TALK the TALK

Popcorn at the Movies

You and a friend go to the movies and decide to share a large bucket of popcorn. Write a story to describe each graph.

1.

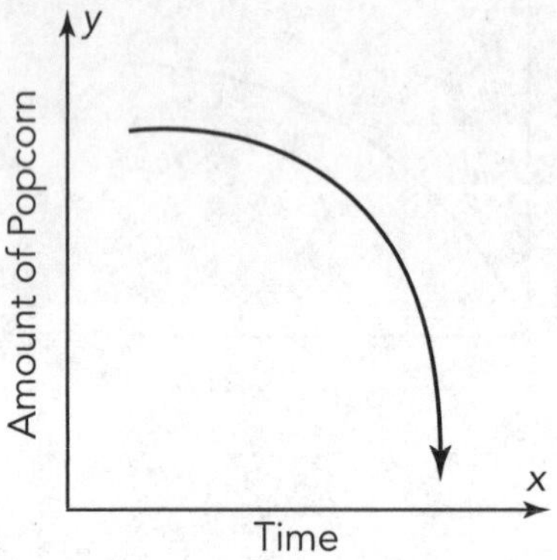

_____

_____

_____

_____

_____

2.

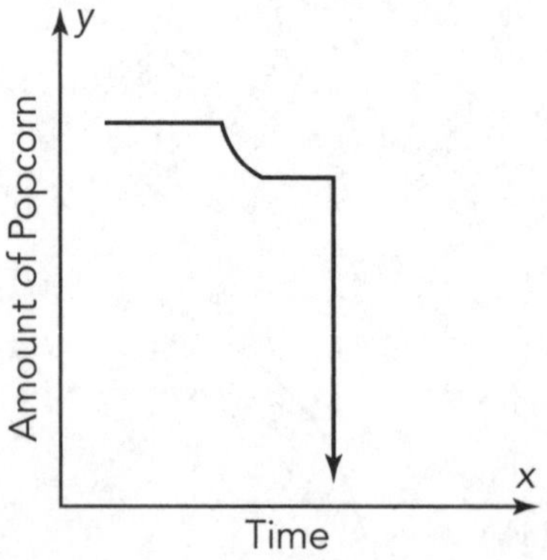

_____

_____

_____

_____

_____

Graph Cutouts

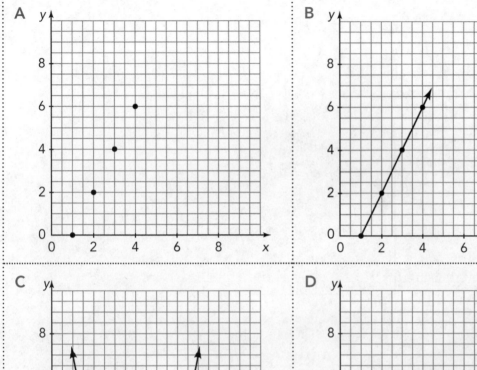

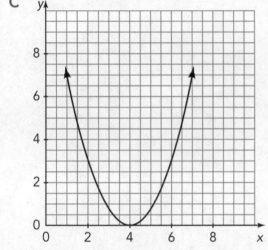

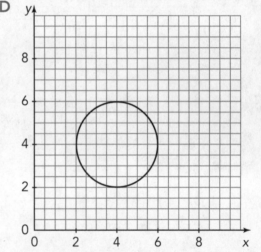

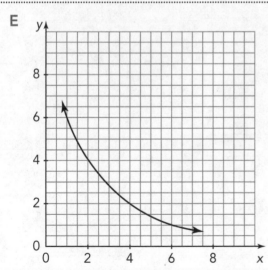

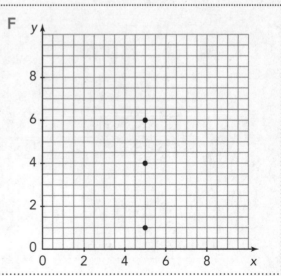

Graph Cutouts

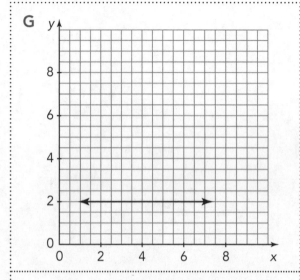

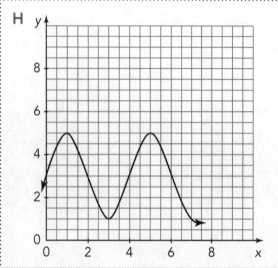

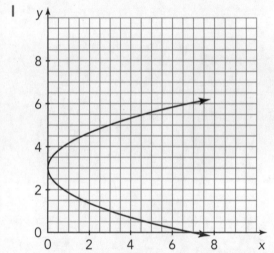

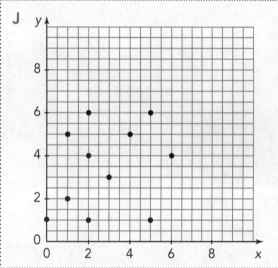

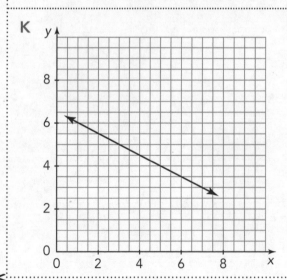

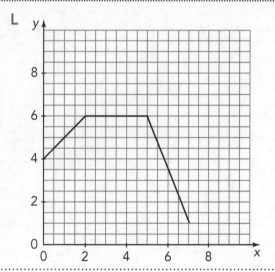

Assignment

Write

Explain the difference between each set of terms.

1. a continuous graph and a discrete graph
2. a linear graph and a non-linear graph

Remember

The graph of a relationship has meaning because it shows how the dependent quantity changes as the independent quantity changes.

Practice

1. Grant is recording the hourly temperatures of Grove City for a science project. He starts at 8:00 AM and records the temperature each hour for 24 hours. The graph represents the temperature of the city x hours after 8:00 AM.

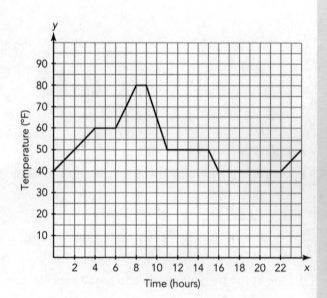

a. Is this graph discrete or continuous? Is the graph increasing, decreasing, or both increasing and decreasing? Is the graph linear or non-linear? Explain.

b. What was the temperature of Grove City at 8:00 AM? What was the temperature of Grove City at noon?

c. Did the temperature change at a constant rate from 8:00 AM to noon? Describe the change in terms of the graph.

d. What was the rate of change of the temperature between 8:00 am and noon?

e. How much did the temperature change from noon to 2:00 PM? What was the rate of temperature change from noon to 2:00 PM?

f. What is the shape of the graph during the time from noon to 2:00 PM?

g. Label each segment of the graph with letters A through I beginning from the left. Create a table to record the time interval for each segment. Then describe whether the temperature was increasing or decreasing, the rate of change, and the final temperature of the time interval.

h. Why does it make sense for the graph of this situation to be continuous rather than discrete?

2. Grant's teacher gave the students the graph of temperatures for a 24-hour period in a different city. Write a story to describe the graph.

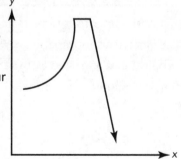

Stretch

Create a situation with an independent and dependent quantity that could match the graph shown.

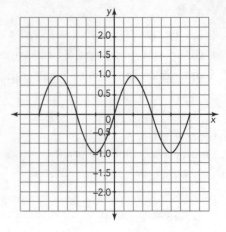

Review

1. Describe the pattern in each sequence and determine the next term of the sequence.
   a. A, C, E, G, . . .
   b. 4, 13, 22, 31, . . .

2. Geoff is training for a charity bike ride. He takes a ride on 49-Mile Scenic Drive in San Francisco. The table shows his time at the beginning and end of the ride. What is Geoff's average speed for the ride?

Time (hours)	Distance (miles)
0	0
3.5	49

3. School event committee members are designing banners for a school dance. They are experimenting by drawing different-sized rectangles. In each rectangle, the width is $\frac{1}{4}$ the length. Complete the table for rectangles with the given lengths.

Length (inches)	4	8	12	16	20
Width (inches)					
Area (square inches)					

   a. Write the ordered pairs from the table, using area as the dependent variable and length as the independent variable.
   b. Is the relationship between the length and the area linear? Explain your reasoning.

4. In each figure, solve for x.
   a.

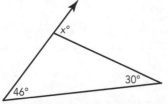

   b.

One or More Xs to One Y

Defining Functional Relationships

WARM UP

Evaluate each expression given the set of values {1, 6, 12, 25}.

1. $5x$

2. $\frac{1}{2}x + 1$

3. $x - 8$

LEARNING GOALS

- Describe a functional relationship in terms of a rule which assigns to each input exactly one output.
- Determine whether a relation (represented as a mapping, set of ordered pairs, table, sequence, graph, equation, or context) is a function.

KEY TERMS

- mapping
- set
- relation
- input
- output
- function
- domain
- range
- scatter plot
- vertical line test

Throughout middle school, you have investigated different types of relationships between variable quantities: additive, multiplicative, proportional, and non-proportional. What are functional relationships?

What's My Rule?

Rules can be used to generate sequences of numbers. They can also be used to generate (x, y) ordered pairs.

1. Write an equation to describe the relationship between each independent variable x and the dependent variable y. Explain your reasoning.

a.

x	y
−6	−12
−3	0
0	12
3	24

b.

x	y
1	−2
5	−10
−1	2
−10	20

You can sketch the graph to help determine the equation.

c.

x	y
−10	9
−2	1
0	−1
5	4

d.

x	y
0	2
4	4
5	4.5
20	12

2. Create your own table and have a partner determine the equation you used to build it.

As you learned previously, ordered pairs consist of an *x*-coordinate and a *y*-coordinate. You also learned that a series of ordered pairs on a coordinate plane can represent a pattern. You can also use a *mapping* to show ordered pairs. A **mapping** represents two sets of objects or items. Arrows connect the items to represent a relationship between them.

When you write the ordered pairs for a mapping, you are writing a set of ordered pairs. A **set** is a collection of numbers, geometric figures, letters, or other objects that have some characteristic in common.

Use braces, { }, to denote a set.

1. **Write the set of ordered pairs that represent a relationship in each mapping.**

a.
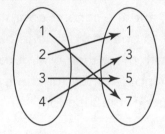

b.
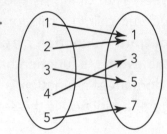

c.
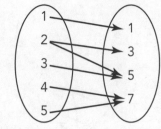

d.
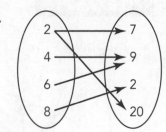

2. **Create a mapping from the set of ordered pairs.**

   a. {(5, 8), (11, 9), (6, 8), (8, 5)}   b. {(3, 4), (9, 8), (3, 7), (4, 20)}

3. Write the set of ordered pairs to represent each table.

a.

Input	Output
−10	−20
−5	−10
0	0
5	10
10	20

b.

x	y
20	−10
10	−5
0	0
10	5
20	10

The mappings and ordered pairs shown in Questions 1 through 3 form *relations*. A **relation** is any set of ordered pairs or the mapping between a set of *inputs* and a set of *outputs*. The first coordinate of an ordered pair in a relation is the **input**, and the second coordinate is the **output**. A **function** maps each input to one and only one output. In other words, a function has no input with more than one output. The **domain** of a function is the set of all inputs of the function. The **range** of a function is the set of all outputs of the function.

Notice the use of set notation when writing the domain and range.

WORKED EXAMPLE

In each mapping shown, the domain is {1, 2, 3, 4}.

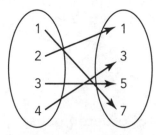

The range is {1, 3, 5, 7}.

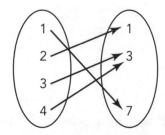

The range is {1, 3, 7}.

Each mapping represents a function because no input, or domain value, is mapped to more than one output, or range value.

WORKED EXAMPLE

In the mapping shown, the domain is {1, 2, 3, 4, 5} and the range is {1, 3, 5, 7}.

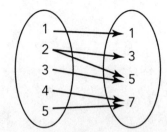

This mapping does not represent a function.

4. State why the relation in the worked example shown is not a function.

5. State the domain and range for each relation in Questions 2 and 3. Then, determine which relations represent functions. If the relation is not a function, explain why not.

Think about the mappings as ordered pairs.

6. Review and analyze Emil's work. Explain why Emil's mapping is not an example of a function.

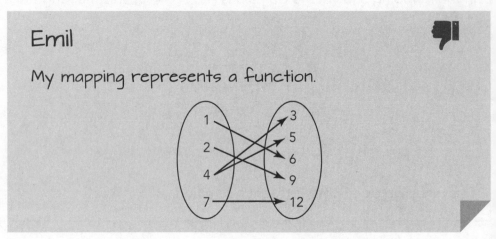

Emil

My mapping represents a function.

7. Determine if each sequence represents a function. Explain why or why not. If it is a function, identify its domain and range. Create a mapping to verify your answer.

a. 2, 4, 6, 8, 10, …

Remember that a sequence has a term number and a term value.

b. 1, 0, 1, 0, 1, …

c. 0, 5, 10, 15, 20, …

Functions as Mapping Inputs to Outputs

You have determined if sets of ordered pairs represent functions. In this activity you will examine different situations and determine whether they represent functional relationships.

Read each context and decide whether it fits the definition of a function. Explain your reasoning.

1. *Input:*   Sue writes a thank-you note to her best friend.
   Output: Her best friend receives the thank-you note in the mail.

2. *Input:*   A football game is being telecast.
   Output: It appears on televisions in millions of homes.

3. *Input:*   There are four puppies in a litter.
   Output: One puppy was adopted by the Smiths, another by the Jacksons, and the remaining two by the Fullers.

4. *Input:*   The basketball team has numbered uniforms.
   Output: Each player wears a uniform with her assigned number.

5. *Input:*   Beverly Hills, California, has the zip code 90210.
   Output: There are 34,675 people living in Beverly Hills.

6. *Input:*   A sneak preview of a new movie is being shown in a local theater.
   Output: 65 people are in the audience.

7. *Input:* Tara works at a fast food restaurant on weekdays and a card store on weekends.

   Output: Tara's job on any one day.

8. *Input:* Janelle sends a text message to everyone in her contact list on her cell phone.

   Output: There are 41 friends and family on Janelle's contact list.

ACTIVITY 3.3

Determining Whether a Relation Is a Function

Analyze the relations in each pair. Determine which relations are functions and which are not functions. Explain how you know.

1. **Mapping A**   **Mapping B**

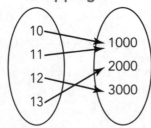 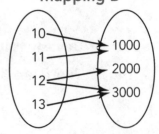

2.

Table A	
Input	Output
−2	4
−1	1
0	0
1	1
2	4

Table B	
x	y
2	−4
1	−1
0	0
1	1
2	4

3. Sequence A
   7, 10, 13, 16, 19, ...

Sequence B
10, 30, 10, 30, 10, ...

4. Set A
   {(2, 3), (2, 4), (2, 5), (2, 6), (2, 7)}

Set B
{(2, 1), (3, 1), (4, 1), (5, 1), (6, 1)}

5. Scenario A
   Input:
   The morning
   announcements
   are read over the school
   intercom system during
   homeroom period.

   Output:
   All students report to
   homeroom at the start of
   the school day to listen
   to the announcements.

Scenario B
Input:
Each student goes
through the
cafeteria line.

Output:
Each student selects a
lunch option from the
menu.

ACTIVITY 3.4 · Functions as Graphs

A relation can be represented as a graph.

A **scatter plot** is a graph of a collection of ordered pairs that allows an exploration of the relationship between the points.

1. Determine if each scatter plot represents a function. Explain your reasoning.

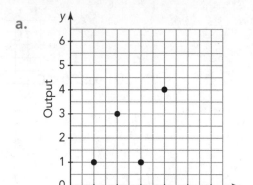

The **vertical line test** is a visual method used to determine whether a relation represented as a graph is a function. To apply the vertical line test, consider all of the vertical lines that could be drawn on the graph of a relation. If any of the vertical lines intersect the graph of the relation at more than one point, then the relation is not a function.

WORKED EXAMPLE

Consider the scatter plot shown.

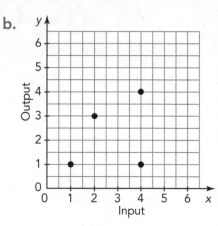

In this scatter plot, the relation is not a function. The input value 4 can be mapped to two different outputs, 1 and 4. Those two outputs are shown as intersections to the vertical line drawn at x = 4.

2. Use the definition of function to explain why the vertical line
   test works.

3. Use the vertical line test to determine if each graph represents
   a function. Explain your reasoning.

a.
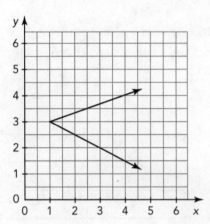

b.
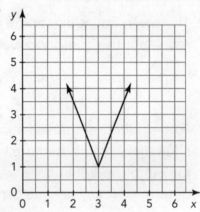

4. Use the 12 cards that you sorted in the previous lesson.
   Sort the graphs into two groups: functions and non-functions.
   Use the letter of each graph to record your findings.

Functions	Non-functions

ACTIVITY 3.5 Functions as Equations

So far, you have determined whether a mapping, context, or a graph represents a function. You can also determine whether an equation is a function.

WORKED EXAMPLE

The given equation can be used to convert yards to feet. Let x represent the number of yards, and let y represent the number of feet.

$$y = 3x$$

To test whether this equation is a function, first, substitute values for x into the equation, and then determine if any x-value can be mapped to more than one y-value. If each x-value has exactly one y-value, then it is a function. Otherwise, it is not a function.

x	y = 3x
1	3
3	9
4	12
8	24

In this case, every x-value can be mapped to only one y-value. Each x-value is multiplied by 3. Some examples of ordered pairs are (2, 6), (10, 30), and (5, 15). Therefore, this equation is a function.

It is not possible to test every possible input value in order to determine whether or not the equation represents a function. You can graph any equation to see the pattern and use the vertical line test to determine if it represents a function.

1. Determine whether each equation is a function. List three ordered pairs that are solutions to each. Explain your reasoning.

If you do not recognize the graph of the equation, use a graphing calculator to see the pattern.

a. $y = 5x + 3$

b. $y = x^2$

c. $y = |x|$

d. $x^2 + y^2 = 1$

e. $y = 4$

f. $x = 2$

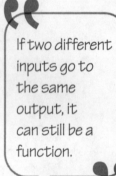

If two different inputs go to the same output, it can still be a function.

2. Explain what is wrong with Taylor's reasoning.

Taylor

The equation $y^2 = x$ represents a function.

x	y
4	2
9	3
25	5

TALK the TALK

Function Organizer

1. Complete the graphic organizer for the concept of function. Write a definition for *function* in your own words. Then, create a problem situation that can be represented using a function. Finally, create a table of ordered pairs and sketch a graph to represent the function.

Definition

Problem Situation

Function

Graph

Table/
Ordered Pairs

Assignment

Write

Write the term from the box that best completes each sentence.

scatter plot	output	relation	input	vertical line test
mapping	set	domain	range	function

1. A(n) _____ is any set of ordered pairs or the mapping between a set of inputs and a set of outputs.
2. The first coordinate of an ordered pair in a relation is the _____.
3. The second coordinate of an ordered pair is the _____.
4. A(n) _____ maps each input to one and only one output.
5. A(n) _____ is a graph of a collection of ordered pairs.
6. The _____ is a visual method of determining whether a relation represented as a graph is a function by visualizing whether any vertical lines would intersect the graph of the relation at more than one point.
7. A(n) _____ shows objects in two sets connected together to represent a relationship between the two sets.
8. A(n) _____ is a collection of numbers, geometric figures, letters, or other objects that have some characteristic in common.
9. The _____ of a function is the set of all inputs of the function.
10. The _____ of a function is the set of all outputs of the function.

Remember

A relation is any set of ordered pairs or the mapping between a set of inputs and a set of outputs.

A relation is a function when each input value maps to one and only one output value.

Practice

1. A history teacher asks six of her students the number of hours that they studied for a recent test. The diagram shown maps the grades that they received on the test to the number of hours that they studied.
   a. Is the relation a function? If the relation is not a function, explain why not.
   b. Write the set of ordered pairs to represent the mapping.
   c. What does the first value in each ordered pair in part (b) represent? What does the second value in each ordered pair represent?
   d. Create a scatter plot. Does the graph agree with your conclusion from part (a)? Explain your reasoning.

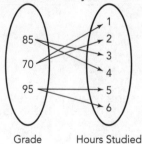

Grade   Hours Studied

2. The science teacher created the set of ordered pairs {(100, 6), (90, 5), (80, 3), (70, 1), (90, 4), (80, 2)} to represent six students' grades on the midterm to the number of hours that they had studied. Create a mapping from this set of ordered pairs.

   a. Is the relation a function? If the relation is not a function, explain why not.

   b. List all the inputs of the relation.

   c. List all the outputs of the relation.

   d. Instead of mapping grades to hours studied, the teacher decides to create a new diagram. This diagram maps hours studied to grades. Show the mapping that would result.

   e. Write the set of ordered pairs to represent the mapping in part (d).

   f. Is the relation in part (d) a function? If the relation is not a function, explain why not.

   g. Create a scatter plot. Does the graph agree with your conclusion from part (f)? Explain your reasoning.

3. At the end of the year, a principal decides to create the given mapping.

   Input: the 82 total students in the history class

   Ouput: the final grades they received for the class

   Does this mapping fit the definition of a function? Explain your reasoning.

4. Use the vertical line test to determine if each graph represents a function. Explain your reasoning.

   a.

   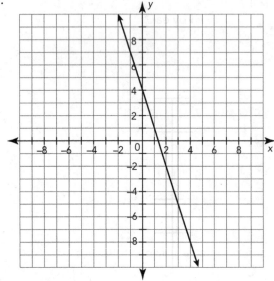

   b.

   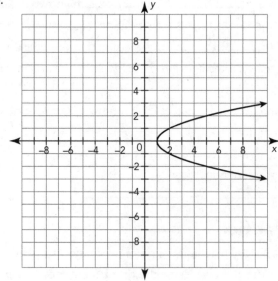

Stretch

Describe how you can tell from an equation whether a function is increasing, decreasing, or constant.

Review

Tell whether each graph is discrete or continuous. Also, tell whether each graph is increasing, decreasing, both, or neither.

1.

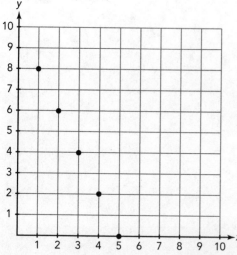

2.

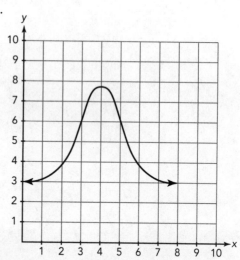

Determine the slope and y-intercept of the linear relationship described by each equation.

3. $y = \frac{x}{2} + 5$

4. $y = \frac{x}{4}$

Calculate the slope of the line represented by each table.

5.

x	y
2	−1
3	1.5
4	4
5	6.5

6.

x	y
2	8
4	2
6	−4
9	−13

Over the River and Through the Woods

Describing Functions

WARM UP

Does the table describe a function? Explain your reasoning.

x	y
0	1
1	2
2	3
−1	2
−2	3

LEARNING GOALS

- Analyze a problem situation using multiple representations.
- Determine characteristics of linear functions.
- Graph linear functions and describe them as functions whose graphs are straight lines.
- Identify intervals of increase, decrease, and constant values of a function.
- Define, graph, and analyze non-linear functions and give examples of functions that are not linear.

KEY TERMS

- linear function
- increasing function
- constant function
- decreasing function
- interval of increase
- interval of decrease
- constant interval
- absolute value function
- quadratic function
- cubic function

You have examined a number of different functional relationships. How are functions categorized in terms of direction and shape?

To Grandmother's House We Go

Little Red Riding Hood is traveling to Grandmother's house to bring her cookies and tea. However, Little Red Riding Hood often gets distracted on her way to Grandmother's house.

1. **Select one of the graphs that could be her journey and describe Red's journey to Grandmother's house.**

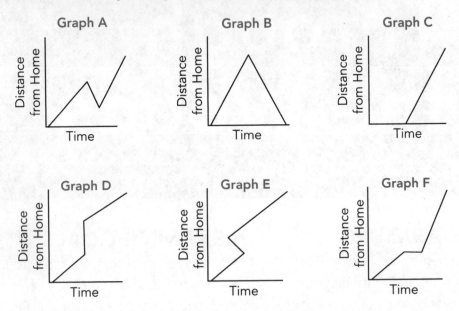

2. **Which of the graphs could not be a graph of Red's journey to Grandmother's? Explain your reasoning.**

3. **Which of the graphs represent functions?**

You and your friends are rock climbing a vertical cliff that is 108 feet tall along a beach. You have been climbing for a while and are currently 36 feet above the beach when you stop on a ledge to have a snack. You then begin climbing again. You can climb about 12 feet in height each hour.

1. Consider your height from when you begin climbing after your break.

   a. Define variables for the changing quantities and explain which is the independent quantity and which is the dependent quantity.

   b. Sketch a graph for your journey up the cliff after the break.

   c. Which quantities are changing? Which quantities remain constant?

   d. Write an equation for the dependent quantity as a function of the independent quantity.

Drawing a line through the data set of a graph is a way to model or represent relationships.

e. **Create a graph to represent the situation. Label your axes appropriately.**

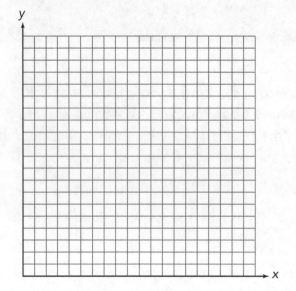

f. **State the domain and range for the situation.**

Is this a proportional relationship?

g. **Does this situation represent a function? Explain your reasoning.**

When you graph the input and output values of some functions, the graph forms a straight line. A function whose graph is a straight line is a **linear function**.

2. Consider what you know about linear relationships.

a. **Is every line a linear function? Explain your reasoning.**

b. **Is every linear function also a proportional relationship? Is every proportional relationship a linear function?**

c. Describe how the independent and dependent values change in linear functions.

d. Write the equation of a linear function with slope m, initial value b, independent quantity x, and dependent quantity y.

3. Write an equation to model each linear function.

a. Lin is tracking the progress of her plant's growth. Today the plant is 5 centimeters high. The plant grows 1.5 centimeters per day. Write an equation that relates h, the height of the plant after d days.

b. Carmen initially has money in her bank account. Each week she withdraws the same amount of money from her account. Write an equation that relates b, her account balance after w weeks.

Week	Account balance (dollars)
1	825
2	750
3	675
4	600

c. A rental car agency charges a fixed daily rate with an additional charge per mile driven. Write an equation that relates t, the total cost for a rental car, after m miles driven.

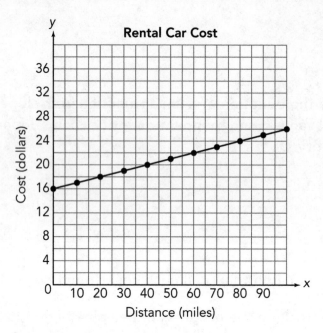

Rental Car Cost

d. Write an equation that relates y, the dependent quantity, to x, the independent quantity, if the slope is $\frac{2}{3}$ and the y-intercept is -7.

Increasing, Decreasing, or Constant

Saturday morning, Erika walked for 30 minutes at a steady rate from her house to a park 3 miles away. When she arrived, she played basketball for an hour, and then she caught a ride home with Kendall. They traveled at a constant speed from the park to Erika's house and arrived in 12 minutes.

1. Define variables for the time since Erika left home in minutes, and for her distance from home in miles.

2. Sketch a graph for Erika's morning.

3. Determine the rate at which Erika walked to the park and the rate at which she and Kendall drove home. Express the rates in miles per minute.

4. Determine the domain (time) and range (distance from home) for each part of Erika's morning.

Activity	Domain	Range
Walking to Park		
Playing Basketball		
Riding Home		

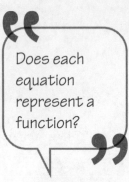

> Does each equation represent a function?

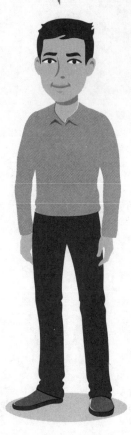

5. Write an equation that can be used to model each statement.

   a. Erika's distance from home as she walked to the park

   b. Erika's distance from home while she was playing basketball

   c. Erika's distance from home as she rode home from the park

6. Describe what happens to Erika's distance from home in each part her morning as time increases.

   a. Erika's walk to the park

   b. Playing basketball

   c. Erika's ride home

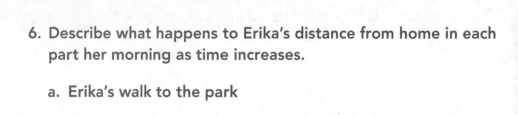

You can describe a function by analyzing the values of the function.

- When both values of a function increase together, the function is called an **increasing function**.
- When the *y*-value of a function does not change, or remains constant, the function is called a **constant function**.
- When the value of a dependent variable decreases as the independent variable increases, the function is called a **decreasing function**.

7. Create a graph of Erika's morning. Label each axis.

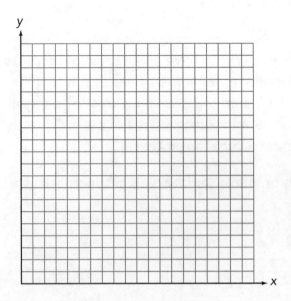

8. Consider the graph of Erika's morning.

   a. What are the domain and range for Erika's morning in this problem?

   b. Does the graph of Erika's morning represent a function? Explain your reasoning.

   c. List the parts of the function that are increasing, decreasing, or constant. Also list their equations and domains.

Activity	Behavior	Equation	Domain
Walking to Park			
Playing Basketball			
Riding Home			

You can describe the intervals of a function by analyzing what happens at specific independent values.

- When a function is increasing for some values of the independent variable, it is said to have an **interval of increase**.
- When a function is decreasing for some values of the independent variable, it is said to have an **interval of decrease**.
- When a function is constant for some values of the independent variable, it is said to have a **constant interval**.

9. Describe any intervals of increase, intervals of decrease, and constant intervals.

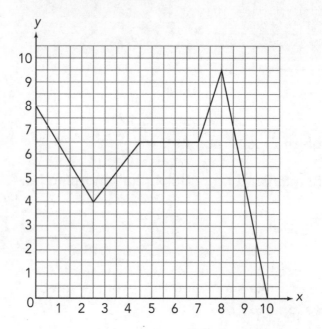

10. Explain how the behavior of each part of the function relates to the slope for that part of the function.

Analyzing Non-Linear Functions

In this activity, have someone in your class think of a whole number from 1 to 20. One-by-one ask each of your classmates to guess what the number is. Then record each guess without revealing the mystery number.

1. Record and analyze the results of each guess.

   a. After each guess, plot a point to represent the relationship between the value of the guess and its distance from the mystery number.

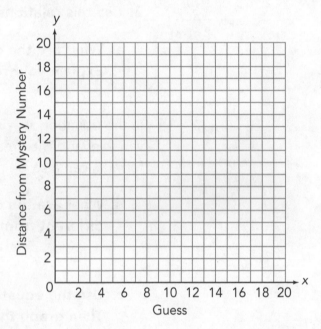

   b. What is the mystery number? Explain your reasoning.

   c. Does this graph represent a function? Explain your reasoning.

   d. Is this a linear function? Explain how you know.

   e. Identify the domain and range for this situation.

   f. Describe when the graph increases, decreases, or is constant.

The graph of the relationship between the value of the guess and its distance from the mystery number is an example of an *absolute value function*. Recall that the absolute value of a number is the distance from the number to zero on a number line. An **absolute value function** is a function that can be written in the form $y = |x|$, where x is any number or expression.

g. Write the equation that describes this absolute value function. How does the equation relate to the graph?

Let's consider a different situation. Recall that the area of a square is equal to the side length, s, multiplied by itself and is written as $A = s^2$.

2. Use this relationship to answer each question.

a. What are the domain and range for $A = s^2$? Explain your reasoning.

In the equation $A = s^2$, the side length of a square is the independent variable, and the area of the square is the dependent variable. This formula can also be modeled by the equation $y = x^2$.

b. What are the domain and range for $y = x^2$? How is this different from $A = s^2$?

c. Use the equation $y = x^2$ to complete the table of values. Then graph the values on the coordinate plane.

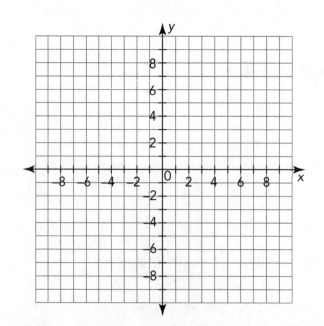

x	$y = x^2$
−3	
−2	
−1	
−0.5	
0	
2	
2.3	
3	

d. Does this graph represent a function? Explain your reasoning.

e. Is this a linear function? How do you know?

f. Describe when the graph increases, decreases, or is constant.

The graph of the relationship between the side length of a square and its area is an example of a *quadratic function*. A **quadratic function** is a function that can be written in the form $y = ax^2 + bx + c$, where a, b, and c are any real numbers and a is not equal to zero.

g. What are the values for a, b, and c in this equation? How does your equation fit the definition of a quadratic function?

Let's consider one more situation. Recall that the volume of a cube is equal to the side length, s, cubed and is written as $V = s^3$.

3. Use this relationship to answer each question.

a. What are the domain and range for $V = s^3$? Explain your reasoning.

In the equation $V = s^3$, the side length of a cube is the independent variable, and the volume of the cube is the dependent variable. This formula can also be modeled by the equation $y = x^3$.

b. What are the domain and range for $y = x^3$? How is this different from $V = s^3$?

c. Use the equation $y = x^3$ to complete the table of values. Then graph the values on the coordinate plane.

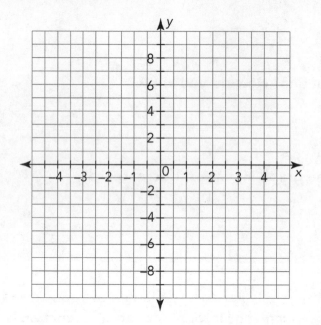

x	$y = x^3$
−2	
−1.5	
−1	
−0.5	
0	
1.5	
2	

d. Does this graph represent a function? Explain your reasoning.

e. Is this a linear function? How do you know?

f. Describe when the graph increases, decreases, or is constant.

The graph of the relationship between the side length of a cube and its volume is an example of a *cubic function*. A **cubic function** is a function that can be written in the form $y = ax^3 + bx^2 + cx + d$, where each coefficient or constant a, b, c, and d is a real number and a is not equal to zero.

g. What are the values for a, b, c, and d in this equation? How does your equation fit the definition of a cubic function?

TALK the TALK 💬

Show the Horse the Way

1. Sketch a graph for each set of given characteristics.

   a. increases over its entire domain

   b. decreases when $x < -2$ and increases when $x > -2$

   c. includes an interval of decrease, an interval of increase, and a constant interval

2. Write a possible story for the graph described in part (c).

   _____

   _____

   _____

   _____

3. Write an equation for each function description.

a. a linear function

b. a decreasing function

c. a constant function

d. an increasing function

e. a decreasing and increasing function

Assignment

Write

Complete each sentence by writing the correct term or phrase from the lesson.

1. When the value of a dependent variable decreases as the independent variable increases, the function is said to be a(n) _____.

2. When both the dependent and independent values of a function increase, the function is said to be a(n) _____.

3. When a function is decreasing for some values of the independent variable, it is said to have a(n) _____.

4. When the dependent variable does not change as the independent value of a function increases, the function is said to be a(n) _____.

5. When a function is constant for some values of the independent variable, it is said to have a(n) _____.

6. When a function is increasing for some values of the independent variable, it is said to have a(n) _____.

7. When a function is a straight line that can be written in the form $y = mx + b$, it is said to be a(n) _____.

Remember

A function can be linear or non-linear, and functions are often represented using equations, graphs, and tables. Functions can be used to model everyday situations with specific domains.

Practice

1. Create a table of values for each situation and identify the domain and range.
   a. Linear function
   b. Non-linear function
   c. Function that decreases and then increases
   d. Constant function

2. For each graph describe each interval of increase, interval of decrease, or constant interval.

a.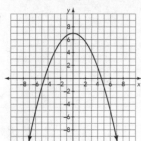

b.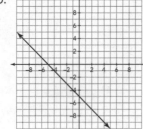

c.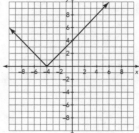

d.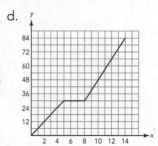

3. When Randall wakes up Thursday morning, there are 15 inches of snow on the ground. The meteorologist reports that because the air temperature is slowly increasing, the snow will melt at a rate of 1.5 inches per day for the next 8 days. Then extremely cold temperatures over the following 3 days will prevent the snow from melting anymore. However, on day 11 of this streak of winter weather, the meteorologist predicts steady snow for the next 5 days, but only $\frac{1}{2}$ of an inch will accumulate per day. Let d represent the time in days since Thursday, and let h represent the height of the snow.

a. Graph the function for the height of the snow over time.

b. Describe each interval of increase, interval of decrease, or constant interval.

Stretch

Create the graph of a function that includes at least three of the following: a constant function, an absolute value function, a quadratic function, and a cubic function.

Review

1. State the domain and range of each relation. Then determine whether each is a function. Explain your reasoning.

a.

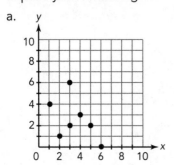

b. Sequence: 4, 14, 24, 34, 44, ...

2. Graph each line using the information contained in the equation.

a. $y = 2x - 5$

b. $y - 4 = -\frac{3}{2}(x + 7)$

3. Use the graph shown to answer each question.

a. What is the speed of the car in miles per hour?

b. What is the cost of one snack?

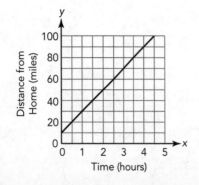

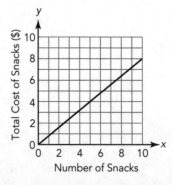

Comparing Apples to Oranges

Comparing Functions Using Different Representations

WARM UP

1. Determine the slope described by the table of values shown.

x	y
−1	15
0	25
2	45
5	75

2. Determine the slope described by the equation $-12x + 2y + 30 = 0$.

3. Determine the hourly rate of change described in the situation given. Jane is a tutor and is paid $20 for a half hour session.

LEARNING GOALS

- Compare properties of two functions, each represented in a different way (equation, table, context, or graph).
- Compare the slopes of two functions, each represented in a different way.

You have represented functions as ordered pairs, mappings, sequences, tables, equations, and graphs. How can you compare functions when they are displayed using different representations?

Comparing Apples to Apples

Examine each set of functions and determine which has the greater rate of change, if either. Explain your reasoning.

1. Table A

x	y
−2	−8
2	−5
6	−2

Table B

x	y
−5	−46
1	−38
7	−30

2. Graph A

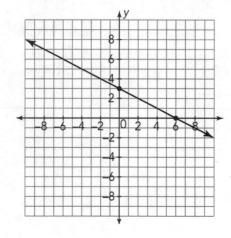

Graph B

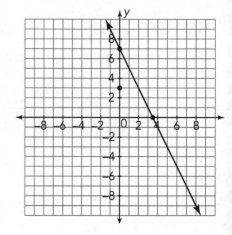

3. Equation A

$5x + 6y = 60$

Equation B

$y = -\frac{1}{4}x - 2$

4. An ice cream shop is choosing a milk delivery service. The Spotted Cow charges $2.80 per gallon, plus a $2 delivery fee. Dairy Farms charges $2.10 per gallon, plus a $10 delivery fee.

Comparing Linear Functions

You have worked with many linear functions presented in real-world and mathematical problems. You have also represented various linear functions through equations, tables, and graphs. In this lesson, you will compare the rates of change in different representations of two or more linear functions.

In Questions 1 through 3, analyze the two distinct linear functions. Identify which function has the greater rate of change. Explain your reasoning.

1. **Function A**

   $y = 8x - 3$

   Function B

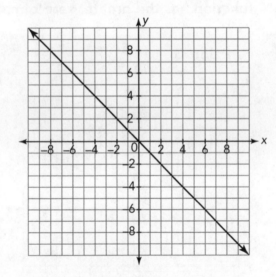

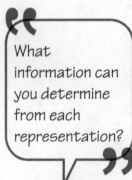

What information can you determine from each representation?

2. **Function C**

x	y
−1	−6
0	−3
2	3
5	12

Function D

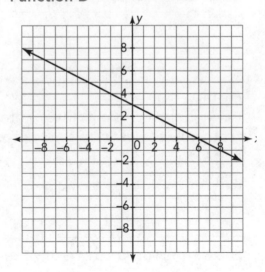

3. **Function E**

6x + y = 1

Function F

x	y
−1	−6
1	6
3	18
5	30

4. Alicia, Cherie, and John had been studying rates of change and were discussing the best way to determine which linear function has the greater rate of change.

Function G

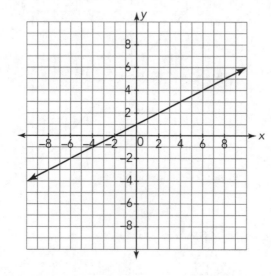

Function H

x	y
0	1
1	3
2	5
3	7

Alicia

I can identify two points from the graph and two points from the table and use the formula $\frac{y_2 - y_1}{x_2 - x_1}$ to calculate the slope.

Function G: (0, 1) and (2, 2)

$m = \frac{2 - 1}{2 - 0} = \frac{1}{2}$

Function H: (0, 1) and (1, 3)

$m = \frac{3 - 1}{1 - 0} = 2$

Function H has a rate of change of 2, which is greater than Function G's rate of change of $\frac{1}{2}$.

Cherie

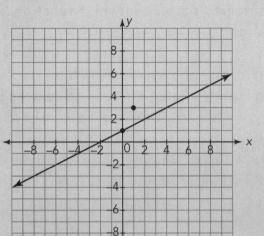

I started plotting Function H on the graph with Function G. I noticed that the functions have the same y-intercept but Function H is steeper than Function G. This means that Function H has a greater rate of change than Function G.

John

I can see from the graph of Function G that the vertical distance increases by one unit for every two units of increase in the horizontal distance. The rise/run is $\frac{1}{2}$, so the rate of change of Function G is $\frac{1}{2}$.

In the table, as the x-values increase by 1, the y-values increase by 2. The rate of change of Function H is $\frac{2}{1} = 2$. Function H has the greater rate of change.

a. How is Cherie's method different from John's and Alicia's methods?

b. Compare John's method to Alicia's method.

c. Which method is the most efficient in this situation?

5. John and Alicia then encountered the two linear functions shown. Again, they wanted to determine which function had the greater rate of change.

Alicia said that it was necessary to use a formula to calculate the rate of change for Function I and to rearrange Function J into the slope-intercept form of a linear equation.

John said that would take too much time. He says he only needs to rewrite Function J in slope-intercept form.
Who is correct?

Function I

x	y
−4	4
−2	4
0	4
2	4

Function J

$4x - y = 0$

Comparing Functions in Context

Read each problem situation and use the different representations to answer the questions.

1. Charlie is an avid reader and purchases e-books. For his birthday, his grandparents want to enroll him in a book of the month club. They plan to purchase a $100 gift certificate to the e-book club. In their research, they found two plans with comparable book offerings.

   Readers-R-Us automatically loads the book of the month onto the e-reader at the beginning of each month, and for this service, the club charges each member $4.50 per month. Consider an equation in which y represents the amount of money remaining in Charles's account and is expressed as a function of the number of months Charlie is a member.

   A second company, Bookworms, presents the table shown to illustrate their plan, given a purchase of a $100 gift certificate.

Months	Balance ($)
0	100
5	75
10	50
15	25

   a. Identify which function has the greater rate of change. Explain your reasoning.

   b. Which plan should Charlie's grandparents choose? Explain your reasoning.

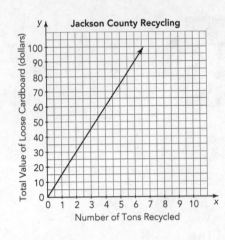

Jackson County Recycling

Total Value of Loose Cardboard (dollars) — *y*-axis: 0, 10, 20, 30, 40, 50, 60, 70, 80, 90, 100

Number of Tons Recycled — *x*-axis: 0 1 2 3 4 5 6 7 8 9 10

2. Washington County Recycle Center currently pays $20 per ton of loose cardboard. Jackson County Recycling represents their pay rate for cardboard using the graph shown.

   After moving from one county to the other, Lashonda needs to recycle her moving boxes. If Lashonda wants to earn the most money possible for her cardboard, which recycling center should she choose? Explain your reasoning.

3. Bobby's Recycle Center currently pays $1.59 per pound of aluminum cans. Bobby needs to write a formula to enter into his spreadsheet to keep a record of how much he has paid for cans. Consider a formula in which y represents the total value of the aluminum cans and is expressed as a function of the number of pounds of recycled aluminum cans. He entered the following into his spreadsheet:

	A	B	C
1	POUNDS of CANS	AMOUNT PAID	
2	1	=A2+1.59	
3	2		
4	3		
5	4		
6			

   a. Is Bobby's formula correct? Explain your reasoning.

   b. Will the spreadsheet show that he has paid out more or less than his actual pay-outs? Explain using your knowledge of rates of change.

1. Consider each representation of four distinct linear functions.
   Order the functions from least to greatest rate of change.
   Justify your ordering.

Function A

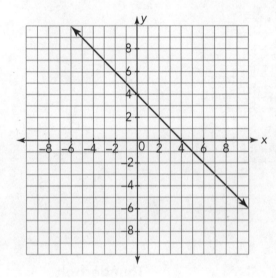

Function B

$4y + x = 12$

Function C

x	y
−2	4
0	7
2	10
4	13

Function D

The Used Book Store will pay $0.50 for each box of hardcover books.

2. Each linear function shown describes the steepness of the initial climb of the roller coaster track. For each representation, let y represent the height of the coaster in feet, and let x represent the horizontal distance in feet. List the roller coasters in order with respect to the steepness.

Jack Rabbit

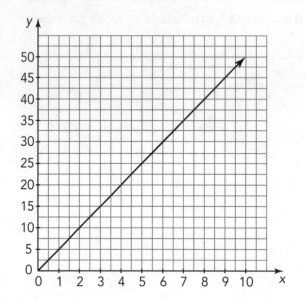

Racer

$2y - 9x = 4$

Pippin

x	y
0	2
1	7.5
3	18.5
5	29.5

Thunderbolt

The track rises 3 feet per 1 horizontal foot.

3. The linear functions shown describe the bank accounts of four students. The y-values represent the dollar amounts in the bank accounts, and the x-values represent the time in months since September 1st. If each student continues to save money at the constant rate shown, who will be the first to save $500? Justify your response.

D'Andre

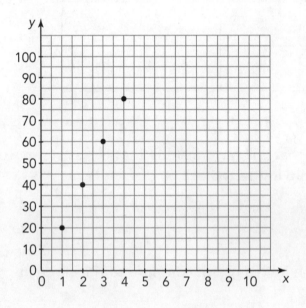

Fiona

$y - 12x = 100$

Sam

x	y
−1	45
0	60
1	75
2	90

Michelle

Michelle opened her bank account on September 1st with $25 and continues to deposit $25 each month.

TALK the TALK 💬

The Whole Fruit Basket

1. Create a situation to represent the table of values shown.

x	−1	0	2	5
y	5	10	20	35

2. Write an equation that will have a slope that is less steep than the relationship in the table.

3. How does the slope in this graph compare to the slope in Questions 1 and 2?

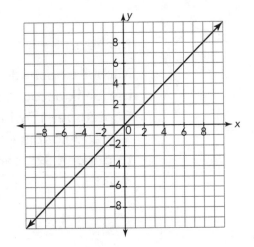

4. What strategies did you use to create your linear functions and to compare the slopes?

Assignment

Write

Explain how to determine the slope from a table, from an equation in any form, from a context, and from a graph.

Remember

Information visible in a table, context, equation, or graph often can be used to compare slopes without determining the actual values for the slopes.

Practice

1. Shawna is a professional dog walker. She offers two different payment plans. In each plan, she agrees to walk your dog twice a day for at least one mile per walk. Suppose you want to employ Shawna but need to choose between the two payment plans.

   The first plan charges a rate of $5 per day.
   The second plan is described using a table of values, and you must purchase 20 days' worth of services per month.

Days	Cost ($)
20	85
24	102

   Consider an equation in which y represents the total cost of dog walking, in dollars, and is expressed as a function of the number of days.

   a. Identify which function has the greater rate of change and explain your reasoning.

   b. Which plan should you choose? Explain your reasoning.

2. Shawna wants to begin offering pet boarding. She is considering charging $32 for 24-hour pet boarding. If she does not board the pet for 24 hours, she will only charge for the number of hours she kept the pet. Her competitor, the Pampered Pet Spa, presents their fee for pet boarding as a table of values, which increases at a constant rate.

Hours	Cost ($)
5	7.50
8	12
11	16.50

   Consider an equation in which y represents the total cost of boarding a pet, in dollars, and is expressed as a function of the number of hours.

   a. Identify which function has the greater rate of change and explain your reasoning.

   b. Suppose you plan on boarding your dog for seven days. Which plan should you choose? Explain your reasoning.

3. Shawna is rethinking her pet boarding business and is considering daily pet boarding that includes play time and regular walks. She is interested in how other businesses charge for similar services. Consider the four companies she researched.

For each company, consider the representation where the dependent value is the total cost, in dollars, to board a pet, and the independent value is the number of hours for the pet's stay.

Beautiful Fur Babies displays the equation $y = 5 + 3x$.

Darling Divas charges $2.75 per hour to board a pet.

Absolutely Perfect Pets:

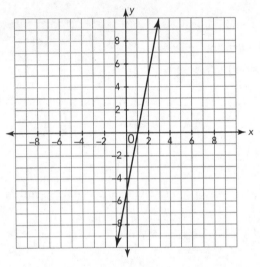

Cozy Critters:

Hours	Cost ($)
2	7
4	14
6	21
8	28

a. Order the businesses by rate of change. Justify your order.

b. If each business requires a two hour minimum stay and a pet owner wants to board a cat for two hours, which business should the pet owner choose?

c. Shawna wants to compete with these local pet boarding businesses. Design a fee schedule for Shawna's pet boarding business.

Stretch

Compare the rates of change for the given functions.

Function A:

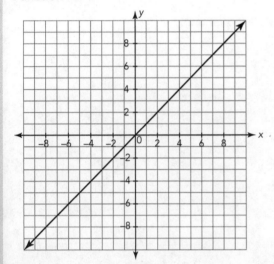

Function B: $y = x^2$

Function C:

x	y
−3	2
−1	0
0	1
1	2
2	3

Review

Describe each interval of increase, interval of decrease, and constant interval for the graphs shown.

1.

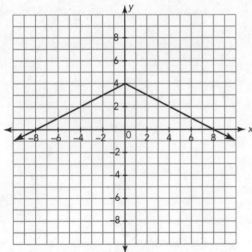

2.

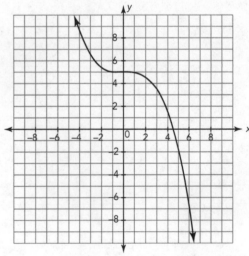

Write an equation for a line with the given characteristics.

3. Passes through the points $(-3, 17)$ and $(5, -8)$

4. Slope of the line is $\frac{8}{5}$ and passes through the point $(0, \frac{1}{4})$

Determine the slope and y-intercept of the line represented by each equation.

5. $12x + 4y = 24$

6. $-x + 3y = 18$

Introduction to Functions Summary

KEY TERMS

- sequence
- term
- ellipsis
- discrete
- continuous
- collinear points
- non-linear
- mapping
- set

- relation
- input
- output
- function
- domain
- range
- scatter plot
- vertical line test
- linear function

- increasing function
- constant function
- decreasing function
- interval of increase
- interval of decrease
- constant interval
- absolute value function
- quadratic function
- cubic function

LESSON 1

Patterns, Sequences, Rules . . .

A **sequence** is a pattern involving an ordered arrangement of numbers, geometric figures, letters, or other objects. A **term** in a sequence is , , , , . . . an individual number, figure, or letter in the sequence. Often only the first few terms of a sequence are listed, followed by an ellipsis. An **ellipsis** is a set of three periods, which stands for "and so on." An example of a sequence is 2, 4, 6, 8, 10, 12, . . .

There are many different patterns that can generate a sequence. The next term in a sequence is calculated by determining the pattern of the sequence and then using that pattern on the last known term of the sequence.

Once Upon a Graph

A **discrete** graph is a graph of isolated points. The values between each point on a discrete graph are not a part of the relationship. A **continuous** graph is a graph with no breaks in it. All the points in a continuous graph can be a part of the relationship.

A linear graph is a graph that is a line or a series of collinear points. **Collinear points** are points that lie in the same straight line. A **non-linear** graph is a graph that is not a line and therefore not a series of collinear points.

For example, Graph A is a discrete graph made of collinear points. Graph B is a non-linear continuous graph.

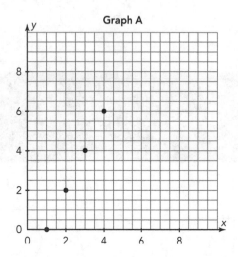

Graph A

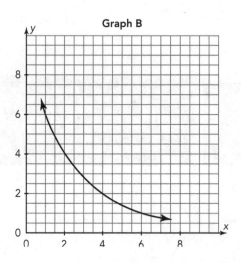

Graph B

The graph of a relationship has meaning because it shows how the dependent quantity changes as the independent quantity changes.

You can use a mapping to show ordered pairs. A **mapping** represents two sets of objects or items. Arrows connect the items to represent a relationship between them. When you write the ordered pairs for a mapping, you are writing a set of ordered pairs. A **set** is a collection of numbers, geometric figures, letters, or other objects that have some characteristic in common. A **relation** is any set of ordered pairs or the mapping between a set of inputs and a set of outputs. The first coordinate of an ordered pair in a relation is the **input**, and the second coordinate is the **output**. A **function** maps each input to one and only one output. The **domain** of a function is the set of all inputs of the function. The **range** of a function is the set of all outputs of the function.

For example, in the mapping shown, the set of ordered pairs is {(1, 7), (2, 1), (3, 5), (4, 3)}. The domain is {1, 2, 3, 4}, and the range is {1, 3, 5, 7}.

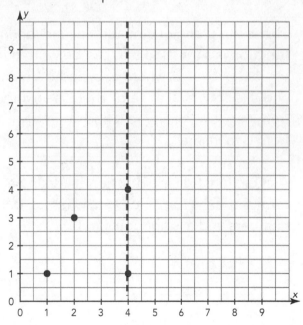

This mapping represents a function because each input, or domain value, is mapped to only one output, or range value.

A relation can be represented as a graph. A **scatter plot** is a graph of a collection of ordered pairs that allows an exploration of the relationship between the points.

The **vertical line test** is a visual method used to determine whether a relation represented as a graph is a function. To apply the vertical line test, consider all of the vertical lines that could be drawn on the graph of a relation. If any of the vertical lines intersect the graph of the relation at more than one point, then the relation is not a function.

In this scatter plot, the relation is not a function. The input value 4 can be mapped to two different outputs, 1 and 4. Those two outputs are shown as intersections to the vertical line drawn at $x = 4$.

A function whose graph is a straight line is a **linear function**. When both values of a function increase, the function is called an **increasing function**. When the y-value of a function does not change, or remains constant, the function is called a **constant function**. When the value of the dependent variable decreases as the independent variable increases, the function is called a **decreasing function**.

When a function is increasing for some values of the independent variable, it is said to have an **interval of increase**. When a function is decreasing for some values of the independent variable, it is said to have an **interval of decrease**. When a function is constant for some values of the independent variable, it is said to have a **constant interval**.

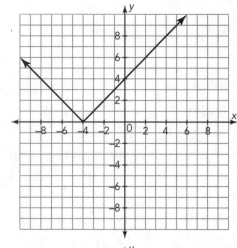

This is the graph of an absolute value function. An **absolute value function** is a function that can be written in the form $y = |x|$, where x is any number or expression. There is an interval of decrease from negative infinity to −4 and an interval of increase from −4 to infinity.

This is the graph of a quadratic function. A **quadratic function** is a function that can be written in the form $y = ax^2 + bx + c$, where a, b, and c are any real numbers and a is not equal to zero. There is an interval of increase from negative infinity to 0 and an interval of decrease from 0 to infinity.

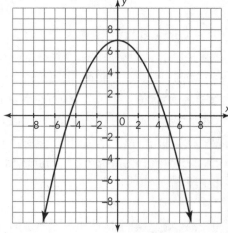

A **cubic function** is a function that can be written in the form $y = ax^3 + bx^2 + cx + d$, where a, b, c, and d are real numbers and a is not equal to 0.

Slopes of functions can be compared when linear functions are modeled using different representations (equations, graphs, and tables).

Suppose there were 4 baby pandas born in the U.S. last year. Compare the rate at which each panda has gained weight over their first 4 weeks.

Panda A

Panda A weighed 0.5 lb at birth and gained 2 lb per week.

Panda B

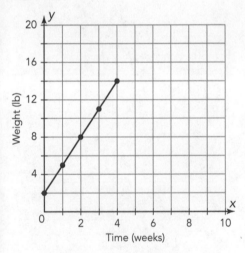

Panda C

Week	Weight (lb)
0	1
1	1.5
2	2
3	2.5
4	3

Panda D

$y = 0.75x + 1.5$

Panda C gained weight at the slowest rate, which was 0.5 lb each week. Next is Panda D, who gained 0.75 lb per week. Panda B gained 1.5 lb each week. Panda A gained weight the fastest at 2 lb per week.

TOPIC 4
Patterns in Bivariate Data

In 2015, a little over a quarter of publishers' revenue was from bookstore sales.

Module 2: Developing Function Foundations

TOPIC 4: PATTERNS IN BIVARIATE DATA

In this topic, students review the statistical process and investigate associations in bivariate data, both quantitative and categorical. On scatter plots, students informally fit lines of best fit, determine the equations of those lines, interpret the slopes and y-intercepts of the lines, and use the equations to make and judge the reasonableness of predictions about the data. Students construct and interpret two-way frequency tables for bivariate categorical data.

Where have we been?

Just as students previously have done with interpreting points on coordinate planes in the context of a scenario, they identify in this topic specific points on scatter plots and informally explain patterns they notice. Students then use their intuition and new vocabulary to describe patterns in provided scatter plots.

Where are we going?

In this topic, students begin examining possible associations between two categorical variables. These experiences provide the foundation for using two-way tables to calculate joint, marginal, and conditional relative frequencies and to determine independence of probabilistic events in high school.

Approximating a Line of Best Fit for Data

A line of best fit can be drawn for data to approximate the data as a linear relationship, even when the data are clearly not linear. The oval shows that these data tend to decrease from left to right. A line drawn through the center of this oval might approximate a line of best fit.

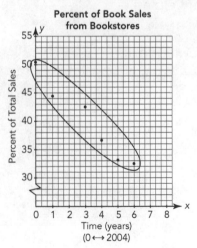

Percent of Book Sales from Bookstores

Myth: "I learn best when the instruction matches my learning style."

If asked, most people will tell you they have a learning style—the expressed preference in learning by seeing images, hearing speech, seeing words, or being able to physically interact with the material. Some people even believe that it is the teacher's job to present the information in accordance with that preference.

However, it turns out that the best scientific evidence available does not support learning styles. In other words, when an auditory learner receives instruction about content through a visual model, they do just as well as an auditory learner who receives spoken information. Students may have a preference for visuals or writing or sound, but sticking to their preference doesn't help them learn any better. Far more important is ensuring the student is engaged in an interactive learning activity and the new information connects to the student's prior knowledge.

#mathmythbusted

Talking Points

You can support your student's learning by resisting the urge, as long as possible, to get to the answer in a problem that your student is working on. Students will learn the algebraic shortcuts that you may know about, but only once they have experience in mathematical reasoning. This may seem to take too long at first. But if you practice asking good questions instead of helping your student arrive at the answer, they will learn to rely on their own knowledge, reasoning, patience, and endurance when struggling with math.

Key Terms

positive association
Two variables have a positive association if, as the independent variable increases, the dependent variable also increases.

negative association
Two variables have a negative association if, as the independent variable increases, the dependent variable decreases.

line of best fit
A line of best fit is a line that is close to as many points as possible, but doesn't have to go through all the points.

relative frequency
A relative frequency is the ratio or percent of occurrences within a category to the total of the category.

Pass the Squeeze

Analyzing Patterns in Scatter Plots

WARM UP

Describe the relationship, if there is one, between the number of hours spent in a bookstore and the amount of money spent.

Hours In the Bookstore	Amount of Money Spent
0.5	60
3	0
2.5	20
4	25
1	85
1.5	10
2	35
3.5	100

LEARNING GOALS

- Define bivariate data.
- Collect and record bivariate data.
- Construct and interpret scatter plots for bivariate data to investigate patterns of association.
- Interpret collected data displayed on a scatter plot and in a table.
- Use a scatter plot to determine if there is no relationship or a linear or non-linear relationship between two quantities.
- Identify potential outliers in a scatter plot.

KEY TERMS

- bivariate data
- explanatory variable
- response variable
- association
- linear association
- positive association
- negative association
- outlier

You have analyzed relationships and characteristics of many graphs. How can you describe patterns of association in a scatter plot of bivariate data?

You Have the Nerve

Your class is going to explore the speed of nerve impulses in the body by performing an experiment that involves a human chain.

- In this experiment, a group of students forms a circle with each person gently holding the wrist of the person to his or her right.

- Another student must be the timekeeper.

- During the experiment, group members must keep their eyes closed.

- To begin the experiment, the timekeeper says, "Go," and the first student carefully, but quickly, squeezes the student's wrist to the right, and then this next student squeezes a wrist, and so on.

- After the last student's wrist is squeezed, he or she says, "Stop," and releases the first student's wrist.

- The amount of time from when the word "Go" is spoken until the word "Stop" is spoken (the amount of time it takes to complete the chain) is recorded by the timekeeper.

In the next activity, you will conduct the experiment 10 times, using a different number of students in the chain each time. For each number of students in the chain, three trials will be conducted and the times averaged.

The Statistical Process
- Formulate a Question
- Collect Data
- Analyze Data
- Interpret the Results

1. **Why do you think three trials are needed for each number of students in the chain?**

2. **Make a prediction about what will happen during the experiment.**

Analyzing Scatter Plots

It's time to run the Human Chain experiment.

1. Record the data for the experiment in the table shown. Then, calculate the mean time for each row and record the result in the last column of the table. Round your average times to the nearest tenth.

Human Chain Experiment Results

Chain Length (number of students)	Trial 1	Trial 2	Trial 3	Average Time (seconds)

2. Write the ordered pairs from the table with the number of students in the chain as the independent variable and the mean time as the dependent variable.

3. Create a scatter plot of the ordered pairs on the coordinate plane.

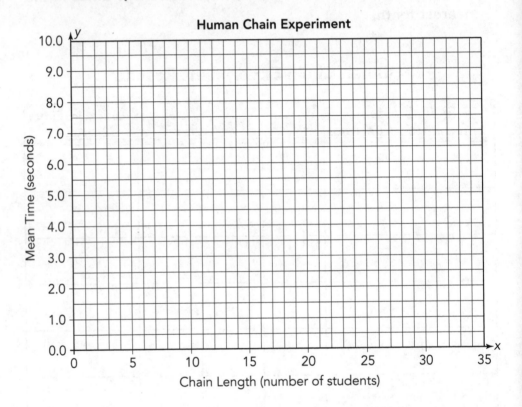

4. On the scatter plot, identify the point representing the longest chain. Then, identify the values of the point in the table. Explain how you identified the point and values.

5. On the scatter plot, identify the point representing the least mean time. Then, identify the values of the point in the table. Explain how you identified the point and values.

6. What pattern(s) do you notice about the scatter plot? Compare the scatter plot with your prediction.

**ACTIVITY
1.2** **Bivariate Data**

The School Spirit Club plans to sell sweatpants and sweatshirt sets with the school's logo. The club is determining if there is a way to package sweatshirt and sweatpants sets so that most of the students can buy a set that will fit.

1. Do you think there might be a relationship between the sweatpant size and the sweatshirt size a person would buy? Why or why not?

This is an example of a statistical question. What data might you collect to answer the question?

When collecting information about a person or thing, the specific characteristic of the information gathered can be called a variable. Previously, you have seen variables in mathematics refer to a letter or symbol to represent a number. In this case, a variable can refer to any characteristic that can change, or vary.

2. **Name a variable that can affect a sweatshirt size.**

3. **Do you think collecting information about one sweatshirt characteristic is enough to determine which shirt sizes should be paired with which pant sizes?**

The School Spirit Club decides to collect students' heights and arm spans. They hope that collecting this information can determine if there is a relationship between sweatshirt size and sweatpant size. When you collect information about two separate characteristics for the same person, thing, or event, you have collected **bivariate data**.

4. **Why is it important to record each student's height and arm span?**

One way to show the relationship between bivariate data is to create a graph that can represent the two variables. The School Spirit Club created a scatter plot using height as the x-coordinate and arm span as the y-coordinate.

5. What patterns do you notice in the scatter plot?

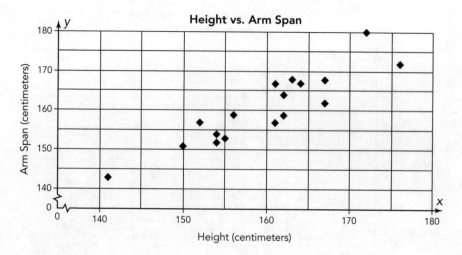

The symbol, ⌇, represents a break in the graph.

6. Now that you have informally analyzed the data represented by a scatter plot, what conclusions can you reach about the relationship between a student's height and arm span?

7. How could your conclusions help the School Spirit Club decide how to package their sets of sweatshirts and sweatpants?

How *do* you think Ms. Liu collected this data? How might her methods bias the data?

Ms. Liu is trying to determine if there is a relationship between the math grade percent of her students, and the time spent playing video games. She constructed the scatter plot for the number of hours her math students spent playing video games per weeknight (Monday through Thursday), and their grade percent in her math class.

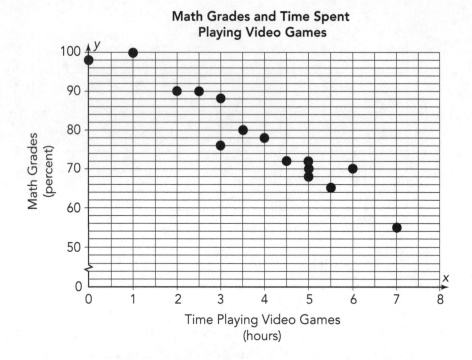

8. Circle the point (3.5, 80) on the scatter plot. Explain the meaning of the point.

9. Describe any patterns you see in Ms. Liu's scatter plot.

10. What conclusions can you make about the relationship between math grade percent and time spent playing video games?

When you look for a relationship in bivariate data, often you are interested in determining whether one variable causes a change in the other variable. In this case, one variable, the *explanatory variable*, is designated as the independent variable, and the *response variable*, is designated as the dependent variable.

1. Erica, who is an oceanographer, is measuring the temperature of the ocean at different depths. Her results are listed in the table.

Depth (m)	100	200	300	400	500	600	700	800	900
Temperature (°F)	76	73	70	66	61	56	52	48	43

   a. Identify the explanatory and response variables in Erica's data table.

   b. Create a scatter plot using the data Erica gathered for the ocean temperatures at different depths.

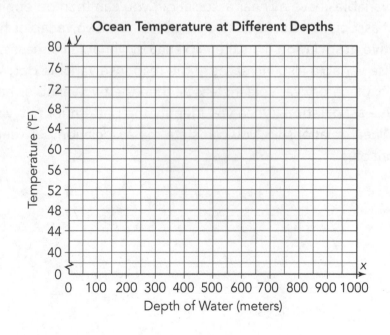

> The independent variable can also be called the **explanatory variable**. The dependent variable can also be called the **response variable**, because this is the variable that responds to what occurs to the explanatory variable.

c. Explain the meaning of the point (400, 66).

d. What relationship does the scatter plot show between the depth of the ocean water and the temperature of the water?

A **linear association** occurs when the points on the scatter plot seem to form a line.

As you have experienced, scatter plots can be great tools to identify patterns in bivariate data. Sometimes, these patterns or relationships are called **associations.** One common pattern that exists in data is when the points on a scatter plot form a *linear association.* In that case, the data values are arranged in such a way that, as you look at the graph from left to right, you can imagine a line going through the scatter plot with most of the points being close to the line.

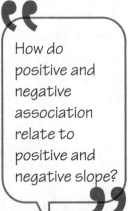

How *do positive and negative association relate to positive and negative slope?*

e. Explain how there seems to be a linear association between the depth of the ocean water and the water temperature.

If two variables have a linear association, you can then determine the type of association between two variables. The two variables have a **positive association** if, as the explanatory variable increases, the response variable also increases. If the response variable decreases as the explanatory variable increases, then the two variables have a **negative association**. Once you identify the pattern for two variables with a linear relationship, you can state the association between the two variables.

f. Describe the type of association that exists between the depth of the ocean water and the water temperature. State the association in terms of the variables.

2. Analyze each scatter plot shown. Identify the explanatory and response variables. Then determine whether the scatter plot shows a linear association. If there is a linear relationship, determine whether it has a positive association or a negative association, and state the association in terms of the variables.

a.

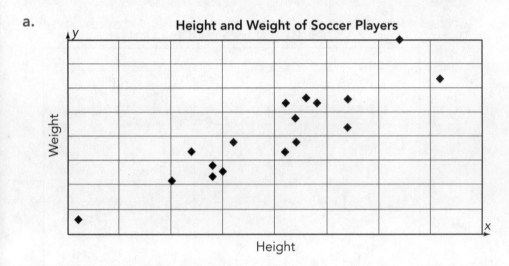

Height and Weight of Soccer Players

Weight

Height

b.

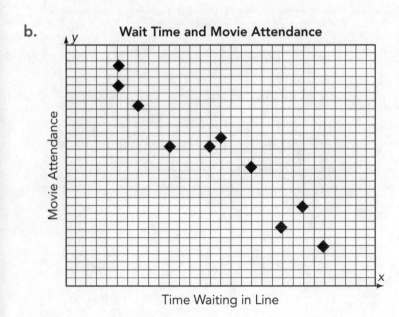

Wait Time and Movie Attendance

Movie Attendance

Time Waiting in Line

c.

Student Grades in Homeroom 6

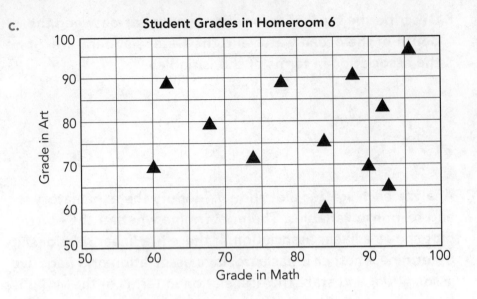

d.

Temperature in Fahrenheit and Celsius

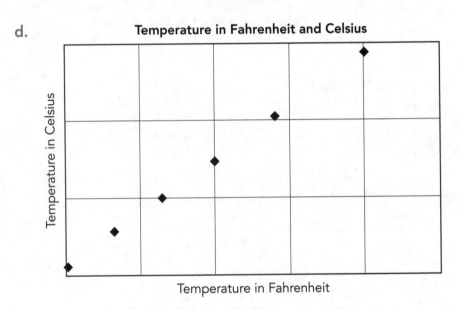

e.

Height of Ball Tossed into Air

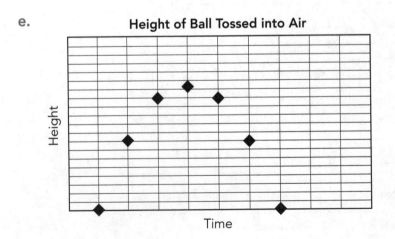

f.

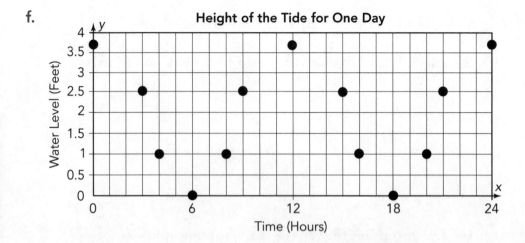

Height of the Tide for One Day

To be a safe driver, you need to understand the factors that affect a car's stopping distance. The stopping distance depends on two factors:

- The thinking distance is the distance travelled in between the driver realizing he needs to brake and actually braking.
- The braking distance is the distance taken to stop once the brakes are applied.

The graph shows how, under normal driving conditions, thinking distance and braking distance depend on the speed of the car.

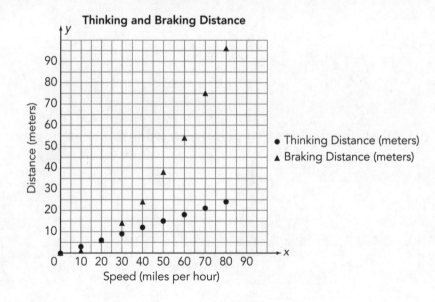

Thinking and Braking Distance

- Thinking Distance (meters)
- ▲ Braking Distance (meters)

3. Use the scenario and graph to answer each question.

    a. Identify the explanatory and response variables.

    b. Do you think that there is a linear, non-linear, or no relationship between the speed and the thinking distance? Explain your reasoning.

    c. Do you think that there is a linear, nonlinear, or no relationship between the speed and the braking distance? Explain your reasoning.

    d. What conclusions can you make from this scatter plot?

Another pattern that can occur in a scatter plot is an *outlier*. An **outlier** for bivariate data is a point that varies greatly from the overall pattern of the data.

Fat (g)	Calories
10	300
11	275
12	325
13	350
15	400
15	450
17	500
20	600
22	575
23	625
25	300

1. The scatter plot shows the fat and calories in 11 different foods.

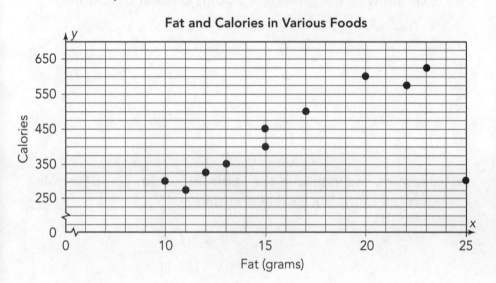

a. Determine the explanatory and response variables in the bivariate data set.

b. Does there appear to be a linear association between the fat and calories of the foods?

So, an outlier is like a point that doesn't belong.

c. Do any of the points appear to vary greatly from the other points? If so, circle any outliers in the scatter plot and identify the outlier in the table.

d. Explain why the point (25, 300) is a potential outlier.

e. Examine the values in the table. How can you determine that (25, 300) is a possible outlier?

f. Use your finger to cover up the point (25, 300) and examine the scatter plot. What do you notice?

2. The scatter plot shows the amount of time bookstore customers spent in the store and the amount of money they spent.

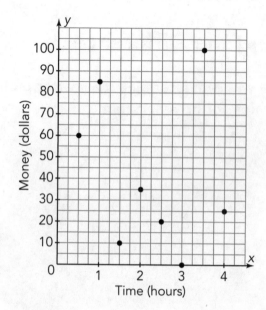

a. Does there appear to be a linear association between the time and money?

b. Use your finger to cover up the point (3.5, 100) and examine the scatter plot. What do you notice?

TALK the TALK 💬

Recognizing the Difference

1. Explain how you can determine if a scatter plot shows a linear, non-linear or no association.

2. Explain the difference between a positive association and a negative association of bivariate data.

3. Explain how you can identify an outlier in bivariate data. Do the data need to have a linear association?

Assignment

Write

Match each term to its corresponding definition.

1. explanatory variable
2. response variable
3. linear association
4. cluster
5. positive association
6. negative association
7. outlier

a. when points on a scatter plot seem to form a line

b. when, as the independent variable increases, the dependent variable also increases

c. the variable whose value is not determined by the other variable

d. a point that varies greatly from the overall pattern of the data

e. when points on a scatter plot are not in a perfect line but are grouped close to an imagined line

f. the variable that changes according to changes in the other variable

g. when the dependent variable decreases as the independent variable increases

Remember

A scatter plot is a graph of a set of ordered pairs. The points in a scatter plot are not connected, but they allow you to investigate patterns in bivariate data. Bivariate data is used when collecting information regarding two characteristics for the same person, thing, or event.

Practice

1. Determine whether each scatter plot represents a linear relationship, a non-linear relationship, or no relationship.

a.
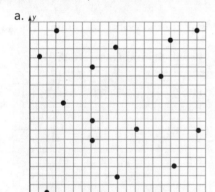

b.
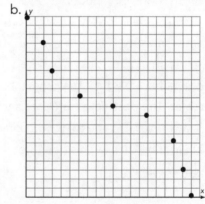

c.
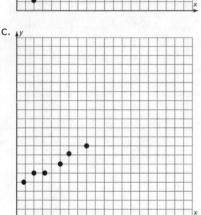

d.
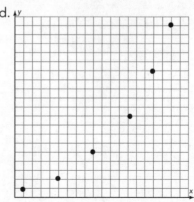

2. Mr. Grayson's 12th grade biology class is studying genetics. They are talking about traits that can be passed on from generation to generation and wondered if they could predict a father's height if they knew the height of his son. Mr. Grayson asks the boys in the class to measure and record their heights. Then he asks them to go home and measure and record their fathers' heights. The results are shown in the table.

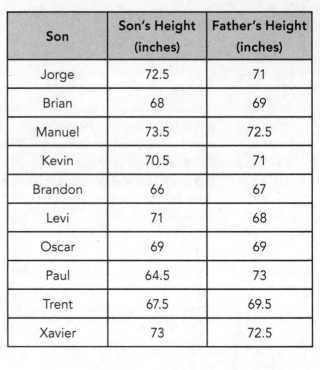

Son	Son's Height (inches)	Father's Height (inches)
Jorge	72.5	71
Brian	68	69
Manuel	73.5	72.5
Kevin	70.5	71
Brandon	66	67
Levi	71	68
Oscar	69	69
Paul	64.5	73
Trent	67.5	69.5
Xavier	73	72.5

a. Identify the explanatory and response variables.

b. Construct a scatter plot using the data. Be sure to label the axes and the graph.

c. What relationship seems to exist between the heights of the students and the heights of their fathers?

d. Explain the meaning of the point (70.5, 71).

e. Does there appear to be a linear association between the height of the students and the height of their fathers?

f. What type of association exists between the students' heights and their fathers' heights? State the association in terms of the quantities.

g. Do any of the points appear to vary greatly from the other points? Identify the potential outlier. Explain why it is a potential outlier.

3. Mr. Grayson's 12th grade biology class wondered if they could predict a father's height if they knew the height of his daughter. The class collected data and displayed it as a scatter plot. Do you think you could predict a father's height by knowing his daughter's height? Explain your reasoning.

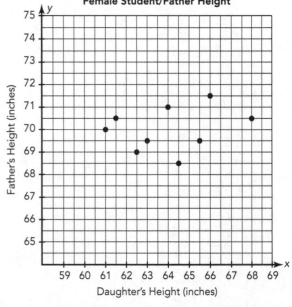

4. Ms. Brubaker is a guidance counselor at Apple Grove High School. She is giving a presentation to the freshman class about the importance of studying and getting good grades. In her talk, she likes to show the freshmen data she has collected about some students who went to the high school and their progress in college. The data for 12 students includes their high school GPA, as well as their first year college GPA. The table shows the data she has collected.

a. Identify the explanatory and response variables.

b. Construct a scatter plot using the data. Be sure to label the axes and the graph.

c. Does there appear to be a linear association between the high school GPA and the college GPA? Explain your reasoning.

d. Is there a positive or negative association between high school GPA and college GPA?

e. Write the ordered pair for the student with the highest high school GPA. Then explain the meaning of each of the coordinates.

f. Write the ordered pair for the students who have the same college GPA. What was the college GPA for each student, and what was their high school GPA?

Student	High School GPA	College GPA
1	2.22	2.35
2	2.50	2.80
3	3.42	3.88
4	3.45	3.40
5	2.45	2.95
6	2.67	3.10
7	3.24	3.55
8	3.80	3.92
9	3.11	3.40
10	3.15	3.50
11	3.25	3.52
12	2.88	2.90

Stretch

Pose a statistical question that can be answered by collecting bivariate data. Identify the explanatory and response variables. Collect and record the data. Construct a scatter plot. Describe the relationship between the variables and note any possible outliers.

Review

1. Explain how you could graph each equation using transformations of the basic function $y = x$.

   a. $y = 3x - 7$

   b. $y = -x + 5$

2. Tell a story to describe each graph.

   a.

   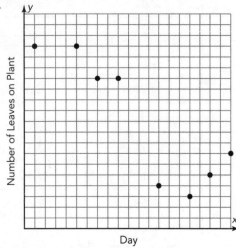

   b.

   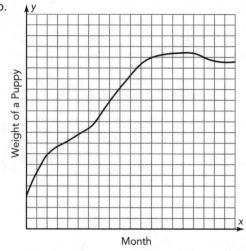

3. Calculate the slope of the line represented by each table.

a.

x	y
3	6
6	8
15	14
21	18

b.

x	y
0	10
4	5
8	0
16	−10

Where Do You Buy Your Books?

Drawing Lines of Best Fit

WARM UP

1. Solve for x.
   a. $50 = 3.5x + 24.2$
   b. $30 = -2.9x + 50.3$

2. Solve for y when x = 6.
   a. $y = 3.5x + 24.2$
   b. $y = -2.9x + 50.3$

LEARNING GOALS

- Identify the line of best fit as a straight line used to model relationships between two quantitative variables.
- Informally fit a straight line to a set of data.
- Write and interpret the equation of a line of best fit.
- Use a line of best fit to make predictions.
- Compare lines of best fit.

KEY TERMS

- line of best fit
- model
- trend line
- interpolating
- extrapolating

You have used equations to represent graphs of linear relationships. How do you create a model for a scatter plot that displays a linear association?

Brick-and-Mortar Book Sales

You can purchase books from many different places: a bookstore, a department store, the Internet, a book club, and many other places. The source for purchasing books changes as the available formats for books change.

Suppose the table and scatter plot show the percent of book sales that came from bookstores for the years 2004 through 2010, but the data for 2006 is missing.

Year	Percent of Total Book Sales
2004	50.8
2005	44.5
2007	42.5
2008	36.8
2009	33.2
2010	32.5

When you use 0 to indicate a particular year, such as 2004, you should indicate this on your graph with the appropriate axis label. One way to do this is to use a double arrow: 0 ↔ 2004. You can think of the double arrow as meaning "is the same as."

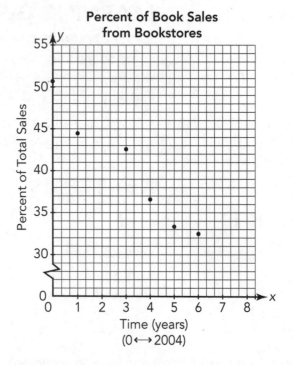

Percent of Book Sales from Bookstores

1. Describe the relationship between the explanatory and response variables.

2. Do all of the points in the scatter plot lie on the same line? What does this tell you about the percent of total sales as the time changes?

3. Use a piece of thin pasta as a "movable line" to estimate the percent of book sales from bookstores in the year 2006. Explain your strategy.

4. Explain why you should not use this graph to estimate the percent of book sales from bookstores in the year 2016.

A Line of Best Fit

When you use a line of best fit, the line and its equation are often referred to as a **model** of the data, or a **trend line**.

Sometimes, it may seem that there is not a linear relationship between the data points in a scatter plot. However, some of the data points may be close to where a straight line might pass. Although a straight line will not pass through all of the points in your scatter plot, you can use a line to approximate the data as closely as possible. This kind of line is called a *line of best fit*. A **line of best fit** is a line that is as close to as many points as possible but doesn't have to go through all of the points.

When data is displayed with a scatter plot, constructing a line of best fit is helpful to predict values that are not displayed on the plot. You want to begin by analyzing the data and asking yourself these questions:

- Does the data look like a line?
- Does the data seem to have a positive or negative association?

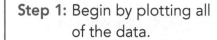

WORKED EXAMPLE

Let's construct a line of best fit.

Try to draw a smooth and relatively even shape that represents how the data is clustered.

Step 1: Begin by plotting all of the data.

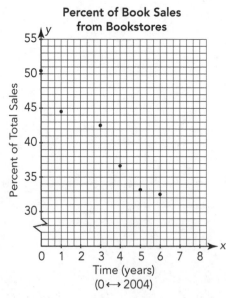

Step 2: Draw a shape that encloses all of the data.

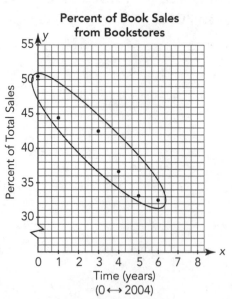

Step 3: Draw a line that divides the enclosed area of the data in half.

Note that the line of best fit does not have to go through any of the data values.

Step 4: Determine the equation of your line of best fit.

- Begin by identifying two points on your trend line. In this example, two points were chosen and marked with an "x." The estimated ordered pairs are (0, 49.2) and (3, 40.5). These points may or may not be data points, but they must be on the trend line.

- Calculate the slope of the line through the two points.

$$m = \frac{49.2 - 40.5}{0 - 3} = \frac{8.7}{-3}$$

$$= -2.9$$

- Write the equation of the line.

  Let x represent the number of years since 2004, and let y represent the percent of all sales.

$$y = -2.9x + 49.2$$

Percent of Book Sales from Bookstores

Percent of Total Sales (y-axis, 30 to 55)

Time (years) (0 ↔ 2004) (x-axis, 0 to 8)

The idea is that you want to identify a line that divides the area in half.

It is possible to choose two different points and estimate those ordered pairs in a slightly different way. Determining the line of best fit may lead to different equations depending upon the estimated ordered pairs chosen to construct the line. However, if the data closely fit a line, the slopes of the different lines of best fit should be close together.

1. Identify the slope of the line of best fit and what it represents in this problem situation.

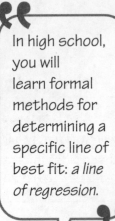

2. Identify the *y*-intercept of the line of best fit and what it represents in this problem situation.

If you are predicting values that fall within the plotted values, you are **interpolating**. If you are predicting values that fall outside the plotted values, you are **extrapolating**.

3. You have already predicted the percent of book sales in 2006. Let's compare that prediction with a prediction using the equation for the line of best fit.

   a. Is predicting the percent of book sales from book stores in 2006 interpolation or extrapolation?

   b. Use the equation from the worked example to predict the book sales from bookstores in 2006.

   c. The actual percent in 2006 was 42.4. How does this compare to your predictions from the graph and the equation?

   d. How is making a prediction different when using a graph versus an equation?

4. Use the line of best fit equation to predict the percent of book sales from bookstores in each given year.

   a. 2011

   b. 2013

   c. 2015

   d. Do you think the line of best fit provides reasonable predictions for these years? Explain your reasoning.

5. Use the line of best fit equation to predict the year in which bookstore sales will be a certain percent of total book sales.

   a. 60% of total book sales

   b. 40% of total book sales

   In 2015, book store sales accounted for 26.2% of publishers' revenue. Is this consistent with your model?

   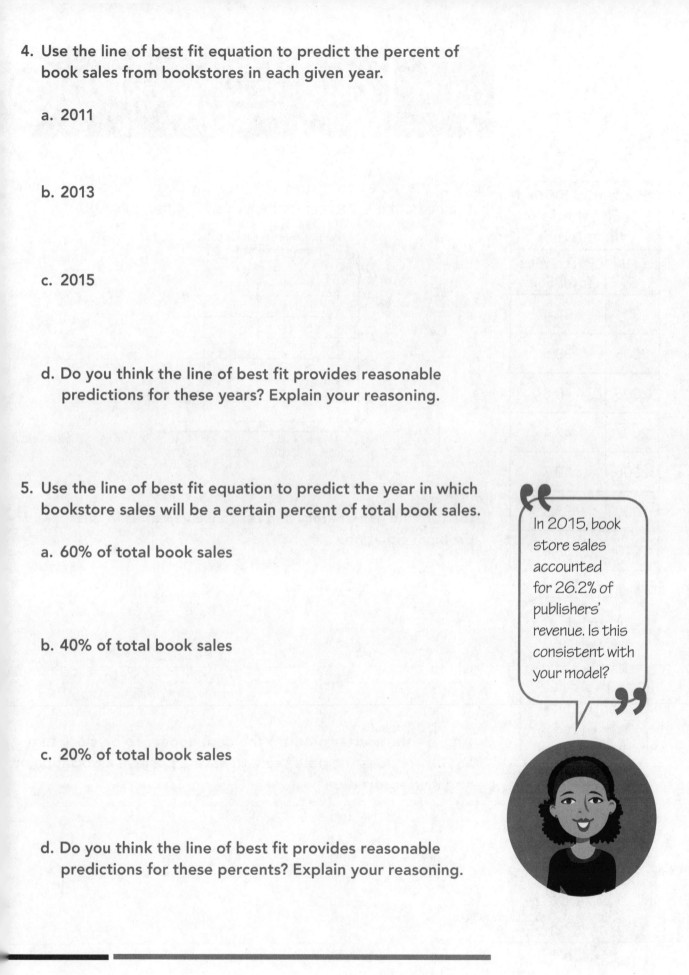

   c. 20% of total book sales

   d. Do you think the line of best fit provides reasonable predictions for these percents? Explain your reasoning.

ACTIVITY
2.2 Another Line of Best Fit

Percent of Printed Book Sales from the Internet	
Year	**Percent of Total Sales**
2004	34.4
2005	38.5
2006	40.8
2007	42.4
2008	50.7
2009	52.8
2010	53.8

Suppose the table and scatter plot show the percent of all book sales that came from the Internet for the years 2004 through 2010.

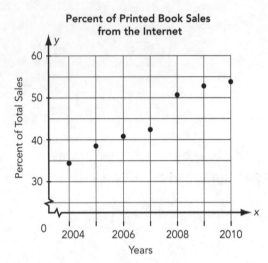

1. Identify the explanatory and response variables in this problem situation.

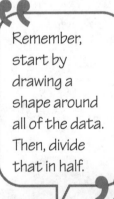

Remember, start by drawing a shape around all of the data. Then, divide that in half.

2. Analyze the scatter plot. Do the data appear to be close to a line? If so, does the data seem to have a positive association or negative association?

3. Use a straightedge to draw the line that best fits your data on the graph. Then, write the equation of the line. Define your variables and include the units.

4. Interpret the meaning of the slope in this problem situation.

5. Interpret the meaning of the y-intercept in this problem situation.

6. Compare the actual values to values using your equation.

a. How close is the value of the y-intercept to the actual value?

b. Use your equation to predict the percent of Internet book sales in 2006. How close is this answer to the actual data?

7. **Use your equation to predict the percent of book sales from the Internet for each given year.**

   a. 2011

   b. 2013

eBooks consisted of about 20% of overall trade book revenue in 2015, down from 2014 revenue. Do you think the same happened with print books purchased on the Internet?

   c. 2015

   d. **Do you think the line of best fit provides reasonable predictions for these years? Explain your reasoning.**

8. **Use your equation to predict the year in which Internet sales will be a certain percent of total book sales. Compare the predictions with the actual data.**

   a. 60% of total book sales

   b. 40% of total book sales

   c. 20% of total book sales

9. Pose and answer a statistical question that might lead to this analysis.

10. Consider both sets of data in this lesson.

   a. Do you think that the data from the two data sets are related?

   b. Which percent of book sales is changing faster: bookstore sales or Internet sales? Explain your reasoning.

   c. Which equation models its data better? Explain your reasoning.

TALK the TALK

eBook Sales

The table and scatter plot show the percent of net publisher revenue attributed to eBook sales during selected years from 2006 until 2015. The scatter plot includes three proposed lines of best fit.

Year	Percent of Net Revenue
2006	0.5
2007	0.8
2008	1.2
2009	3.2
2010	8.3
2011	17
2012	22.6
2014	23
2015	20

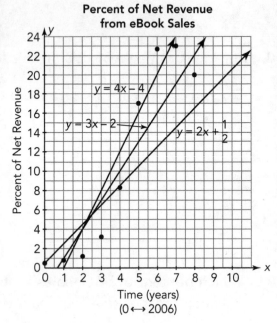

Percent of Net Revenue from eBook Sales

1. Determine which line provides the best fit. Explain your reasoning.

2. Which line would you use to determine the percent of net revenue for 2013? Use the equation for the line of best fit to predict the percent of net revenue for 2013.

3. Which line would you use to determine the percent of net revenue for 2016? Use the equation for the line of best fit to predict the percent of net revenue for 2016.

Assignment

Write

Explain the relationship between the terms *line of best fit, trend line,* and *model.*

Remember

A line of best fit is a straight line that is as close to as many points as possible but does not have to go through any of the points on the scatter plot.

A line of best fit can be used to make predictions about bivariate data through interpolation and extrapolation.

Practice

1. Estimate the equation of the line of best fit for each graph.

a.

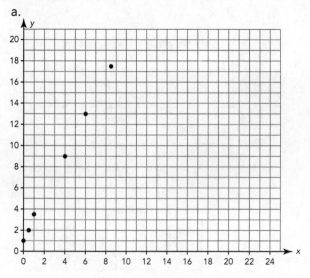

b.

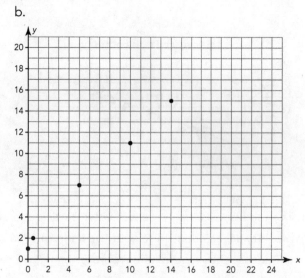

c.

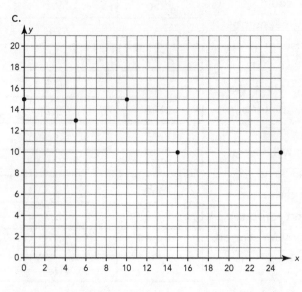

d.

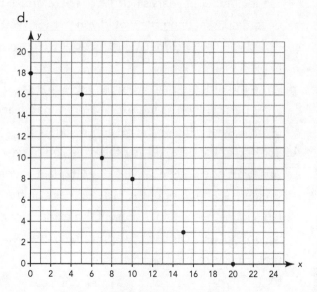

2. Compare each pair of graphs to determine which line is a better fit for the data.

a.

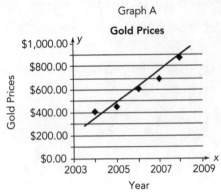

b.

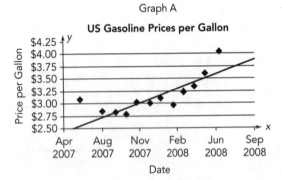

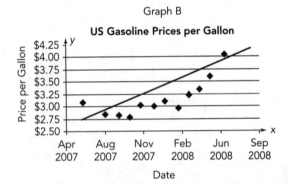

3. The table shows the percent of voter participation in US presidential elections in selected years from 1956 to 2000.

   a. Because the x-coordinates represent time, we can define time as the number of years since 1956. Therefore, 1956 would become 0. What number would you use for 1960? What number would you use for 1964? What number would you use for 1968? Explain your reasoning.

   b. Write the ordered pairs from the table that show the percent of voter participation as the explanatory variable and the number of years since 1956 as the response variable.

   c. Looking at the data, do you think the line of best fit will have a positive slope or a negative slope? Explain your reasoning.

   d. Create a scatter plot of the ordered pairs on the grid shown. First, label the axes to represent the explanatory and response variables. Next, choose the appropriate intervals for your scatter plot. Finally, name your scatter plot.

Election Year	Voter Participation as Percent
1956	59.3
1960	62.8
1964	61.9
1968	60.9
1972	55.2
1976	53.5
1984	53.1
1988	50.2
1992	55.9
1996	49.0
2000	50.7

e. Use a straightedge to draw the line that best fits your data on the graph. Then, write the equation of the line. Define your variables and include the units.

f. Interpret the slope and *y*-intercept of the equation in terms of the problem situation.

g. Use your equation to determine what the voter participation was in 1980. How does the value from your equation compare with the actual turnout of 54%?

h. Use your equation to predict the percent of voter participation in 2016. How does your prediction compare with the actual voter turnout of 58.6%?

i. Use your equation to predict the year in which the voter participation will be 50%.

j. For what years is your model reliable for predicting voter turnout in presidential elections?

Stretch

An *influential point* is an outlier that greatly affects the slope of the line of best fit. One way to test if an outlier is an influential point is to determine a line of best fit with and without the point and then compare the slopes of the lines. For the given data, determine a line of best fit. Then, identify a potential influential point and determine the line of best fit without that point. Compare the slopes of the lines and state if you think the point was influential.

x	0	1	2	4	5	6	8	10	11	25
y	95	80	93	70	85	70	84	60	80	70

Review

1. Identify the explanatory and response variables in each. Determine whether the scatter plot shows an association or not, and if so, tell if it is positive or negative. State the association in terms of the variables. Identify any outliers.

a.

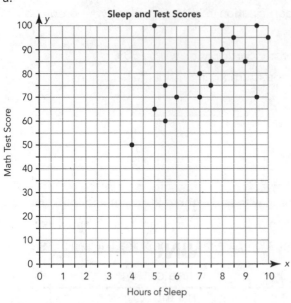

b.

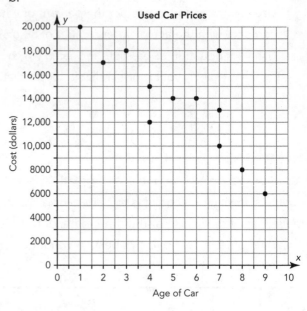

2. Tell whether each relation is a function. Justify your answer.

a.

Input	Output
15	0
10	5
5	10
10	15
15	20

b.

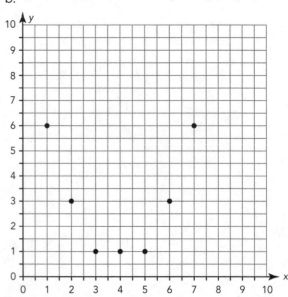

3. Determine the slope and y-intercept of the line represented by each equation.

a. $2x - 5y = 30$

b. $4y = 40 - 8x$

Mia Is Growing Like a Weed

Analyzing Lines of Best Fit

WARM UP

Complete each statement.

1. If a line has a positive slope, then, as the x-values increase, the y-values _____.
2. If a line has a negative slope, then, as the x-values increase, the y-values _____.
3. If a line has a slope of 7, then, as the x-values increase by one unit, the y-values _____.
4. If a line has a slope of 7, then, as the x-values increase by 5 units, the y-values _____.

LEARNING GOALS

- Draw a line of best fit.
- Write and interpret an equation of a line of best fit.
- Use the equation of a line of best fit to make predictions and solve problems in the context of bivariate data, interpreting slope and intercept.
- Assess the fit of a linear model.

You have used lines of best fit to make predictions. How can you use interpolation and extrapolation to make predictions over time?

Mighty Mia

Mia was born a healthy, happy baby girl to the Sanchez family. At each doctor's visit, Mia's height and weight were recorded. Her records from birth until she was 18 months old are shown in the table.

Age (months)	Weight (pounds)
0.0	6.1
1.0	8.1
1.8	10.0
2.3	10.3
4.0	13.7
6.0	17.0
8.0	21.0
10.0	22.0
12.0	23.0
15.0	23.0
18.0	25.1

Consider the relationship between Mia's age and her weight.

1. What happens to Mia's weight as she gets older?

2. Do you think she will continue growing at this rate? Why or why not?

Analyzing Mia's Weight

Use the information about Mia's age and weight to answer each question.

1. Use the data in the table to determine and analyze unit rates for Mia's weight gain.

   a. Write a unit rate that compares Mia's weight change to her change in age from age 4 months to age 6 months. Explain how you calculated your answer.

   b. Write a unit rate that compares Mia's weight change to her change in age from 6 months to 8 months. Explain how you calculated your answer.

   > Remember, a unit rate is a comparison of two measurements in which the denominator has a value of one unit.

   c. Was Mia gaining weight faster from 4 months to 6 months, or from 6 months to 8 months? Explain your reasoning.

2. Create a scatter plot that shows Mia's age as the explanatory variable and her weight as the response variable.

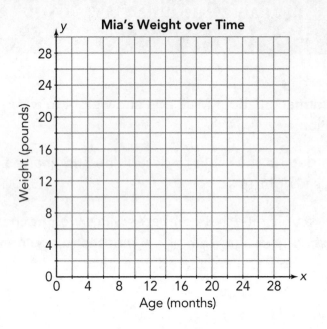

Mia's Weight over Time

3. Do all the points in your scatter plot lie on the same line? What does this tell you about Mia's weight change as time changes? Explain your reasoning.

Remember, after you draw the line, pick two points from your line to write the equation.

4. Use a straightedge to draw the line that best fits the data on the graph.

5. Write the equation of your line. Be sure to define your variables and include the units. Identify the slope and y-intercept of your line.

6. Use the equation of your line to answer each question. Explain how you determined your answers.

   a. Approximately how many pounds did Mia gain each month from the time she was born until she was 18 months old?

   b. Approximately how many pounds did Mia weigh at birth?

7. Predict Mia's weight at each given age if she continues to grow at the same rate. Then analyze your predictions.

   a. 2 years old

   b. 5 years old

   c. 18 years old

   d. Do all your predictions make sense? Explain your reasoning.

8. What can you conclude about the accuracy of your model?

Are you interpolating or extrapolating?

ACTIVITY 3.2   Analyzing Mia's Height

Analyze the table shown with the data of Mia's age and her height.

Age (months)	Height (inches)
0.0	17.9
1.0	20.5
1.8	21.0
2.3	21.8
4.0	25.0
6.0	25.8
8.0	27.0
10.0	27.0
12.0	29.3
15.0	30.5
18.0	32.5

1. **Consider the relationship between Mia's age and her height. What happens to Mia's height as she gets older?**

2. **Create a scatter plot that shows Mia's age as the explanatory variable and her height as the response variable. First, label the axes to represent the explanatory and response variables. Next, choose the appropriate intervals for your scatter plot.**

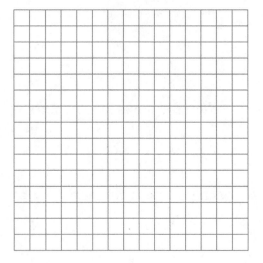

3. **Can these data be exactly represented by a linear equation? Explain your reasoning.**

4. Use a straightedge to draw the line that best fits your data on your graph. Then, write the equation of your line. Be sure to define your variables and include the units.

5. Interpret the slope and *y*-intercept of your line in terms of Mia's height.

6. Predict Mia's height at each given age if she continues to grow at the same rate. Then analyze your predictions.

   a. 2 years old

   b. 5 years old

   c. 18 years old

   d. Do all of your predictions make sense? Explain your reasoning.

What are these heights in terms of feet?

7. What can you conclude about the accuracy of your model?

The table shows Mia's growth from age 2 to age $5\frac{1}{2}$.

Age (years)	Age (months)	Weight (pounds)	Height (inches)
2.0		27.3	34.5
2.5		30.0	35.8
3.0		32.0	36.6
3.5		33.0	38.0
4.5		39.0	42.0
5.5		44.0	45.0

1. Complete the table shown by converting each age from years to months.

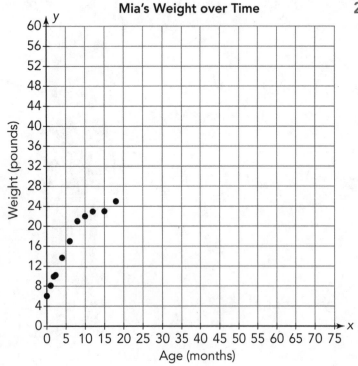

2. The scatter plot shown relates Mia's age to her weight.

   a. Plot the new data from the table.

   b. Draw the line of best fit. Then determine the equation of the line.

   c. Interpret the slope and y-intercept in terms of Mia's weight.

3. The scatter plot shown relates Mia's age to her height.

   a. Plot the new data from the table.

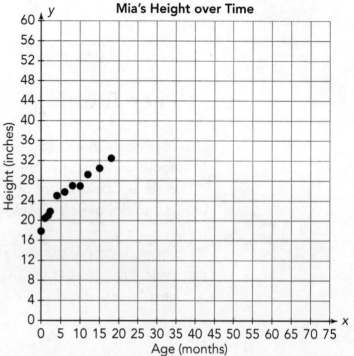

Mia's Height over Time

   b. Draw the line of best fit. Then determine the equation of the line.

   c. Interpret the slope and y-intercept in terms of Mia's height.

4. Use your new lines of best fit to determine Mia's height and weight when she is 18 years old.

5. How do these predictions compare to your previous predictions? Are these predictions reasonable? Explain your reasoning.

6. Do you think that extending the lines of best fit for Mia's weight and height over time helped to make predictions about her weight and height beyond 6 years?

7. Propose a strategy for developing more accurate models for Mia's height and weight over time.

TALK the TALK

Peer Tutoring

Your classroom partner, Terrence, was absent when you learned about drawing appropriate lines of best fit. After he completed a make-up assignment on sketching lines of best fit, Terrence asked you to double-check his work.

For each graph, determine what Terrence misunderstands about sketching lines of best fit. Then sketch another possible line of best fit and explain your strategy.

1.

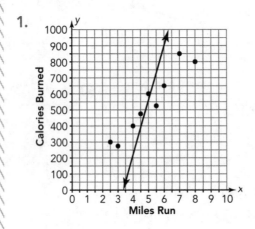

2.

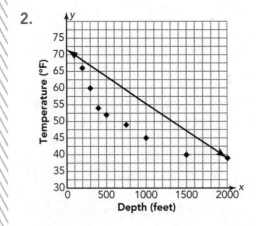

Assignment

Write

Explain the difference between interpolating and extrapolating when making predictions from a line of best fit.

Remember

The equation for the line of best fit can be used to make predictions about the related problem.

Practice

1. The typical gestational period (time from conception to birth) for a human baby is about 40 weeks. Recent developments in ultrasound scanning allow doctors to make measurements of parts of a baby's body while it is still in the womb. The table contains data about the length of a baby's femur (thigh bone) during gestation.

Gestation Time (weeks)	Femur Length (centimeters)
14	1.5
14.5	1.6
15	2.0
16	2.1
20	3.3
25	4.8
30	6.2
40	8.0

   a. Write unit rates that compare the baby's change in femur length to the change in gestation time from 14 weeks to 14.5 weeks, from 16 weeks to 20 weeks, and from 30 weeks to 40 weeks.

   b. Create a scatter plot to show the relationship between gestation time and femur length. First, label the axes to represent the explanatory and response variables. Next, choose the appropriate intervals for your scatter plot. Finally, name your scatter plot.

   c. Do all of the data points in your scatter plot lie on the same line? What does this tell you about the baby's femur length change over time? Explain your reasoning.

   d. Use a straightedge to draw the line that best fits your data in your graph. Then, write the equation of your line. Be sure to define your variables and include the units.

   e. According to the line you drew, approximately how many centimeters did the femur grow each week from 14 weeks to 40 weeks? How did you determine your answer?

   f. According to the line you drew, approximately how long would the baby's femur have been when the gestation time was 7 weeks?

   g. According to the line you drew, approximately how long would the baby's femur have been when the gestation time was 8 weeks?

2. Use the data given in the table to create a scatter plot. Draw the line of best fit on the scatter plot. Determine the equation for the line of best fit.

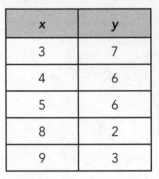

x	y
3	7
4	6
5	6
8	2
9	3

3. Predict each score. Explain your strategy.
   a. Predict the 2005 mathematics SAT score for Connecticut.

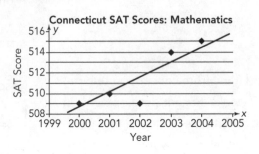

   b. Predict the 2005 mathematics SAT score for New York.

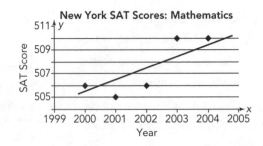

4. An animal's weight varies with age when it is young. In parts (a) through (c), for each specified set of data, complete each task.
   a. Create a scatter plot of the data of each table.
   b. Draw the line of best fit. Then determine the equation.
   c. Interpret the meaning of the slope and y-intercept for each.
   d. Predict the weight of a 15-week-old female Chihuahua.
   e. Predict the weight of a 9-week-old male Chihuahua.

Chihuahua's Weight (male)	
Age (weeks)	Weight (oz)
6	15
12	30
16	39
24	46
30	51

Chihuahua's Weight (female)	
Age (weeks)	Weight (oz)
6	11
12	19
16	25
24	30
30	33

Stretch

Because the relationships in bivariate data can change for different ranges of values of the explanatory variable (e.g., age, time), sometimes the best model for a data set includes more than one line.

Consider the data set for the temperature in Washington, DC since 8 AM on a day in winter.

- Create a scatter plot.
- Split the data into sections that show increasing, decreasing, or constant associations, and draw lines for each section.
- Determine an equation for the line of best fit for each section of the scatter plot. Specify for which domain each equation is the trend line.

Time Since 8 AM (hours)	0	1	2	3	4	5	6	7	8	9	10	11	12	13	14
Temperature (°F)	20	23	31	35	38	45	45	45	45	45	40	29	27	16	11

Review

1. Compare each pair of graphs to determine which line is a better fit for the data.

a.

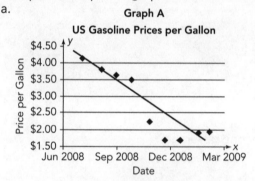

Graph A

US Gasoline Prices per Gallon

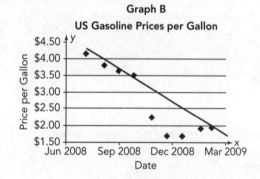

Graph B

US Gasoline Prices per Gallon

b.

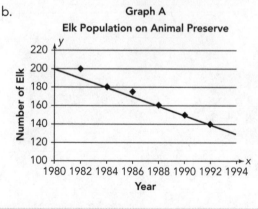

Graph A

Elk Population on Animal Preserve

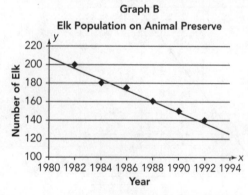

Graph B

Elk Population on Animal Preserve

2. Jerry puts a different type of fertilizer on each of his two pumpkin patches. A pumpkin from Patch A measures 13 ounces in week 1 and grows at a rate of 3.2 ounces per week. A pumpkin from Patch B measures 9 ounces in week 1 and grows at a rate of 3.6 ounces per week.

a. Write equations for the weight of pumpkins from each patch over time.

b. Create a graph that contains both lines.

c. Explain the conditions for which Jerry should use each fertilizer.

3. The graph models the amount of money Ella has in her savings account. What is Ella's rate of saving? Write your answer as a unit rate and include units.

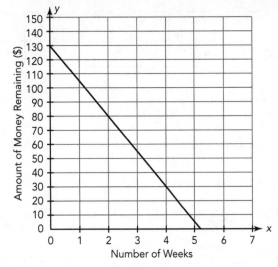

4. The graph models the sale of beverages. What is the cost of one beverage?

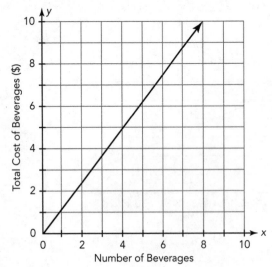

The Stroop Test

4

Comparing Slopes and Intercepts of Data from Experiments

WARM UP

1. Use the given data to create a scatter plot.

x	y
5	0
4	2
3	3
2	5
9	3

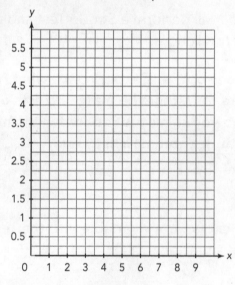

2. Draw a line of best fit on the scatter plot.

3. Determine the equation for the line of best fit.

LEARNING GOALS

- Write a linear function as a line of best fit for a set of data.
- Interpret the slope and y-intercept of a linear function modeling a set of data.
- Perform experiments and compare the results of different experiments.

Scatterplots and lines of best fit are used in many different fields of study to make predictions based on a collected data set. How can you collect data and make predictions about how your brain functions?

Reading Is Automatic

The Stroop Test is an experiment that studies how people read text. The test uses lists of color words. Each word is written in one of the four colors. A person who participates in the Stroop Test experiment receives one of two lists, a matching list or a non-matching list, with a varying number of words. In a matching list, the ink color matches the color of the word. In a non-matching list, the ink color does not match the color of the word.

Participants in the Stroop Test experiment are given one of the two kinds of lists, matching or non-matching, and are asked to say aloud the ink color in which each word is written. The time it takes for the person to say the correct ink color for all the words in the list is recorded, along with the total number of words in the list. The experiment is repeatedly performed with different people until enough data are collected to make a conclusion about the experiment.

For example, in a matching list, the word **purple** would be shown in purple. In a non-matching list, the word purple might be shown in black.

In this lesson, you will perform a Stroop Test and calculate a line of best fit to make predictions.

1. Before you perform this experiment, what results do you expect to see for either the matching lists or non-matching lists? How do you think the results for the matching lists will compare with the non-matching lists?

2. Identify the explanatory variable and the response variable in this problem situation.

3. Write a statistical question you can ask that the Stroop Test experiment can help to answer.

Comparing Slopes and *y*-Intercepts of Lines of Best Fit

Let's perform the Stroop Test!

1. Perform three trials of the Stroop Test for each type of list—matching and non-matching. Then, vary the test length by increasing or decreasing the number of words in the matching and non-matching lists. Record the list's data in the correct table. You will complete the last column of the table later.

Matching Lists				
List Length (words)	Time 1 (seconds)	Time 2 (seconds)	Time 3 (seconds)	

Non-Matching Lists				
List Length (words)	Time 1 (seconds)	Time 2 (seconds)	Time 3 (seconds)	

2. Record the mean time in seconds for each list length in the empty column of each table.

3. Create a scatter plot of the ordered pairs for the matching and non-matching list on the grids shown. First, label the axes to represent the explanatory and response variables. Next, choose the appropriate intervals for each scatter plot. Finally, name each scatter plot.

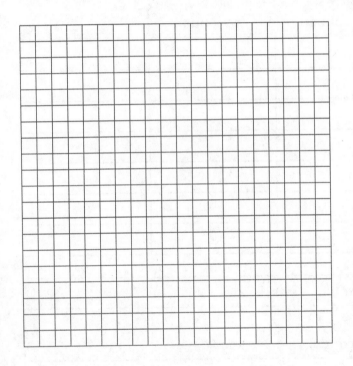
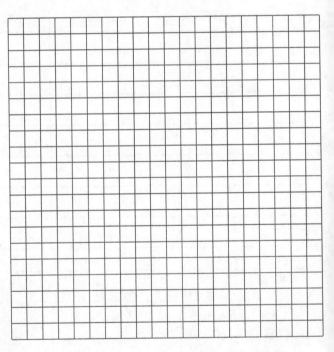

4. Use a straightedge to draw the line of best fit for each data set. Then, write the equation of each line.

5. Determine the y-intercept of each line. Interpret the meaning of the y-intercept in this situation.

6. Determine the slope of each line. Interpret the meaning of the slope in this situation.

7. Use your equations to answer each question.

   a. About how many seconds should it take a person to say 25 words from a matching list? from a non-matching list?

   b. About how many seconds should it take a person to say 10 words from a matching list? from a non-matching list?

   c. If given 2 minutes, about how many words should a person be able to say from a matching list? from a non-matching?

   d. If given 5 minutes, about how many words should a person be able to say from a matching list? from a non-matching?

TALK the TALK 💬

Interpret the Results

1. Compare your results for the matching lists to the results for the non-matching lists. Do your results seem reasonable? Explain your reasoning.

2. Revisit the statistical question you asked at the beginning of the lesson. How did the results of the experiment help to answer this question? Explain your reasoning.

3. What conclusions do you think a cognitive psychologist might draw from your experiment results?

Assignment

Write

Write a scenario that could be modeled by the data and line of best fit shown. Interpret the slope and *y*-intercept of the data.

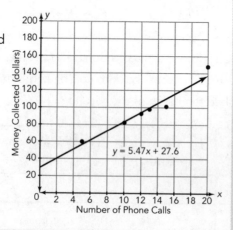

$y = 5.47x + 27.6$

Number of Phone Calls

Remember

You can interpret the slope and *y*-intercept of a line of best fit by looking at the problem situation and the explanatory and response variables.

Practice

1. The goal of a word recall experiment is to see how many words from a list that is read aloud a person can memorize and repeat back. Five word lists are given.

   5-Word List: chair, shoe, horse, suitcase, lamp

   7-Word List: animal, sweater, cheetah, avocado, back, desk, plant

   10-Word List: stereo, basketball, violin, teacher, pear, baby, table, zoo, curtains, ox

   15-Word List: cup, barn, paper, book, fire, comb, glass, vacuum, cloud, road, suit, stereo, computer, trunk, television

   20-Word List: football, hair, pizza, scarf, sandwich, T-shirt, microphone, screen, clock, fingers, coat, watch, tires, candles, cushions, earrings, heater, picture, keyboard, soda

   a. If you were to perform a word recall experiment, what results would you expect to see as the number of words increases? Do you expect people to remember more words or fewer words? Do you think people will remember the same percent of words as the length of the list increases?

   b. Identify the explanatory variable and response variable.

c. Perform the experiment for each word list. Read each list of words slowly and clearly to someone, but do not repeat any of the words. After you have finished reading each list, the person should repeat any words he or she remembers back to you. Do not allow the person to write anything down. Keep track of the number of words the person correctly repeats back to you by completing the table. Repeat this experiment two more times and calculate the mean of the results.

List Length (words)	Time 1 (words recalled)	Time 2 (words recalled)	Time 3 (words recalled)	Average (words recalled)
5-Word List				
7-Word List				
10-Word List				
15-Word List				
20-Word List				

d. Write the ordered pairs from the table that show the average number of words recalled as the response variable and the number of words in the list as the explanatory variable.

e. Create a scatter plot of the ordered pairs on the grid shown. First, label the axes to represent the explanatory and response variables. Next, choose the appropriate intervals for your scatter plot. Finally, name your scatter plot.

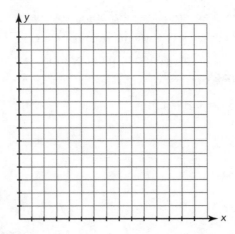

f. Use a ruler to draw a line of best fit. Then, write the equation of your line. State the y-intercept of your line. What does the y-intercept represent in this situation?

g. State the slope of your line. What does the slope represent in this situation?

h. What is the average number of words that should be recalled from a list of 25 words? 35 words? 50 words? Show your work.

i. What length should the word list be if a person recalls 20 words? Show your work.

Stretch

Two experiments are conducted to compare how long it takes inkjet printers to print in black-and-white and how long it takes them to print in color. The number of pages printed using black-and-white can be expressed by the line of best fit $p_b = 33.8t + 5.3$, and the number of pages printed using color can be expressed by the line of best fit $p_c = 21t + 2.7$, where p is the total number of pages printed, and t is the time in minutes. If you only had 15 minutes to use an inkjet printer, how many more black-and-white pages could you print than color pages?

Review

Draw a line of best fit for each scatter plot. Then, write the equation for each line.

1. (0, 18), (5, 16), (7, 10), (10, 8), (15, 3), (20, 0)

2. (0, 10), (5, 5), (6, 4), (7, 3), (10, 0)

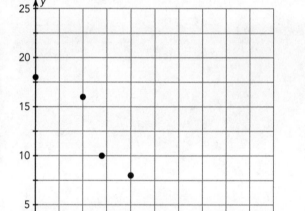 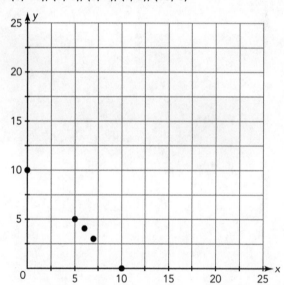

Determine the next term in each sequence. Explain the rule you used.

3. 1, 1, 2, 3, 5, 8, 13, 21, 34, . . .

4. 2, 3, 3, 5, 10, 13, 39, 43, 172, 177, 885, 891, . . .

Write the equation of the translated line.

5. Given the equation of the line $y = -3x - 1$, rewrite the equation to represent this line translated 2 units up.

6. Given the equation of the line $y = 2x + 6$, rewrite the equation to represent this line translated 8 units down.

Would You Rather . . .?

Patterns of Association in Two-Way Tables

WARM UP

In Ms. Snyder's math class, she noticed that she had 14 female students and 12 male students. Out of the 14 female students, 8 students wear either glasses or contact lenses. Out of the 12 male students, 5 students wear either glasses or contact lenses.

1. What percent of Ms. Snyder's class
   a. are female?
   b. wear either glasses or contact lenses?
   c. are female and wear either glasses or contact lenses?

LEARNING GOALS

- Interpret frequencies in two-way tables for bivariate categorical data.
- Construct two-way frequency tables.
- Construct and interpret two-way relative frequency tables for categorical data.

KEY TERMS

- categorical data
- two-way table
- frequency
- relative frequency

You know how to collect numerical data, display it on a scatterplot, and determine if the variable quantities have a positive association, negative association, or no association. What if your statistical question relies on categorical data? How do you determine an association for bivariate categorical data?

Would You Rather . . .?

1. Answer the "Would You Rather" questions. Then complete the survey questions. Record the results when everyone in the class is finished with the survey.

Would You Rather . . .

a. be able to fly?   or   be able to read minds?

b. go way back in time?   or   go way into the future?

c. be able to talk to animals?   or   be able to speak all languages?

d. Which of these topics would you most prefer to study?

   • math   • history

   • science   • Spanish

e. Which of these careers would most interest you?

   • university professor   • software engineer

   • veterinarian   • psychologist

f. Which choice describes your fear of heights?

   • not at all afraid

   • a little afraid

   • mildly afraid

   • very afraid

2. Analyze the data collected. For your class, do you think the data would show an association:

   a. between a person's fear of heights and whether he or she would like to be able to fly?

   b. between a person's choice as veterinarian for a career and whether he or she would like to talk to animals?

   c. between choosing history and choosing to go way back in time?

3. Describe how you could organize the survey data in order to determine associations between people's preferences.

ACTIVITY 5.1

Constructing and Interpreting Two-Way Frequency Tables

Ms. Carter is an athletic coordinator at Liberty Middle School. She is developing an after-school sports program. Ms. Carter has a budget to follow and needs to determine which sports she will include in the program. She surveys students in her eighth-grade class in order to determine which sports the students prefer. The results are shown in the table.

Name	Gender	Favorite Sport	Name	Gender	Favorite Sport
Sue	Female	Soccer	Jon	Male	Soccer
Jorge	Male	Basketball	Rose	Female	Volleyball
Alex	Male	Baseball	Donna	Female	Volleyball
Maria	Female	Volleyball	Suzi	Female	Soccer
Tamika	Female	Volleyball	Kayla	Female	Basketball
Sarah	Female	Basketball	Ashley	Female	Soccer
Beth	Female	Soccer	Devon	Male	Basketball
Sam	Male	Soccer	Carson	Male	Baseball
Eric	Male	Volleyball	Dawn	Female	Volleyball
Marcus	Male	Basketball	Eryn	Female	Soccer
Carla	Female	Baseball	Harley	Male	Soccer
Ben	Male	Soccer	Abigail	Female	Basketball
Will	Male	Basketball	Jordan	Male	Basketball
Yasmin	Female	Basketball	Nicole	Female	Volleyball
Paulos	Male	Volleyball	Bert	Male	Baseball

1. Identify the variables in the table.

Previously, you explored relationships between two variables whose data were quantitative or numerical. Not all data are numerical. Data that can be grouped into categories are called **categorical** (or qualitative) **data.**

One method of organizing categorical data is in a *two-way table*. A **two-way table** displays categorical data that shows the number of data points that fall into each group for two variables. One variable is divided into rows, and the other is divided into columns.

WORKED EXAMPLE

The two-way table displays the favorite sports of students in Ms. Carter's eighth-grade class. For example, you can use the two-way table to record the females who preferred soccer.

- There are two groups for the variable gender. The two groups are male and female.

- There are four groups for the variable sport. The four groups are baseball, basketball, soccer, and volleyball.

Favorite Sports of Students in Ms. Carter's Eighth-Grade Class

Gender	Baseball	Basketball	Soccer	Volleyball
Male				
Female			ⅢⅡ	

To record information in the two-way table, you can use tally marks to ensure each variable of a data point is recorded.

Therefore, since five females prefer soccer, you would use 5 tally marks in the category for female and soccer.

Analyzing the data is an important step in the statistical process. Analyzing includes organizing the data in a way to make interpreting the data most effective.

2. Complete the two-way table in the worked example for all students in Ms. Carter's class.

Once you have recorded all of the data with tally marks, you can count the tally marks in each cell of the two-way table, and then you can write the *frequency* for each variable. The **frequency** of a variable is the number of times it appears in a data set.

3. Record the frequency in the two-way table. Then, calculate the totals.

Favorite Sports of Students in Ms. Carter's Eighth-Grade Class Sport

		Baseball	Basketball	Soccer	Volleyball	Total
Gender	**Male**					
	Female					
	Total					

4. Add the total number of males and females. Then, add the total number of students who preferred baseball, basketball, soccer, and volleyball. What does this tell you?

> This two-way table has three rows and five columns now. Why is it important to know the totals for the data set?

5. Which sport is the least favorite and most favorite

   a. of the students?

   b. of the male students?

   c. of the female students?

6. According to the survey, which sports should not be included in Ms. Carter's after-school program? Explain your reasoning.

7. What other conclusions can you draw about the favorite sports of students in Ms. Carter's eighth-grade class?

8. Construct a two-way frequency table to compare the fears of heights reported by students in your class who chose the ability to fly versus those students who chose the ability to read minds. What conclusions can you draw?

A recent study has estimated that between 70% and 90% of the world's population is right-handed. Another study suggests that almost 90% of athletes are right-handed. And yet another study shows that left-handed people have a higher percentage of participants in individual sports, such as wrestling or golf.

Mr. Harris's math class thinks that these figures may be incorrect. They decide to conduct a random survey to determine which hand is favored, and whether the favored hand affects if a person participates in certain types of sports, or no sports at all. The results are shown in the two-way table.

Sports Participation

Hand Favored		Individual	Team	Does Not Play	Total
	Left	3	13	8	
	Right	6	23	4	
	Mixed	1	3	2	
	Total				

1. Name the two variables displayed in the table.

2. Which hand was favored most in the survey?

3. Which hand was favored least in the survey?

4. Calculate the total for each row and each column in the table.

   a. How many total people participated in the survey?

   b. Out of all the people surveyed, how many were left-handed?
       right-handed? mixed-handed?

   c. Out of all of the people surveyed, how many participated in
       individual sports? participated in team sports? did not
       participate in any sports?

You cannot verify that the studies' figures are correct by simply looking at the frequencies. Instead you must determine the *relative frequencies*. A **relative frequency** is the ratio or percent of occurrences within a category to the total of the category. To determine the ratio of each category, determine the part to the whole of each category. To determine the percent of each category, set up a fraction with the denominator being the total number of each row.

5. Complete the relative frequencies for each favored hand category. Round decimals to the nearest thousandth.

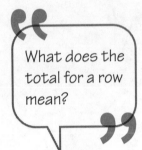

What does the total for a row mean?

Sports Participation

Hand Favored		Individual	Team	Does Not Play	Total
	Left	$\frac{3}{24} = 0.125$			
	Right		$\frac{23}{33} = 0.70$		
	Mixed				

6. Interpret each of the relative frequencies for each category.

   a. left-handed people

   b. right-handed people

   c. mixed-handed people

7. Determine the percent of people who participated in individual and team sports.

   a. left-handed people

   b. right-handed people

   c. mixed-handed people

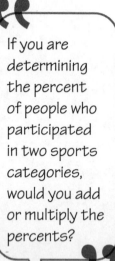

If you are determining the percent of people who participated in two sports categories, would you add or multiply the percents?

8. Which group of people had the greatest number participate in sports?

9. Complete the relative frequencies for each sports participation. Round decimals to the nearest thousandth.

Sports Participation

		Individual	Team	Does Not Play
Hand Favored	Left	$\frac{3}{10} = 0.3$	$\frac{13}{39} = 0.33$	
	Right			$\frac{4}{14} = 0.29$
	Mixed			
	Total	$\frac{10}{10} = 1$		

10. Interpret each of the relative frequencies for the type of sports participation.

11. In completing the relative frequency tables, did the studies' figures seem accurate?

TALK the TALK

Going Back in Time

1. What is the difference between numerical data and categorical data?

2. What is a relative frequency of categorical data?

3. Look back at your Would You Rather questions and survey results.

a Construct a two-way relative frequency table to determine if there is an association between choosing veterinarian as a career preference and choosing the ability to talk to animals.

b. Is there an association between a preference to go back in time and a preference for studying history? Show your work.

Assignment

Write

Define each term in your own words.

1. categorical data
2. two-way table
3. frequency
4. relative frequency

Remember

Two-way tables can show that two variables in a categorical data set are associated. They cannot show that one variable caused another variable.

Practice

Tracey manages the local movie theaters. She wants to ensure that she is showing the most popular movies and serving the most popular snacks for her theater patrons.

1. She surveys the movie-goers in the theater one evening in order to determine if they prefer to watch a drama, comedy, thriller, or documentary. The results are shown in the table.

Name	Gender	Movie Preference
Kimberly	Female	Comedy
John	Male	Comedy
Ernestine	Female	Drama
Mary	Female	Drama
Alice	Female	Drama
Damon	Male	Comedy
Katie	Female	Comedy
Jeff	Male	Documentary
Derrick	Male	Thriller
Sarina	Female	Drama
Brian	Male	Thriller
Sean	Male	Documentary
Sarah	Female	Comedy
Cecelia	Female	Comedy
Benjamin	Male	Comedy

Name	Gender	Movie Preference
David	Male	Documentary
Sophie	Female	Comedy
Grace	Female	Documentary
John David	Male	Comedy
Earl	Male	Thriller
Jacob	Male	Drama
Maggi	Female	Comedy
Morgan	Female	Documentary
Tre	Male	Drama
Kendall	Female	Thriller
Elizabeth	Female	Thriller
Kasey	Female	Thriller
Ruth	Female	Documentary
Rodney	Male	Documentary
Faith	Female	Thriller

a. Identify the variables in the table.

b. Complete the two-way table to display the data from Tracey's survey.

Movie Preference of Movie-Goers

Type of Movie

		Drama	Comedy	Thriller	Documentary	Total
Gender	Male					
	Female					
	Total					

c. How many males were surveyed? How many females were surveyed?

d. How many movie-goers prefer to watch a comedy? a thriller? a documentary? a drama?

e. Which type of movie is the least popular among the movie-goers surveyed?
   Explain your reasoning.

f. Which type of movie is the most popular among the females surveyed?
   Explain your reasoning.

g. Which type of movie is the least popular among the males surveyed? Explain your reasoning.

2. Tracey goes through the receipts at the theater to determine the types of snacks that were purchased during each of the evening's movie showings. She constructs this two-way table to compare the different types of snacks purchased.

Types of Snacks Purchased

Snack Types

		Popcorn	Nachos	Hot Dog	Candy	Total
Movie Showings	5:00 PM	200	125	75	100	
	7:00 PM	350	175	150	125	
	9:00 PM	425	225	175	125	
	11:00 PM	100	65	10	75	
	Total					

a. Name the two variables displayed in the table.

b. Calculate the total for each row and each column in the table.

c. During which movie showing were the most snacks sold?

d. Which type of snack was sold the most this evening?

e. Complete the relative frequencies for each row. Round decimals to the nearest hundredth.

Types of Snacks Purchased

Snack Types

	Popcorn	Nachos	Hot Dog	Candy	Total
5:00 PM	$\frac{200}{500} = 0.4$				$\frac{500}{500} = 1$
7:00 PM			$\frac{150}{800} \approx 0.19$		
9:00 PM		$\frac{225}{950} \approx 0.24$			
11:00 PM				$\frac{75}{250} = 0.3$	

Movie Showings

f. Interpret each of the relative frequencies.

g. Complete the relative frequencies for each column. Round decimals to the nearest hundredth.

Types of Snacks Purchased

Snack Types

	Popcorn	Nachos	Hot Dog	Candy
5:00 PM	$\frac{200}{1075} \approx 0.19$			
7:00 PM			$\frac{150}{410} \approx 0.37$	
9:00 PM		$\frac{225}{950} \approx 0.38$		
11:00 PM				$\frac{75}{425} \approx 0.18$
Total		$\frac{590}{590} = 1$		

Movie Showings

h. Interpret each of the relative frequencies.

Stretch

Thirty students were surveyed. One-fourth of the boys prefer chocolate ice cream. One-third of the people who like vanilla are girls. Twice as many girls as boys prefer coffee.

Use this information to construct a two-way table.

Review

1. The data on the graph show the foot lengths and forearm lengths for a group of people. The line of best fit for the data is shown. Use the equation of the line of best fit to predict the length of a person's forearm if the length of his or her foot is 8 inches.

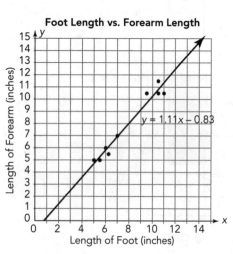

2. Estimate the slope of the line of best fit for these data.

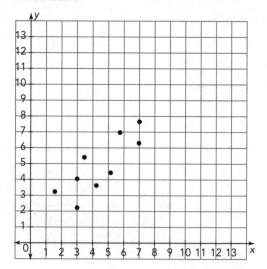

3. Determine whether each relation shown is a function. Explain your reasoning.

   a.
   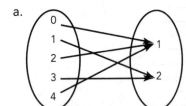

   b.

x	y
−5	6
−4	7
−4	8
−5	9

   c. {(−3, 10), (0, 8), (-1, 10), (9, 2)}

Patterns in Bivariate Data Summary

KEY TERMS

- bivariate data
- explanatory variable
- response variable
- association
- linear association
- positive association

- negative association
- outlier
- line of best fit
- model
- trend line
- interpolating

- extrapolating
- categorical data
- two-way table
- frequency
- relative frequency

LESSON 1

Pass the Squeeze

When you collect information about two separate characteristics for the same person, thing, or event, you have collected **bivariate data**. A scatter plot is a graph of a set of ordered pairs. The points in a scatter plot are not connected, but they allow you to investigate patterns in bivariate data by comparing the two variables.

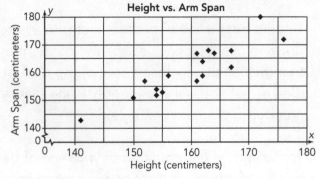

Height vs. Arm Span

For example, the scatter plot shown represents height as the x-coordinate and arm span as the y-coordinate.

When you look for a relationship in bivariate data, often you are interested in determining whether one variable causes a change in the other variable. In this case, one variable, the **explanatory variable**, is designated as the independent variable, and the **response variable**, is designated as the dependent variable, because this is the variable that responds to what occurs to the explanatory variable. In the scatter plot above, height is the explanatory variable and arm span is the response variable.

Sometimes the relationships seen in scatter plots are called **associations**. A **linear association** occurs when the points on the scatter plot are arranged in such a way that, as you look at the graph from left to right, you can imagine a line going through the scatter plot with most of the points being close to the line. In a linear association, the two variables have **positive association** if, as the explanatory variable increases, the response variable also increases. If the response variable decreases as the explanatory variable increases, then the two variables have **negative association**. For example, the scatter plot comparing height and arm span appears to have a positive linear association.

Another pattern that can occur in a scatter plot is an outlier. An **outlier** for bivariate data is a point that varies greatly from the overall pattern of the data. If the point (150, 180) were added to the scatter plot comparing height and arm span, it could be considered an outlier.

LESSON 2

Where Do You Buy Your Books?

Although a straight line will not pass through all of the points in a scatter plot, you can use a line to approximate the data as closely as possible. This kind of line is called a *line of best fit*. A **line of best fit** is a line that is as close to as many points as possible but doesn't have to go through all of the points. When you use a line of best fit, the line and its equation are often referred to as a **model** of the data, or a **trend line**. Constructing a line of best fit is helpful to predict values not displayed on the plot.

To construct a line of best fit, first plot all the data. Next, draw an oval that encloses all the data. Then draw a line that divides the enclosed area of the data in half. The idea is that you want to identify a line that has an equal number of points on either side.

To determine the equation of your line of best fit, begin by identifying two points on your trend line. These points may or may not be data points, but they must be on the trend line. Use the slope formula to calculate the slope of the line through the two points. Then use the slope and the formula to determine the *y*-intercept of the line to write the equation in slope-intercept form.

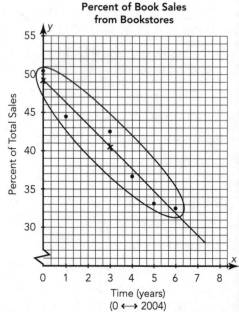

Percent of Book Sales from Bookstores

Percent of Total Sales (y-axis)

Time (years) (0 ⟷ 2004) (x-axis)

If you are predicting values that fall within the plotted values of a scatter plot, you are **interpolating**. If you are predicting values that fall outside the plotted values, you are **extrapolating**. For example, predicting the percent of book sales from book stores in 2006 using the line of best fit is an example of interpolation, while predicting the percent of book sales from book stores in 2012 using the same line would be an example of extrapolation.

LESSON 3

Mia Is Growing Like a Weed

The equation for the line of best fit can be used to make predictions about a problem. Be sure that your line of best fit is drawn in such a way that an equal number of data points fall on either side of the line, or your predictions may not be reasonable. Also consider the variables being compared to decide if a prediction is reasonable or unreasonable in context.

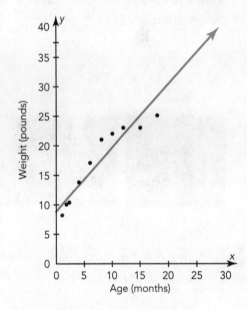

For example, the graph of the line can be represented by the equation $y = 1.1x + 8.6$. You can use this equation to estimate the child's weight at 9 months.

$$y = 1.1(9) + 8.6 = 18.5 \text{ pounds}$$

However, if you use the equation to estimate the weight of the child at 12 years old, the prediction does not seem reasonable.

$$y = 1.1(144) + 8.6 = 167 \text{ pounds}$$

The Stroop Test

You can interpret the slope and *y*-intercept of a line of best fit by looking at the problem situation and the explanatory and response variables.

For example, in the scatter plot shown, the *y*-intercept is 18.3 and the slope is approximately −1. When Therefore, every time the *x*-value increases by 1, the *y*-value decreases by approximately 1.

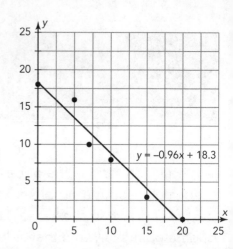

$y = -0.96x + 18.3$

Would You Rather . . .?

Not all data are numerical. Data that can be grouped into categories are called **categorical (or qualitative) data**.

One way of organizing categorical data is in a two-way table. A **two-way table** displays categorical data that shows the number of data points that fall into each group for two variables. One variable is divided into rows, and the other is divided into columns.

For example, the two-way table displays the favorite pets of students in Ms. Kutner's eighth-grade class. There are four males who prefer cats.

Favorite Pets in Ms. Kutner's Class

	Cat	Dog	Other
Male	IIII		
Female			

To record information in the two-way table, you can use tally marks to ensure each variable of a data point is recorded. Therefore, since four males prefer cats, you would use 4 tally marks in the category of female and soccer.

Once you have recorded all of the data with tally marks, you can count the tally marks in each cell of the two-way table, and then you can write the frequency for each variable. The **frequency** of a variable is the number of times it appears in a data set.

For example, this two-way table records the frequency of each pet preference in Ms. Kutner's class.

Favorite Pets in Ms. Kutner's Class

	Cat	Dog	Other	Total
Male	4	8	2	14
Female	7	6	3	16

A **relative frequency** is the ratio or percent of occurrences within a category to the total of the category. To determine the ratio of each category, determine the part to the whole of each category. To determine the percent of each category, set up a fraction with the denominator being the total number of each row.

For example, this two-way table shows the relative frequencies for each row of the table.

	Cat	Dog	Other	Total
Male	$\frac{4}{14} \approx 0.29$	$\frac{8}{14} \approx 0.57$	$\frac{2}{14} \approx 0.14$	$\frac{14}{14} = 1$
Female	$\frac{7}{16} = 0.4375$	$\frac{6}{16} = 0.375$	$\frac{3}{16} = 0.1875$	$\frac{16}{16} = 1$

MODULE 3

MODELING

LINEAR EQUATIONS

The lessons in this module build on your experiences of solving two-step equations and graphing linear equations. You will apply number properties as strategies to write equations in equivalent forms and explore strategies for solving equations with variables on both sides of the equals sign. You will write and solve equations to answer questions about real-world situations. You will also use systems of linear equations to solve real-world problems.

Solving Linear Equations

The game of Bingo dates back to 16th century Italy. The modern version of the game was copyrighted by Hugh Ward of Pittsburgh, Pennsylvania, in 1924.

Module 3: Modeling with Linear Equations

TOPIC 1: SOLVING LINEAR EQUATIONS

In this topic, students increase the range of one-variable linear equations they can solve. Students solve equations with variables on both sides of the equals sign. They review and learn strategies, including the use of properties of arithmetic, to efficiently solve equations with rational number coefficients. Students develop an understanding of the conditions that lead to equations with one solution, no solution, or infinite solutions.

Where have we been?

In grade 7, students have solved equations of the form $px + q = r$ and $p(x + q) = r$, where p, q, and r are rational numbers. They have also used properties, including the Distributive Property, to factor and expand algebraic expressions. Now, just as they did in grade 7, students review and/or learn strategies in this topic to make solving such equations more efficient.

Where are we going?

This topic provides the bridge from solving one-variable equations with variables on one side of the equals sign to solving systems of linear equations algebraically. Solving equations with no solution or with infinite solutions also prepares students to solve, algebraically, systems of linear equations with no solution or infinite solutions.

Using the Properties of Equality to Solve Equations

Students have been using these Properties of Equality throughout elementary and middle school. Understanding these properties allows students to understand much of the logic behind solving equations.

Properties of Equality	For all numbers a, b, and c, ...
Addition Property of Equality	If $a = b$, then $a + c = b + c$.
Subtraction Property of Equality	If $a = b$, then $a - c = b - c$.
Multiplication Property of Equality	If $a = b$, then $ac = bc$.
Division Property of Equality	If $a = b$ and $c \neq 0$, then $\frac{a}{c} = \frac{b}{c}$.

Myth: "Just give me the rule. If I know the rule, then I understand the math."

Memorize the following rule: *All quars are elos*. Will you remember that rule tomorrow? Nope. Why not? Because it has no meaning. It isn't connected to anything you know. What if we change the rule to: *All squares are parallelograms*. How about now? Can you remember that? Of course you can, because now it makes sense.

Learning does not take place in a vacuum. It **must be** connected to what you already know. Otherwise, arbitrary rules will be forgotten.

#mathmythbusted

Talking Points

You can further support your student's learning by making sure they eat right and get enough sleep. Healthy bodies make for healthy minds, and both diet and sleep have significant effects on learning.

Key Terms

no solutions

An equation may have no solutions. The equation $x = x + 2$, for example, has no solutions. No value of x can make the equation true.

one solution

An equation may have one solution. The equation $8 = x + 2$, for example, has one solution. The value $x = 6$ makes the equation true.

infinite solutions

An equation may have an infinite number of solutions. The equation $x(1 + 1) = 2x$, for example, has infinite solutions. An infinite number of values for x make the equation true.

Strategic Solving

Equations with Variables on Both Sides

1

WARM UP

Solve each equation.

1. $2.5x + 100 = 600$

2. $10 = 2x - 4$

3. $\frac{1}{4}x + 5 = 30$

LEARNING GOALS

- Use strategies to solve linear equations with variables on both sides of the equals sign.
- Solve linear equations with rational number coefficients.
- Combine like terms and use the Distributive Property to solve linear equations.

You have solved equations by combining like terms and using inverse operations. How can you solve equations when there are variables on both sides of the equation?

Build It Up and Break It Down

The Properties of Equality allow you to solve equations.

Properties of Equality	For all numbers a, b, and c
Addition Property of Equality	If $a = b$, then $a + c = b + c$.
Subtraction Property of Equality	If $a = b$, then $a - c = b - c$.
Multiplication Property of Equality	If $a = b$, then $ac = bc$.
Division Property of Equality	If $a = b$ and $c \neq 0$, then $\frac{a}{c} = \frac{b}{c}$.

These properties also allow you to create more complex equations. For example, given the equation $x = 2$, you can use the Addition Property of Equality to create $x + 1 = 2 + 1$, which is the same as $x + 1 = 3$. Since you used the Properties of Equality, the two equations have the same solution.

To solve a two-step equation, isolate the variable term on one side of the equation and the constant on the other side of the equation. Then multiply or divide both sides of the equation by the numeric coefficient to determine the value of the variable.

1. Consider each given equation. Use the Properties of Equality to create an equivalent equation in the form $ax + b = c$, where a, b, and c can be any number. Record the Properties of Equality you used to create your new equation.

   a. $x = 5$ b. $x = -1$

2. Give each of your equations to a partner to verify that each equation has the correct solution.

ACTIVITY 1.1   Factoring to Solve Equations

You have previously solved two-step equations using a variety of strategies. In this activity you will learn different strategies to solve equations with variables on both sides. Remember, to solve an equation means to determine the value of the unknown that makes the equation true.

Consider the equation $5x + 3 = 2x + 5$.

Teddy and Topher each solved it in a different way. Analyze their solution strategies.

To begin solving an equation with variables on both sides of the equation, move all the variable terms to one side of the equation and all the constants to the other side of the equation.

Teddy 👍

$$5x + 3 = 2x + 5$$
$$-5x \qquad -5x$$
$$\overline{\qquad 3 = -3x + 5}$$
$$-5 \qquad -5$$
$$\overline{\quad \frac{-2}{-3} = \frac{-3x}{-3}}$$
$$\frac{2}{3} = x$$
$$x = \frac{2}{3}$$

Topher 👍

$$5x + 3 = 2x + 5$$
$$-2x \qquad -2x$$
$$\overline{\quad 3x + 3 = \qquad 5}$$
$$-3 \qquad -3$$
$$\overline{\qquad 3x = 2}$$
$$x = \frac{2}{3}$$

1. Compare the two solution strategies.

   a. How were their solution strategies the same? How were they different?

   b. Which strategy do you prefer? Explain your choice.

2. Solve each equation. Describe why you chose your solution strategy.

   a. $x - 6 = 5x + 10$ b. $2x - 7 = -5x + 14$

Consider the two different equations that Sandy and Sara solved.

Sandy 👍

$3x + 9 = 6x - 30$

$\dfrac{3x + 9}{3} = \dfrac{6x - 30}{3}$

$x + 3 = 2x - 10$

$-x -x$

$\overline{}$

$3 = x - 10$

$+10 +10$

$\overline{}$

$13 = x$

$x = 13$

Sara 👍

$-x - 2 = -4x - 1$

$\dfrac{-x - 2}{-1} = \dfrac{-4x - 1}{-1}$

$x + 2 = 4x + 1$

$-x -x$

$\overline{}$

$2 = 3x + 1$

$-1 -1$

$\overline{}$

$1 = 3x$

$\dfrac{1}{3} = \dfrac{3x}{3}$

$\dfrac{1}{3} = x$

$x = \dfrac{1}{3}$

3. Sandy and Sara each divided both sides of their equations by a factor and then solved.

   a. Explain the reasoning used by each.

   b. Do you think this solution strategy will work for any equation? Explain your reasoning.

4. Solve each equation using the strategy similar to Sandy and Sara.

   a. $-4x + 8 = 2x + 10$ 　　　b. $-42x = -4x - 1$

Solving Equations with Efficiency

As you saw in the last activity, there can be more than one way to solve an equation. Sometimes an efficient strategy involves changing the numbers in the equation—in mathematically appropriate ways.

> A savvy mathematician (you!) can look at an equation, see the structure of the equation, and look for the most efficient solution strategy.

WORKED EXAMPLE

Consider the equation $\frac{1}{3}(2x + 7) + \frac{5}{6} = \frac{5}{3}x$.

You can multiply both sides of the equation by the least common denominator (LCD) of the fractions to convert the fractions to whole numbers.

$\frac{1}{3}(2x + 7) + \frac{5}{6} = \frac{5}{3}x$ ← The LCD of the fractions is 6.
    Multiply both sides by 6.

$2(2x + 7) + 5 = 10x$ ← Rewrite using the Distributive Property.
$4x + 14 + 5 = 10x$

1. Explain how both sides of the equation were multiplied by 6 in the first step.

2. What is the solution to the equation $\frac{1}{3}(2x + 7) + \frac{5}{6} = \frac{5}{3}x$? Check your solution.

3. Explain why Cody's reasoning is incorrect.

Cody

$$-\frac{3}{4}x = \frac{1}{2}x + \frac{5}{4}$$

$$4\left(-\frac{3}{4}x\right) = 4\left(\frac{1}{2}x + \frac{5}{4}\right)$$

$$-3x = 2x + 5$$

$$-5x = 5$$

$$x = -1$$

Since I multiplied both sides by 4 to get the solution, I have to divide the solution by 4:

$$x = -\frac{1}{4}$$

4. Solve each equation by first multiplying both sides of the equation by the LCD. Check your solutions.

   a. $\frac{1}{4}(x - 5) + 9 = \frac{1}{2}x$ b. $\frac{5}{4}(x + \frac{1}{2}) + 8 = \frac{1}{8}x$

5. Mindy and David multiplied both sides of the equation $2.5x + 1.4 = 0.5x + 2$ by 10 before solving the equation. The first step of each strategy is shown. Who's correct? What is the error in the other strategy?

You can multiply both sides of an equation by powers of 10 to convert all numbers to whole numbers.

Mindy

$25x + 14 = 5x + 2$

David

$25x + 14 = 5x + 20$

Solve each equation.

1. $12.6 + 4x = 9.6 + 8x$

2. $-12.11x - 10.5 = 75.6 - 3.5x$

3. $\frac{10x + 2}{2} = 4x + \frac{1}{4}$

4. $\frac{3}{8}(x + 8) = \frac{1}{2}(x + 5) + \frac{1}{4}$

5. $\frac{-2(5x + 4)}{3} = -3(3x + 2) - \frac{7}{3}$

TALK the TALK 💬

Building Strategically

Use each starting equation to build an equation with variables on both sides that can be solved using the given strategy. Then, give your equations to a partner to solve.

1. $h = 1.6$, factor out a number from both sides

2. $j = 5$, multiply both sides by the LCD to rewrite fractions as whole numbers

3. $k = \frac{1}{3}$, multiply both sides by a power of 10 to rewrite decimals as whole numbers

Assignment

Write

Explain the process of solving an equation with variables on both sides.

Remember

You can use Properties of Equality to rewrite equations and increase your efficiency with solving equations.

- Factor out a number from both sides.
- Multiply both sides of an equation by the least common denominator of the fractions to rewrite fractions as whole numbers.
- Multiply both sides of an equation by a power of 10 to rewrite decimals as whole numbers.
- Use the Distributive Property to rewrite expressions.

Practice

Solve each equation.

1. $5x + 15 = 75 - 25x$

2. $\frac{1}{4}x - 3 = \frac{1}{2}x + 12$

3. $4x = 20x - 24$

4. $11.3x + 12.8 = 7.5x + 35.6$

5. $9.6x - 15.4 = -4.3x + 26.3$

6. $-2x - 1.4 = 6 + 3x$

Stretch

You can solve an equation with two variables by trying different values. What is the solution to the equation $2x + 3y = 13$?

Review

1. Rodell took a survey of his classmates. The data from the survey are shown in the two-way table.

Student's Lunch Preference

		Lunch Options				
		Chicken Nuggets	Peanut Butter & Jelly	Pizza	Salad	Total
Gender	Male	2	3	4	0	9
	Female	3	1	3	4	11
	Total	5	4	7	4	20

a. Which lunch option is the most favorite of the males?

b. Which lunch option is the most favorite of the females?

2. Isabel surveyed three classes about their favorite season. The data from the survey are shown in the two-way table. Complete the relative frequencies for each row. If necessary, round decimals to the nearest thousandth.

Student's Season Preference

Classes		Winter	Spring	Summer	Fall	Total
		Seasons				
	Class A	9	2	7	6	24
	Class B	2	5	9	4	20
	Class C	8	6	10	4	28
	Total	19	13	26	14	72

Student's Season Preference

Classes		Winter	Spring	Summer	Fall	Total
		Seasons				
	Class A	$\frac{9}{24} = 0.375$				
	Class B					
	Class C					

3. Calculate the slope of the line represented by each table.

a.

X	Y
4	8
10	11
16	14
20	16

b.

X	Y
2	5
4	3
5	2
8	−1

MP3s and DVDs

Analyzing and Solving Linear Equations

WARM UP

Members of a community service club are collecting pull tabs from aluminum cans to support a local hospital's initiative.

- Sadie collected the least number of pull tabs.
- Emma collected 15 more pull tabs than Sadie.
- Ricky collected 4 times as many as Emma.
- Lily collected 10 fewer than Ricky.

Define a variable to represent the number of pull tabs that Sadie collected. Then, write algebraic expressions to represent the number of pull tabs that each of the other students collected.

LEARNING GOALS

- Write and solve linear equations in one variable.
- Determine whether an equation has one solution, no solutions, or infinite solutions by successively transforming the equation into simpler forms.
- Interpret expressions in and solutions to equations in the context of problem situations.

You have learned how to use strategies to solve complex equations with variables on both sides. How can you determine when an equation has no solutions or infinite solutions?

No One Knows Exactly

Sometimes, you are asked to determine the value of unknown quantities using only information you have for a quantity.

Five friends have a certain number of DVDs.

- Dan has the fewest.
- Donna has 7 more than Dan.
- Betty has twice as many as Donna.
- Jerry has 3 times as many as Dan.
- Kenesha has 6 fewer than Donna.

1. Define a variable for the number of DVDs that Dan has.

Think about how the numbers of DVDs compare among the friends.

2. Use your defined variable to write algebraic expressions to represent the number of DVDs each person has.

Writing Expressions to Represent Situations

Use the expressions you wrote in the previous activity to answer each question.

1. Is it possible for Jerry and Kenesha to have an equal number of DVDs? Write and solve an algebraic equation to explain why or why not.

2. Kim and Corinne share their own set of DVDs. Kim has 6 times as many as Dan has, and Corinne has twice as many as Jerry has. Can you write and solve an equation to determine how many DVDs each girl has? Explain your reasoning.

3. If the original group of friends has a total of 182 DVDs all together, then how many does each person have? Make sure to check your work.

   a. DVDs that Dan owns: b. DVDs that Donna owns:

   c. DVDs that Betty owns: d. DVDs that Jerry owns:

   e. DVDs that Kenesha owns:

4. Write and solve an algebraic equation to show why Donna's reasoning is incorrect.

Donna

Donna says that the sum of the number of her DVDs and Kenesha's DVDs is the same as the number of DVDs that Betty owns.

Terry, Trudy, Tom, and Trevor have challenged their friends with
this riddle.

- Terry said, "If you add 150 to the number of MP3 downloads Tom
  has, double that number, and finally divide by 3, you have the
  number of MP3 downloads I have."

- Trudy said, "If you take the number of MP3 downloads Tom has,
  subtract 30, multiply that difference by 5, and finally divide that
  product by 4, the result will be the number of MP3 downloads I
  have."

- Trevor said, "Well, if you take twice the number of MP3
  downloads Tom has, add 30, multiply the sum by 4, and finally
  divide that product by 3, you will have the number of MP3
  downloads I have."

1. What do you need to know to determine the number of MP3
   downloads each person has?

2. Define a variable for the number of MP3 downloads Tom has,
   and then write expressions for the number of MP3 downloads
   each of the other people has.

   a. The number of MP3 downloads Terry has:

   b. The number of MP3 downloads Trudy has:

   c. The number of MP3 downloads Trevor has:

3. Suppose Tom has 150 MP3 downloads. Determine how many MP3 downloads each person has.

Terry   Trudy   Trevor

4. What if Terry and Trevor have the same number of MP3 downloads? How many MP3 downloads would each person have?

Tom   Trudy   Trevor and Terry

5. What if the sum of Trudy's and Trevor's MP3 downloads is 39 more than the number Terry has? How many would each person have?

Tom   Trudy

Trevor   Terry

Amy and Damon were solving an equation from their math homework. They came across the equation shown.

$$3x + 7 = 5x + 2(3 - x) + 1$$

Examine each solution strategy.

Amy

$$3x + 7 = 5x + 2(3 - x) + 1$$
$$3x - 5x + 7 = 5x - 5x + 2(3 - x) + 1$$
$$-2x + 7 = 2(3 - x) + 1$$
$$-2x + 7 = 6 + (-2x) + 1$$
$$-2x + 7 = 7 + (-2x)$$
$$-2x + 2x + 7 = 7 + (-2x) + 2x$$
$$7 = 7$$

> What did Damon do differently to solve the equation?

Damon

$$3x + 7 = 5x + 2(3 - x) + 1$$
$$3x + 7 = 5x + 6 + (-2x) + 1$$
$$3x + 7 = 5x + (-2x) + 6 + 1$$
$$3x + 7 = 3x + 7$$
$$3x + 7 + (-7) = 3x + 7 + (-7)$$
$$\frac{3x}{3} = \frac{3x}{3}$$
$$x = x$$

1. Explain why both Amy's and Damon's methods are correct but have different solutions.

2. How would you interpret the final equation in each solution? Is the final equation always true, sometimes true, or never true? Explain your reasoning.

3. Explain whether the equation has one solution, no solution, or an infinite number of solutions.

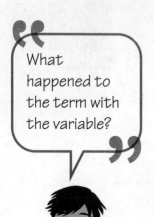

What happened to the term with the variable?

Consider this new equation:

$$3(x - 5) + 11 = x + 2(x + 5)$$

Examine each solution strategy.

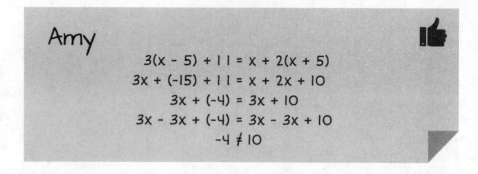

Amy

$$3(x - 5) + 11 = x + 2(x + 5)$$
$$3x + (-15) + 11 = x + 2x + 10$$
$$3x + (-4) = 3x + 10$$
$$3x - 3x + (-4) = 3x - 3x + 10$$
$$-4 \neq 10$$

Damon

$$3(x - 5) + 11 = x + 2(x + 5)$$
$$3x + (-15) + 11 = x + 2x + 10$$
$$3x + (-4) + 4 = 3x + 10 + 4$$
$$3x = 3x + 14$$
$$3x + (-3x) = 3x + (-3x) + 14$$
$$0 \neq 14$$

4. Explain why both Amy's and Damon's methods are correct but have different solutions.

5. How would you interpret the final equation in each solution? Is the final equation always true, sometimes true, or never true? Explain your reasoning.

6. Explain whether the equation has one solution, no solution, or an infinite number of solutions.

ACTIVITY 2.4

Practice Solving Equations with Rational Coefficients

Solve each equation shown. Make sure to check your work.

1. $\frac{3}{4}(2x + 5) = 14$

Pay close attention to the sign of numbers, especially when using the Distributive Property.

2. $2x - 7 + 3x = 4x + 2$

3. $\frac{-7(3x + 6)}{3} = 7$

4. $1.99x + 6 = 2.50x$

5. $40x = -50(x - 2)$

6. $30(x - 10) = 15x$

7. $3(x - 1) + x = 4(x + 2)$

8. $5(2x - 1) + x + 17 = 5x + 6(x + 2)$

9. $\dfrac{-3(-2x - 5)}{4} = -5(3x + 5) + \dfrac{5}{4}$

10. $\dfrac{2}{3}(6x - 5) = 2 - \dfrac{1}{3}(3x - 2)$

TALK the TALK

How Do You Know?

1. When you solve any equation, describe how you know when there will be:

   a. one solution.

   b. no solutions.

   c. infinite solutions.

Assignment

Write

Write three equations, one that has one solution, one that has no solutions, and one that has infinite solutions.

Remember

An equation can have one solution, no solutions, or infinite solutions.

Practice

1. Don has four different chicken coops on his farm. He gathers eggs from each coop every day to sell at the local farmer's market each week. During one week in the summer, the production levels from the coops were compared.
   - The number of eggs from coop B can be found by subtracting 10 from coop A's production, and then multiplying this result by two-fifths.
   - The number of eggs from coop C can be found by adding 3 to coop A's production, multiplying this amount by 3, subtracting 4 from this total, and then dividing the whole result by 4.
   - The number of eggs from coop D can be found by adding 7 to coop A's production, doubling this amount and then dividing the result by 3.
   a. Define a variable for the number of eggs produced by coop A. Then write expressions for the number of eggs produced by the other coops.
   b. If coop A produced 125 eggs, how many did each of the other coops produce?
   c. If the sum of the number of eggs from coop B and coop C was 24 more than the number of eggs from coop D, how many eggs did each coop produce?

2. Three siblings collect rare coins. To determine the number of rare coins that Samantha has, take the number of rare coins Kevin has, add 4, and then divide that sum by 2. To determine the number of rare coins Ben has, double the number of rare coins Kevin has, subtract 4, and then multiply that difference by 2. How many rare coins does each sibling have if they have a total of 49 rare coins?

3. Three teammates had different point totals at the girls' basketball game. To determine the number of points Effie had, multiply Toni's points by 3, subtract 8, and then multiply the difference by 2. To determine the number of points Linda had, add 9 to Toni's points and divide the sum by 3. How many points did each girl have if Effie scored 9 more than Toni and Linda combined?

4. Four members of the track team ran various numbers of miles last week. To determine the number of miles Manuel ran, multiply the number of miles Ewan ran by 3, subtract 15, multiply the difference by 2, and divide this quantity by 5. To determine the number of miles Violet ran, subtract 14 from the number of miles Ewan ran, and then multiply the difference by 3. To determine the number of miles Ling ran, add 30 to the number of miles Ewan ran, and then divide the sum by 5. How many miles did each team member run last week if the total number of miles run by Ewan and Manuel is equal to the total number of miles run by Violet and Ling?

Stretch

When an equation is not a linear equation, it can have more than one solution. The equation $x^2 = 9$ has two solutions, -3 and 3. What are the solutions to the equation $2x^2 + 5 = 77$?

Review

Solve each equation.

1. $\frac{2}{3}(x + 2) = \frac{1}{6}x + \frac{1}{3}$
2. $2.5x - 1 = 10 - 7.5x$

Determine whether there is likely a positive or negative association between the quantities.

Explain your reasoning.

3. Independent quantity: number of sunny days in Year A

   Dependent quantity: number of cloudy days in Year A

4. Independent quantity: number of miles driven

   Dependent quantity: amount of gas in tank

Determine the slope and y-intercept of the line represented by each equation.

5. $36 = 24y + 48x$
6. $y - 14 = 7x + 9$

Tic-Tac-Bingo

Creating Linear Equations

WARM UP

Solve each equation.

1. $\frac{2}{3}(x - 4) = \frac{1}{2}$

2. $0.7(x + 3) = 2.1$

3. $3(-2x + 5) = 5x - 7$

4. $\frac{3x + 11}{2} = x - 4$

LEARNING GOALS

- Solve linear equations with rational coefficients and variables on both sides.
- Give examples of linear equations with one solution, no solutions, or infinite solutions.
- Determine whether an equation has one solution, no solutions, or infinite solutions.

You know how to solve linear equations and determine the number of solutions. How can you create linear equations with zero, one, or infinite solutions?

The Goal

In this lesson, each person in the class will be given a different algebraic expression. Your goal is to locate a classmate and form an equation to meet each of the criteria listed.

a. no solution

b. a non-zero integer solution

c. a negative rational solution

d. a positive rational solution

e. a solution that is neither positive nor negative

f. infinite solutions

1. **For each criterion, provide an example of a final line of the solved equation.**

Use the Tic-Tac-Bingo board at the end of the lesson. The board has 9 spaces. Three spaces are already designated.

1. Fill each remaining space with one of the solution types listed. Each option must be used at least once.

   - positive rational solution

   - negative rational solution

   - non-zero integer solution

> Each equation can only be used in one box, but you can rearrange your equations if you need to.

2. Your teacher will assign your expression. When you and a classmate have created an equation with one of the solution types, write your equation in the corresponding box.

Try to be the first person to get three in a row. Then, try to be the first person to completely fill your board with equations.

TALK the TALK 💬

The Strategy

Think about the strategies you used to play Tic-Tac-Bingo.

1. Describe your general strategy.

2. Reflect on the equations with no solutions and infinite solutions.

   a. How can you look at an equation and determine that there will be no solution?

   b. How can you look at an equation and determine that there will be infinite solutions?

Tic-Tac-Bingo

	Solution is not positive or negative	
Equation: **Solution:**	**Equation:** **Solution:**	**Equation:** **Solution:**
No Solution **Equation:**	 FREE SPACE	**Equation:** **Solution:**
Equation: **Solution:**	**Equation:** **Solution:**	Infinite Solutions **Equation:**

Assignment

Write

Explain the difference between an equation with no solution and an equation with a solution of $x = 0$.

Remember

Linear equations can have no solution, one solution, or infinite solutions.

Practice

1. Set each given expression equal to $7(x - 2) - 4x + 14$. Determine whether the equation formed has no solution, infinite solutions, or a solution of $x = 0$.

   a. no solution $\frac{8x + 4}{2} - \frac{1}{3}(x + 6)$

   b. infinite solutions $2(x - 1) + x$

   c. solution of $x = 0$ $-9x + 12 + 4(3x - 3)$

2. Set each given expression equal to $\frac{7}{3}x + 4 - \frac{x - 6}{3}$. Determine whether the equation formed has no solution, infinite solutions, or a solution of $x = 0$.

   a. no solution $\frac{1}{3}(8x + 18) - \frac{2}{3}x$

   b. infinite solutions $2(3x + 5) - 4$

   c. solution of $x = 0$ $4\left(\frac{1}{2}x - 3\right) + 6$

Stretch

Create an equation with at least one fractional coefficient and at least one negative coefficient with solutions $x = 0$ and $x = \frac{4}{3}$.

Review

1. The Franklin Lee Middle School Glee Club is hosting a talent show competition to raise money for a community that was recently hit by a flood. All of the members are asked to go out in the community to sell tickets to the show.

   - Patrick sold 30 more tickets than Jose.
   - Gabriella sold 25 fewer than two times the number that Patrick sold.
   - Owen sold one-third the number of tickets that Patrick sold.
   - Desmond sold 15 fewer than Owen.

   a. Define a variable for the number of tickets Jose sold. Then write expressions for the number of tickets sold by the other students.

   b. If Jose sold 30 tickets, how many tickets did each of the others sell?

   c. If Gabriella sold 65 tickets, how many tickets did each of the others sell?

   d. If Patrick, Owen, and Desmond sold 175 tickets altogether, how many tickets did each of them sell?

2. Isabel surveyed three classes about their favorite season. The data from the survey are shown in the two-way table.

Student's Season Preference

		Seasons				
		Winter	Spring	Summer	Fall	Total
Classes	Class A	9	2	7	6	24
	Class B	2	5	9	4	20
	Class C	8	6	10	4	28
	Total	19	13	26	14	72

a. Compute the relative frequencies for each row. If necessary, round decimals to the nearest thousandth.

b. What percent of students in Class A prefer winter?

c. Which class has the largest percent of students who prefer summer?

d. Compute the relative frequencies for each column. If necessary, round decimals to the nearest thousandth.

e. What percent of students who prefer winter are from Class C?

f. The smallest percentage of students who prefer summer comes from which class?

3. Determine whether each relation represents a function. Explain your reasoning.

a.

x	y
1	7
5	23
5	35
8	55

b.

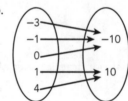

Solving Linear Equations Summary

Strategic Solving

An equation with variables on both sides of the equation can be solved by moving all the variable terms to one side of the equation and all the constants to the other side of the equation.

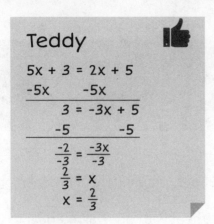

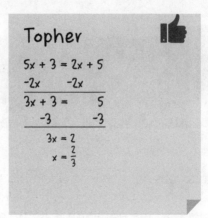

You can use Properties of Equality to rewrite equations and increase your efficiency with solving equations.

- Factor out a number from both sides.

    Consider the equation $3x + 9 = 6x - 30$.
    You can factor out the common factor 3 from both sides of the equation to help you solve.

$$\frac{3x + 9}{3} = \frac{6x - 30}{3} \quad \longrightarrow \quad x + 3 = 2x - 10 \quad \longrightarrow \quad 13 = x$$

- Multiply both sides of an equation by the least common denominator of the fractions to remove the fractions.

  Consider the equation $\frac{1}{3}(2x + 7) + \frac{5}{6} = \frac{5}{3}x$.

  You can multiply both sides of the equation by the least common denominator of the fractions to convert the fractions to whole numbers.

  $\frac{1}{3}(2x + 7) + \frac{5}{6} = \frac{5}{3}x$ The LCD of the fractions is 6. Multiply both sides by 6.

  $2(2x + 7) + 5 = 10x$ Rewrite using the Distributive Property.

- Multiply both sides of an equation by a power of 10 to remove decimals.

  Consider the equation $1.2x + 4.8 = 0.6x - 1.8$.

  $10(1.2x + 4.8) = 10(0.6x - 1.8)$ $\longrightarrow$ Multiply both sides of the equation by 10.

  $12x + 48 = 6x - 18$ $\longrightarrow$ Factor out a 6 from both sides.

  $2x + 8 = x - 3$

LESSON

2

MP3s and DVDs

A linear equation can have one solution, no solutions, or infinitely many solutions.

When the solution to the equation is a true statement with one value equal to the variable, there is only one solution. For example, the equation $x + 2 = 8$ has only one solution: $x = 6$.

When the solution to the equation is a false statement, the equation has no solution. For example, the equation $x + 0 = x + 1$ has no solutions.

When the solution to the equation is a true statement for any value of the variable, such as $x = x$, the equation has infinitely many solutions.

LESSON 3

Tic-Tac-Bingo

Equations can have different kinds of solutions.

For example, the equation $2x - 5 = 10$ has a positive rational solution: $x = \frac{15}{2}$.
The equation $2x + 5 = 0$ has a negative rational solution: $x = -\frac{5}{2}$.

TOPIC 2
Systems of Linear Equations

Intersections are important when solving systems of linear equations.

Module 3: Modeling with Linear Equations

TOPIC 2: SYSTEMS OF LINEAR EQUATIONS

In this topic, students analyze and solve pairs of simultaneous linear equations. Throughout the topic, students write systems of equations to represent problem situations. To build fluency with solving systems of linear equations using inspection, graphing, and substitution, students write and solve additional systems of linear equations, using the structure of the equations in the system to determine the most efficient solution strategy.

Where have we been?

In this topic, students utilize a great deal of what they have learned in this course and previous courses about linear relationships, tables, graphs, and equations, and proportionality to solve problems and investigate solutions to multiple linear equations.

Where are we going?

Students' experiences in this topic provide the foundation for a more rigorous and abstract study of systems of equations in high school. In high school, students will solve systems that include equations that are not linear, and they will use algebraic and graphical techniques to solve systems of inequalities.

Modeling a Solution to a System with a Point of Intersection

If a system of two linear equations has one solution, that solution can be modeled as the point of intersection of the graphs of the two equations. For this system, when $x = 1$ and $y = 6$, both equations are true.

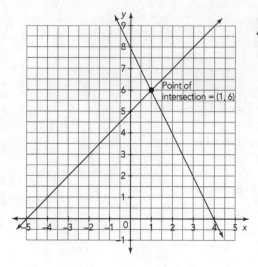

$$\begin{cases} y = x + 5 \\ y = -2x + 8 \end{cases}$$

Myth: Memory is like an audio or video recording.

Let's play a game. Memorize the following list of words: strawberry, grape, watermelon, banana, orange, peach, cherry, blueberry, raspberry. Got it? Good. Some believe that the brain stores memories in pristine form. Memories last for a long time and do not change—like a recording. Without looking back at the original list, was apple on it?

If you answered "yes," then go back and look at the list. You'll see that apple does not appear, even though it seems like it should. In other words, memory is an active, reconstructive process that takes additional information, like the category of words (e.g., fruit), and makes assumptions about the stored information.

This simple demonstration suggests memory is not like a recording. Instead, it is influenced by prior knowledge and decays over time. Therefore, students need to see and engage with the same information multiple times to minimize forgetting (and distortions).

#mathmythbusted

Talking Points

You can further support your student's learning by asking questions about the work they do in class or at home. Your student is learning more about systems of equations and solving systems.

Questions to Ask

- How does this problem look like something you did in class?
- Can you show me the strategy you used to solve this problem? Do you know another way to solve it?
- Does your answer make sense? How do you know?
- Is there anything you don't understand? How can you use today's lesson to help?

Key Terms

break-even point
When one graphed line represents the cost of an item and the other line represents the income from selling the item, the point of intersection is called the break-even point.

solution of a linear system
The solution of a linear system is an ordered pair (x, y) that is a solution to both equations in the system.

substitution method
The substitution method is a process of solving a system of equations by substituting a variable in one equation with an equivalent expression.

Crossing Paths

Point of Intersection of Linear Graphs

LEARNING GOALS
- Write a system of equations to represent a problem situation.
- Analyze and solve a system of simultaneous linear equations graphically.
- Interpret the solution to a system of two linear equations in two variables as the point of intersection of two linear graphs and in terms of the original problem's context.
- Determine a point of intersection in a system of linear equations using tables.

KEY TERMS
- point of intersection
- break-even point

You have modeled different linear equations. How can you model two linear equations on the same graph? What does it mean when two linear graphs intersect?

Long-Sleeved T-Shirts

Profit is the amount of money made after paying all costs. To calculate the profit made from selling T-shirts, subtract the cost of the shirts from the income, which is the money earned from sales.

Your school's parent-teacher organization wants to sell long-sleeved T-shirts as a fundraiser. The business manager found a company that will charge $4 for each long-sleeved T-shirt and a setup fee of $160 to create the design that will be placed on each shirt. The chairman of the fundraising committee suggested selling the long-sleeved T-shirts for $8 each. The organization has asked you to help them analyze the production costs and the amount of money that can be made by this fundraiser.

1. If the shirts are sold for $8 each, at what point will the parent-teacher organization start making a profit? Show your work. Describe the reasoning you used to determine the answer.

Graphing and Interpreting a Point of Intersection

Consider the fundraiser being held by the parent-teacher organization, described in the previous activity. Shirts are sold for $8 each and cost $4 each to make, plus a $160 setup fee.

1. Write an equation to represent the organization's cost, in dollars, to buy the long-sleeved T-shirts. Describe what your variables represent.

2. Write an equation to represent the organization's income from selling the long-sleeved T-shirts. Describe what your variables represent.

3. Complete the table to show the cost, income, and profit for different numbers of long-sleeved T-shirts sold.

Quantity Name	Number of Long-Sleeved T-shirts	Cost	Income	Profit
Unit	Long-Sleeved T-shirts	Dollars	Dollars	Dollars
Expression				
	0			
	10			
	20			
	35			
	50			
	100			

4. Create graphs to represent the cost and the income on the coordinate plane shown. Use the given bounds and intervals.

Variable Quantity	Lower Bound	Upper Bound	Interval
Number of Long-Sleeved T-shirts	0	50	2.5
Money	0	400	20

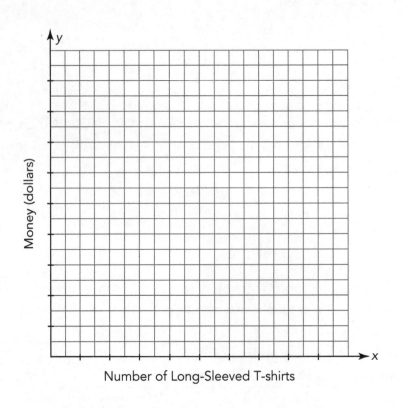

Money (dollars)

Number of Long-Sleeved T-shirts

Be sure to label your lines.

5. Use your graphs to answer each question and describe your reasoning in terms of the graphs.

   a. Determine the number of long-sleeved T-shirts for which the cost is greater than the income.

   b. Determine the number of long-sleeved T-shirts for which the income is greater than the cost.

   c. Determine when the cost is equal to the income.

   d. Verify your solution algebraically.

The **point of intersection** is the point at which two lines cross on a coordinate plane. When one line represents the cost of an item and the other line represents the income from selling the item, the point of intersection is called the **break-even point**.

6. What is the break-even point for making and selling the long-sleeved T-shirts?

7. What is the profit from T-shirts at the break-even point?

8. What are the cost and income at the break-even point?

9. What do the coordinates of the point of intersection mean in terms of the fundraiser?

10. State the number of long-sleeved T-shirts that must be sold for a profit to be made.

A Different Point of Intersection

After the initial analysis, the business manager of the parent-teacher organization called the company that will be producing the shirts. The company agreed to discount the design fee to $80, while maintaining the cost of $4 per shirt. The committee would like you to analyze the profit potential with the new costs and a new selling price of $12 per shirt.

1. Write an equation that represents the cost, in dollars, for the long-sleeved T-shirts. Describe what your variables represent.

2. Write an equation that represents the organization's income from selling the long-sleeved T-shirts. Describe what your variables represent.

3. Complete the table to show the cost, income, and profit for different numbers of long-sleeved T-shirts.

Quantity Name	Number of Long-Sleeved T-shirts	Cost	Income	Profit
Unit	Long-sleeved T-shirts	Dollars	Dollars	Dollars
Expression				
	0			
	5			
	10			
	35			
	50			
	100			

4. Create graphs to represent the cost and the income on the coordinate plane shown. Use the given bounds and intervals.

Variable Quantity	Lower Bound	Upper Bound	Interval
Number of Long-Sleeved T-shirts	0	50	2.5
Money	0	400	20

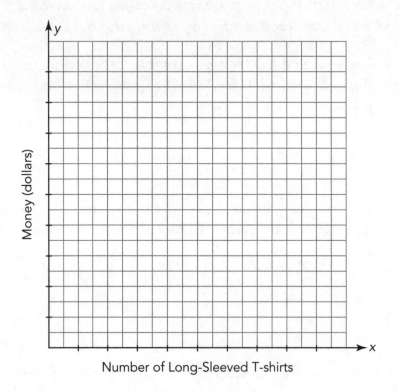

Number of Long-Sleeved T-shirts

5. Use your graphs to answer each question and describe your reasoning in terms of the graphs.

a. Determine the number of long-sleeved T-shirts for which the cost is greater than the income.

b. Determine the number of long-sleeved T-shirts for which the income is greater than the cost.

c. Determine when the cost is equal to the income.

d. Verify your solution algebraically.

6. What is the break-even point for producing and selling the long-sleeved T-shirts?

7. What is the profit from T-shirts at the break-even point?

8. What are the production cost and income at the break-even point?

9. What do the coordinates of the point of intersection mean in terms of the fundraiser?

10. State the number of long-sleeved T-shirts that must be sold for a profit to be made.

Determining a Point of Intersection to Solve a Problem

Serena is ordering lunch from Tony's Pizza Parlor. John told her that when he ordered from Tony's last week, he paid $34 for two 16-inch pizzas and two drinks. Jodi told Serena that when she ordered one 16-inch pizza and three drinks, it cost $23.

1. Write two equations to represent the two statements that Serena hears.

2. Interpret what the point of intersection means for the two lines representing the equations.

3. Verify your answers by graphing the two equations.

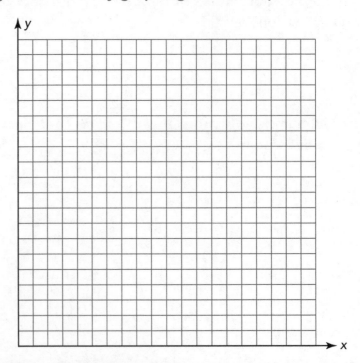

TALK the TALK 💬

Putting It All on the Table

Look back at the tables you used in this lesson.

1. How can you use a table alone to determine the point of intersection of two linear graphs?

2. How does determining a point of intersection from a table compare with determining the point of intersection from a graph and from equations?

Assignment

Write

In your own words, define the terms *point of intersection* and *break-even point*.

Remember

The point where two linear graphs intersect represents the solution to both of the equations that describe the graphs.

Practice

Misha is the manager of Movie Parlor, a video store. She is in charge of buying the videos for the store to sell. She buys videos from a wholesaler that sells them for $8 each. The wholesaler also charges a fee of $200 for each bulk purchase. Misha then sells the videos for $12 each.

1. Write an equation to represent the cost to buy videos from the wholesaler. Describe what your variables represent. Write a second equation to represent the amount of money the store will earn from selling the videos. Describe what your variables represent in this equation.

2. Calculate the cost to buy 30 videos from the wholesaler.

3. Calculate the amount of money the store will earn from selling 30 videos.

4. Calculate the profit the store will make from selling 30 videos. Interpret the meaning of your answer.

5. Calculate the cost to buy 70 videos from the wholesaler.

6. Calculate the amount of money the store will earn from selling 70 videos.

7. Calculate the profit the store will make from selling 70 videos. Interpret the meaning of your answer.

8. Complete the table to show the cost of buying videos from the wholesaler and income for different numbers of videos.

Number of Videos	Cost from Wholesaler ($)	Income ($)
x		
0		
10		
30		
45		
70		
100		

9. Create graphs of both the cost and income equations. Use the given bounds and intervals.

Variable Quantity	Lower Bound	Upper Bound	Interval
Videos	0	70	5
Money	0	900	50

10. Use your graphs to determine the number of videos for which the cost to buy them is greater than the income from selling them. Explain your reasoning.

11. Use your graphs to determine the number of videos for which the income from selling them is greater than the cost to buy them. Explain your reasoning.
12. Determine the break-even point for buying and selling the videos.
13. What is the video store's profit at the break-even point?
14. What is the point of intersection of the two lines you graphed?
15. What do the coordinates of the point of intersection mean in terms of buying and selling videos?
16. Describe the number of videos that must be sold in order for a profit to be made.

Stretch

Suppose a jet plane is traveling at 500 miles per hour at a height of 30,000 feet. If you took off from the ground in a flying car, traveling straight up at 100 miles per hour, how far away would the plane need to be when you take off in order for the car to meet the plane at the same height and time?

Review

Determine whether the equation has one solution, no solutions, or infinite solutions.

1. $3x - 4 = 6x - 8$ 2. $2x + 1 = 2x - 1$

Solve each equation.

3. $-4x - 2 = 6x + 2$ 4. $\frac{1}{2}x - 5 = 8 + 2x$

Describe the pattern of association between the two quantities in each scatter plot.

5.

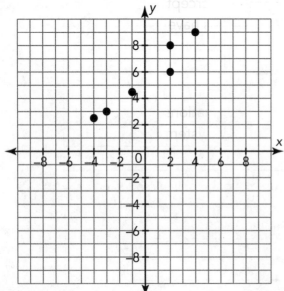

6.

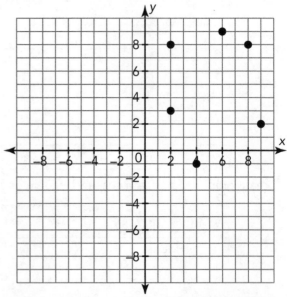

The Road Less Traveled

2

Systems of Linear Equations

WARM UP

1. Graph the equations on the coordinate plane.

   $y = x$

   $y = -x$

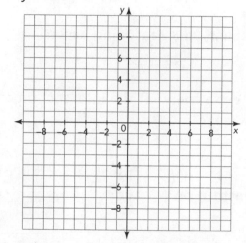

2. What are the coordinates of the point of intersection?

3. Interpret the meaning of the point of intersection.

LEARNING GOALS

- Write a system of equations to represent a problem context.
- Analyze and solve a system of two simultaneous linear equations in two variables graphically.
- Interpret the solution to a system of equations in terms of a problem situation.
- Use slope and y-intercept to determine whether two linear equations have one solution, no solutions, or infinite solutions.

KEY TERMS

- system of linear equations
- solution of a linear system
- consistent system
- inconsistent system

You have graphed linear equations on a coordinate plane. How can you interpret two linear equations together as a system?

According to the Map

Many of the diagonal roads in Washington, DC, are named after US states. Except for California and Ohio, every state provides the name for an avenue. California is a street, and Ohio is a drive. There is also a Puerto Rico Avenue.

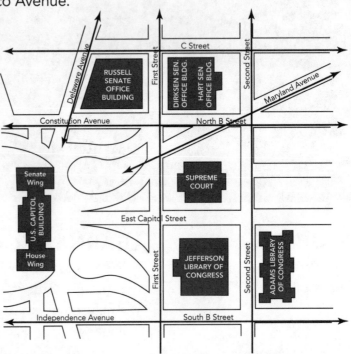

1. Answer each question and explain your reasoning according to the map shown.

   a. Would it be possible to meet a friend at the intersection of First Street and Second Street?

   b. Would it be possible to meet a friend at the intersection of Delaware Avenue and Constitution Avenue?

   c. Would it be possible to meet a friend at the intersection of C Street and Second Street?

2. How many places could you be if you are at the intersection of Independence Avenue and South B Street?

Representing a Problem Situation with a System of Equations

Colleen and Jimmy have part-time jobs after school. Both have decided that they want to see how much money they can save in one semester by placing part of their earnings each week into a savings account. Colleen currently has $120 in her account and plans to save $18 each week. Jimmy currently has $64 in his savings account and plans to save $25 each week.

1. Write an equation for Colleen and for Jimmy that represents the total amount of money, in dollars, in each of their savings accounts, y, in terms of the number of weeks, x, that they place money in their respective accounts.

2. How much money will each person have in his or her savings account after five weeks?

3. Which person will have more money in his or her savings account after five weeks?

4. How much money will each person have in his or her savings account after 18 weeks (the amount of time in one semester)?

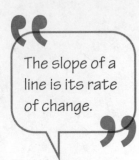

The slope of a line is its rate of change.

5. Which person will have more money in his or her savings account at the end of the semester?

6. Create a graph of each equation on the coordinate plane shown. Choose your bounds and intervals for each quantity.

Variable Quantity	Lower Bound	Upper Bound	Interval

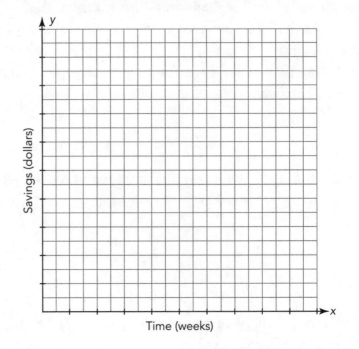

7. Determine the number of weeks after which Colleen and Jimmy will have the same amount of money in their savings accounts.

8. Verify your solution to Question 7 algebraically.

9. Interpret the meaning of the slope of each graph in this problem situation.

10. Which person is saving more money per week?

NOTES

11. How can you tell who is saving more money each week by analyzing the graph?

12. Interpret the meaning of the *y*-intercept of each graph in this problem situation.

When two or more linear equations define a relationship between quantities, they form a **system of linear equations**. The **solution of a linear system** is an ordered pair (*x*, *y*) that is a solution to both equations in the system. Graphically, the solution is the point of intersection, the point at which two or more lines cross.

WORKED EXAMPLE

A system of linear equations is written with a brace as shown:

$$\begin{cases} y = x + 5 \\ y = -2x + 8 \end{cases}$$

You can determine the solution to this system by graphing the equations. The point of intersection is the solution to the system.

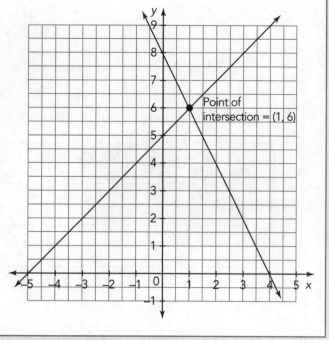

Eric also has a part-time job after school working at the same place as Jimmy. He heard about the money that Colleen and Jimmy were saving and decided that he wanted to save money, also. Eric has $25 in his savings account and will save the same amount as Jimmy, $25 per week.

1. Write an equation that represents the total amount of money in Eric's savings account, y, in terms of the number of weeks, x, that he places money in his savings account.

2. Write a linear system that shows the total amount of money that will be saved by Eric and Jimmy.

3. Create a graph of the linear system on the coordinate plane shown. Choose your bounds and intervals for each quantity.

Variable Quantity	Lower Bound	Upper Bound	Interval

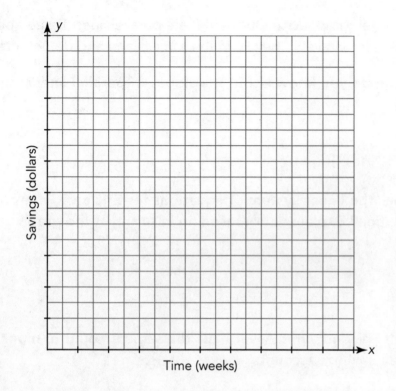

Savings (dollars)

Time (weeks)

4. What does the slope of each graph represent in this problem situation?

5. What is the same for both Eric and Jimmy?

6. What is different for Eric and Jimmy?

7. What is the point of intersection for this system of equations? Explain your reasoning in terms of the graph.

The lines you graphed in Question 3 are parallel lines. Remember that two lines are parallel if they lie in the same plane and do not intersect.

8. What do you know about the slopes of parallel lines?

9. Does the linear system of equations for Eric and Jimmy have a solution? Explain your reasoning in terms of the graph.

10. Will Eric and Jimmy ever have the same amount of money in their savings accounts?

Eric's sister Trish was able to save $475 working part-time during the first semester of school. She recently quit her part-time job to play on the high school's softball team. She is hoping to get a college scholarship to play softball and wants to devote her time to achieving her goal. She will withdraw $25 each week from her savings account for spending money while she is not working.

11. Write an equation that gives the total amount of money in Trish's savings account, y, in terms of the number of weeks, x, that she withdraws money out of her savings account.

12. Write a system of equations that represents the amount of money that Trish and Eric will have in their respective savings accounts.

13. Create a graph of the linear system on the coordinate plane shown. Choose your bounds and intervals for each quantity.

Variable Quantity	Lower Bound	Upper Bound	Interval

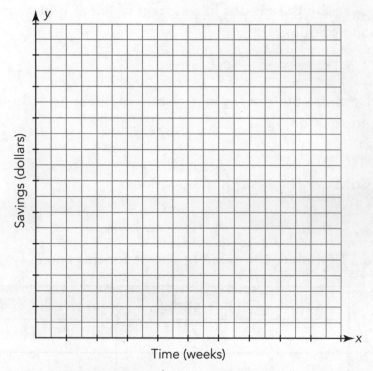

14. What does the point of intersection of the lines represent?

15. Compare the slopes of the lines.

16. According to the graph, approximately when will Trish and Eric have the same amount of money in their savings accounts? How much will they each have?

ACTIVITY
2.3

Systems with Infinitely Many Solutions

You have worked with systems of linear equations that have one solution and no solutions.

1. Describe the graphs in a system of linear equations that has one solution.

2. Describe the graphs in a system of linear equations that has no solution.

3. Consider the system of equations:

$$\begin{cases} y = 3x + 6 \\ y = 3(x + 2) \end{cases}$$

a. Complete the table of values for this linear system.

x	y = 3x + 6	y = 3(x + 2)
−2		
0		
2		
4		
8		
13		
20		

b. Describe the equations that make up this system. What can you conclude about the number of solutions to this type of linear equation?

TALK the TALK

Line Up for Inspection!

Each graph shows a system of two linear relationships.

1. Write the linear system that represents each.

a.

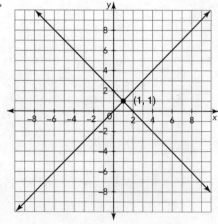

b.

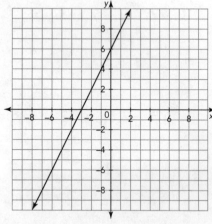

c.

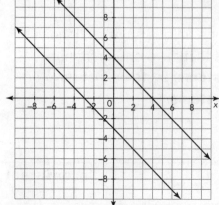

2. Using only the equations, determine whether each system has one solution, no solutions, or infinite solutions. Explain your reasoning.

a. $y = \frac{4}{5}x - 3$ and $y = -\frac{5}{4}x + 6$

b. $y = \frac{2}{3}x + 7$ and $y = \frac{1}{6}(4x + 42)$

c. $y = -2.5x + 12$ and $y = 6 - 2.5x$

d. $y = 5x$ and $y = \frac{1}{5}x$

A system of equations may have one unique solution, infinite solutions, or no solutions. Systems that have one or infinite solutions are called **consistent systems**. Systems that have no solution are called **inconsistent systems**.

3. Complete the table.

	Consistent Systems		Inconsistent Systems
	One Unique Solution	Infinite Solutions	No Solutions
Compare the slopes.			
Compare the y-intercepts.			
Describe the lines.			

Assignment

Write

Complete each sentence by writing the correct term or phrase from the lesson.

1. A(n) _____ is formed when the equations or graphs of two or more linear equations define a relationship between quantities.
2. A(n) _____ is an ordered pair (x, y) that is the point of intersection, the point at which two or more lines cross.
3. A(n) _____ has one or infinite solutions.
4. A(n) _____ has no solution.

Remember

- A system of equations whose graphs intersect at just one point is a system with one solution.
- A system of equations that has parallel line graphs is a system with no solutions.
- A system of equations that has identical graphs is a system with infinite solutions.

Practice

Aiko works in the fish department of a pet store. She is asked to drain, clean, and refill two reef tanks. The first tank holds 175 gallons of water, and the second tank holds 200 gallons of water. The hoses that she uses drain the tanks at a rate of 25 gallons of water per hour.

1. Write an equation for each tank that represents the total amount of water in gallons in the tank, y, in terms of the number of hours, x, that the tanks are draining.
2. How much water is in each tank after 3 hours?
3. Write your equations in the first row of the table. Then, complete the table of values for the linear system.

Number of Hours	First Tank	Second Tank
x		
0		
1		
2		
3		
4		
5		
6		
7		

4. Create a graph of both equations.

5. Interpret the meaning of the slope of each line in this problem situation.

6. What is the same for both tanks?

7. What is different for the two tanks?

8. What is the point of intersection for this system of equations? Explain your reasoning in terms of the graph.

9. When will both tanks have the same amount of water?

10. While Aiko is draining both tanks, she is also filling a 250-gallon tank. The water fills at a rate of 25 gallons per hour. Write an equation that gives the total amount of water in gallons in the third tank, y, in terms of the number of hours, x, that the tank is filling.

Stretch

A system with an equation that has an exponent of 2 can have more than one solution. How many solutions does the system $y = x$ and $y = x^2 - 2$ have? What are the solutions?

Review

1. Billy is selling lemonade for $1 per cup. It costs him 50 cents per cup to make the lemonade. He also has to spend an additional $10 for supplies such as ice, cups, and plastic shakers.

   a. Write a system of equations to represent this situation.

   b. What does the point of intersection represent in this situation?

2. Determine whether the equations have one solution, no solutions, or infinite solutions.

   a. $1.5x + 6.5 = \frac{3}{2}x + \frac{13}{2}$

   b. $-\frac{1}{5}x - 12 = -0.2x - \frac{24}{2}$

3. Solve each equation.

   a. $4(x + 5) = 6(x + 4)$

   b. $-3(p - 4) = -2p + 1$

The County Fair

Using Substitution to Solve Linear Systems

3

WARM UP

Analyze each system of equations. What can you conclude about the value of y in each?

1. $\begin{cases} x = 12 \\ y = x + 22 \end{cases}$

2. $\begin{cases} x = 0 \\ y = x - 45 \end{cases}$

3. $\begin{cases} x = y \\ y = 2x - 10 \end{cases}$

4. $\begin{cases} x = y + 3 \\ y = 2x - 10 \end{cases}$

LEARNING GOALS

- Write a system of equations to represent a problem context.
- Solve a system of equations algebraically using substitution.
- Interpret a solution to a system of linear equations in terms of the problem situation.
- Solve real-world and mathematical problems with two linear equations in two variables.

KEY TERMS

- standard form of a linear equation
- substitution method

Suppose you graph a system of equations, but the point of intersection is not clear from the graph? How can you determine the solution to the system?

Goats, Chickens, and Pigs

At the county fair, farmers bring some of their animals to trade with other farmers. To make all trades fair, a master of trade oversees all trades. Assume all chickens are of equal value, all goats are of equal value, and all pigs are of equal value.

- In the first trade of the day, 4 goats were traded for 5 chickens.
- In the second trade, 1 pig was traded for 2 chickens and 1 goat.
- In the third trade, Farmer Lyndi put up 3 chickens and 1 pig against Farmer Simpson's 4 goats.

1. Is this a fair trade? If not, whose animals are worth more? How could this be made into a fair trade?

Introduction to Substitution

In this lesson, you will explore systems of equations that may or may not be accurately solved using graphs. As you have seen, reasoning can also be used to solve systems. In the next activities, you will learn about solving systems algebraically.

Janet was helping her mother make potato salad for the county fair and was asked to go to the market to buy fresh potatoes and onions. Sweet onions cost $1.25 per pound, and potatoes cost $1.05 per pound. Her mother told her to use the $30 she gave her to buy these two items.

> The **standard form of a linear equation** is $Ax + By = C$, where A, B, and C are constants and A and B are not both zero.

1. Write an equation in standard form that relates the number of pounds of potatoes and the number of pounds of onions that Janet can buy for $30. Use x to represent the number of pounds of onions, and y to represent the number of pounds of potatoes that Janet can buy.

2. Janet's mother told her that the number of pounds of potatoes should be 8 times greater than the number of pounds of onions in the salad. Write an equation in x and y that represents this situation.

3. Will 1 pound of onions and 8 pounds of potatoes satisfy both equations? Explain your reasoning.

4. Create graphs of both equations. Choose your bounds and intervals for each quantity.

Variable Quantity	Lower Bound	Upper Bound	Interval

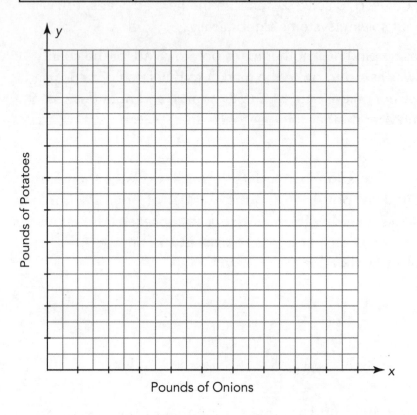

5. Can you determine the exact solution of this linear system from your graph? Explain your reasoning.

6. Estimate the point of intersection from your graph.

In many systems, it is difficult to determine the solution from the graph. There is an algebraic method that can be used called the *substitution method*. The **substitution method** is a process of solving a system of equations by substituting a variable in one equation with an equivalent expression.

The slope-intercept form of a linear equation is $y = mx + b$, where m is the slope of the line and b is the y-intercept of the line.

WORKED EXAMPLE

Let's consider the system you wrote.

$$\begin{cases} 1.25x + 1.05y = 30 \\ y = 8x \end{cases}$$

Because $y = 8x$ is in slope-intercept form, use this as the first equation.

Step 1: To use the substitution method, begin by choosing one equation and isolating one variable. This will be considered the first equation.

Step 2: Now, substitute the expression equal to the isolated variable into the second equation.

Substitute $8x$ for y in the equation $1.25x + 1.05y = 30$.

Write the new equation.

$$1.25x + 1.05y = 30$$
$$1.25x + 1.05(8x) = 30$$

You have just created a new equation with only one unknown.

Step 3: Solve the new equation.

$$1.25x + 8.40x = 30$$
$$9.65x = 30$$
$$x \approx 3.1$$

Therefore, Janet should buy approximately 3.1 pounds of onions.

Now, substitute the value for x into $y = 8x$ to determine the value of y.

$$y = 8(3.1) = 24.8$$

Therefore, Janet should buy approximately 24.8 pounds of potatoes.

Step 4: Check your solution by substituting the values for both variables into the original system to show that they make both equations true.

Keep in mind what the value represents.

7. Check that the solution is correct. Show your work.

8. What is the solution to the system? What does it represent in terms of the problem situation?

9. Compare your solution using the substitution method to the solution on your graph. What do you notice?

Substitution with Special Systems

Samson and Adrian are helping to set up the booths at the fair. They are each paid $7 per hour to carry the wood that is needed to build the various booths. Samson arrives at 7:00 A.M. and begins working immediately. Adrian arrives 90 minutes later and starts working.

1. Write an equation that gives the amount of money that Samson will earn, y, in terms of the number of hours he works, x.

2. How much money will Samson earn after 90 minutes of work?

3. Write an equation that gives the amount of money Adrian will earn, y, in terms of the number of hours since Samson started working, x.

4. How much money will each student earn by noon?

5. Will Adrian ever earn as much money as Samson? Explain your reasoning.

6. Write a system of linear equations for this problem situation.

7. Analyze the system of linear equations. What do you know about the solution of the system by observing the equations? Explain your reasoning.

How is this similar to solving linear equations with no solution or with infinite solutions?

Let's see what happens when we solve the system algebraically.

8. Since both equations are written in slope-intercept form as expressions for y in terms of x, substitute the expression from the first equation into the second equation.

   a. Write the new equation.

   b. Solve the equation for x.

   c. Does your result for x make sense? Explain your reasoning.

9. What is the result when you algebraically solve a linear system that contains parallel lines?

On Monday night, the fair is running a special for the the local schools: if tickets are purchased from the school, you can buy student tickets for $4 and adult tickets for $4. You buy 5 tickets and spend $20.

10. Write an equation that relates the number of student tickets, x, and the number of adult tickets, y, to the total amount spent.

11. Write an equation that relates the number of student tickets, x, and the number of adult tickets, y, to the total number of tickets purchased.

12. Write both equations in slope-intercept form.

13. Analyze the system of linear equations. What do you know about the solution of the system by looking at the equations?

Let's see what happens when you solve the system algebraically.

14. Since both equations are now written in slope-intercept form as expressions for y in terms of x, substitute the expression from the first equation into the second equation.

 a. Write the new equation and solve the equation for x.

 b. Does your result for x make sense? Explain your reasoning.

15. How many student tickets and adult tickets did you purchase?

16. What is the result when you algebraically solve a linear system that contains two lines that are actually the same line?

Write and solve a system of equations to solve each problem.

1. The admission fee for the fair includes parking, amusement
   rides, and admission to all commercial, agricultural, and
   judging exhibits. The cost for general admission is $7, and the
   price for children under the age of 5 is $4. There were 449
   people who attended the fair on Thursday. The admission
   fees collected amounted to $2768.

   a. Write a system of equations in standard form for this
      situation. Use x to represent the number of people 5 and
      over, and use y to represent the number of children under
      5 years of age.

   b. Without solving the system of linear equations, interpret
      the solution.

   c. Solve the system of equations using the substitution method.
      Then interpret the solution of the system in terms of the
      problem situation.

2. The business manager for a band must make $236,000 from ticket sales to cover costs and make a reasonable profit. The auditorium where the band will play has 4000 seats, with 2800 seats on the main level and 1200 on the upper level. Attendees will pay $20 more for main-level seats.

a. Write a system of equations with x representing the cost of the main-level seating and y representing the cost of the upper-level seating.

b. Without solving the system of linear equations, interpret the solution.

c. Solve the system of equations using the substitution method. Then interpret the solution of the system in terms of the problem situation.

3. Ms. Ross told her class that tomorrow's math test will have 20 questions and be worth 100 points. The multiple-choice questions will be 3 points each, and the open-ended response questions will be 8 points each. Determine how many multiple-choice and open-ended response questions will be on the test.

   a. Write a system of equations. Describe your variables.

   b. Without solving the system of linear equations, interpret the solution.

   c. Solve the system of equations using the substitution method. Then interpret the solution of the system in terms of the problem situation.

4. Ashley is working as a cashier at the sports arena. What should she tell the next person in line?

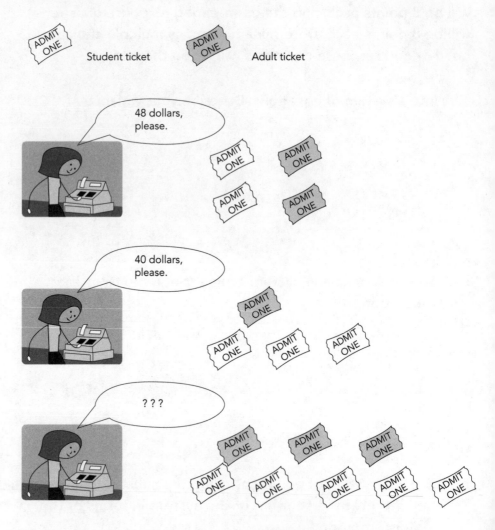

Write and solve a system of equations that represents the problem situation. Define the variables. Then determine the cost of each type of ticket. Finally, state the amount Ashley charges the third person.

5. Alex is applying for positions at two different electronic stores in neighboring towns. The first job offer is a $200 weekly salary plus 5% commission on sales. The second job offer is a $75 weekly salary plus 10% commission.

a. Write a system of equations that represents the problem situation. Define the variables. Then solve the system of linear equations and interpret the solution in terms of the problem situation.

b. What is the difference in the weekly pay between stores if Alex sells $3000?

c. What is the difference in the weekly pay if he sells $4225?

d. Which job offer would you recommend Alex take? Explain your reasoning.

Alex's sales targets for each job would be between $1500 and $3000 weekly. Each manager tells Alex the same thing: "Some weeks are better than others, depending on the time of year and the new releases of technology."

TALK the TALK 💬

The Substitution Train

1. Determine the solution to each linear system by using the substitution method. Check your answers algebraically.

a. $\begin{cases} 2x + 3y = 34 \\ y = 5x \end{cases}$

b. $\begin{cases} y = 4x + 2 \\ y = 3x - 2 \end{cases}$

c. $\begin{cases} 3x + 2y = 4 \\ 2x - y = 5 \end{cases}$

d. $\begin{cases} 3x + y = 8 \\ 6x + 2y = 10 \end{cases}$

Assignment

Write

Explain how to use the substitution method to solve systems of linear equations.

Remember

When a system has no solution, the equation resulting from the substitution step has no solution.

When a system has infinite solutions, the equation resulting from the substitution step has infinite solutions.

Practice

1. Serena is trying to become more environmentally conscious by making her own cleaning products. She researches different cleaners and decides to make furniture polish using olive oil and lemon juice. She wants to make enough to fill two 24-ounce bottles.
   a. Write an equation in standard form that relates the amount of olive oil and lemon juice to the total amount of mixture Serena wants to make. Use x to represent the amount of lemon juice and y to represent the amount of olive oil.
   b. The recommendation for the mixture is that the amount of olive oil be twice the amount of lemon juice. Write an equation in terms of x and y as defined in part (a) that represents this situation.
   c. Use substitution to solve the system of equations. Check your answer.
   d. What does the solution of the system represent in terms of the mixture?
   e. The best price Serena can find for lemon juice is $0.25 per ounce. The best price she can find for olive oil is $0.39 per ounce. She buys a total of 84 ounces of lemon juice and olive oil, and spends $29.40. Write equations in standard form for this situation. Use x to represent the amount of lemon juice she buys, and use y to represent the amount of olive oil she buys.
   f. Solve the system of equations you wrote using the substitution method. Check your answer. Describe the solution in terms of the problem situation.

2. In an effort to eat healthier, Bridget is tracking her food intake by using an application on her phone. She records what she eats, and then the application indicates how many calories she has consumed.
   One day, Bridget eats 10 medium strawberries and 8 vanilla wafer cookies as an after-school snack. The caloric intake from these items is 192 calories. The next day, she eats 20 medium strawberries and 1 vanilla wafer cookie as an after-school snack. The caloric intake from these items is 99 calories.
   a. Write a system of equations for this problem situation. Define your variables.
   b. Without solving the system of linear equations, interpret the solution.
   c. Solve the system of equations using the substitution method. Check your work.
   d. Interpret the solution of the system in terms of the problem situation.
   e. Bridget's friend Monica also has a calorie counting application on her phone. The two friends decide to compare the two programs. Bridget eats 1 banana and 5 pretzel rods, and her application tells her she consumed 657 calories. Monica eats 1 banana and 5 pretzel rods, and her application tells her she consumed 656 calories. The girls want to know how many calories are in each food. Write a system of equations for this problem. Define your variables.
   f. Solve the system of equations using the substitution method. Interpret your answer in terms of the problem.

3. Write a system of linear equations to represent each situation. Then solve the system using substitution. Interpret the solution of the system in terms of the problem situation.

    a. James has 13 coins. The coins are nickels and quarters. The coins have a total value of $2.05. Let n represent the number of nickels, and let q represent the number of quarters.

    b. Ms. Snyder is giving a 28-question test that is made up of 2-point questions and 4-point questions. The entire test is worth 100 points. Let t represent the number of 2-point questions, and let f represent the number of 4-point questions.

    c. The basketball team scored 82 points from 2-point and 3-point baskets. They make 38 baskets altogether. Let a represent the number of 2-point baskets, and let b represent the number of 3-point baskets.

4. Use the substitution method to determine the solution of each system of linear equations. Check your solutions.

    a. $\begin{cases} 9x + y = 16 \\ y = 7x \end{cases}$
          b. $\begin{cases} 3x + \frac{1}{2}y = -3.5 \\ y = -6x + 11 \end{cases}$

    c. $\begin{cases} y = -5x \\ 21x - 7y = 28 \end{cases}$
          d. $\begin{cases} 2x + 4y = -32 \\ y = -\frac{1}{2}x - 8 \end{cases}$

Stretch

Create a system of linear equations with solution (2, 5). Solve the system using substitution to verify your system has the given solution.

Review

1. Graph each system of linear equations to determine the solution to the system.

    a. $y = 34 - \frac{5}{2}x$ and $y = \frac{2}{5}x + 5$
        b. $y = 21x + 144$ and $y = 3(7x + 48)$

2. The population growth (in thousands) for a small town near Bay City can be represented by the expression $x + \frac{4}{5}(x + 315)$, where x represents the number of years since 2005. The population growth (in thousands) for a neighboring town can be represented by the expression $2x - \frac{1}{5}(x - 630)$, where x represents the number of years since 2005. When will the populations of the two towns be the same?

3. Two neighboring towns are not having population growth. In fact, they both have been losing population since 1995. The population decline for one of the towns (in thousands) can be represented by the expression $-\frac{2}{5}(x - 500)$, where x represents the number of years since 1995. The population decline for the other town (in thousands) can be represented by the expression $-\frac{1}{2}x + \frac{1}{10}(x + 2000)$, where x represents the number of years since 1995. When will the populations of the two towns be the same?

4. Solve each equation.

    a. $8(2m + 7) = 10(m + 11)$
        b. $-3(y + 20) = -9y$

Rockin' Roller Rinks

4

Choosing a Method to Solve a Linear System

LEARNING GOALS

- Write a system of linear equations to represent a problem context.
- Interpret the solution of a system of linear equations.
- Choose the best method to solve a system of linear equations.

Now that you know how to solve systems of linear equations by graphing, by inspection, and by substitution, how do you decide which method to use?

So Many Possibilities

Tickets for a movie cost $8 for evenings and $5 for matinees. There were 440 tickets sold, and $3130 was collected in ticket sales.

1. Consider each system of equations. Determine which system(s) could be used to calculate the number of matinee tickets sold. Explain your reasoning.

   a. $\begin{cases} x + y = 3130 \\ 5x + 8y = 440 \end{cases}$

   b. $\begin{cases} x + y = 440 \\ 5x + 8y = 3130 \end{cases}$

   c. $\begin{cases} x + y = 3130 \\ 8x + 5y = 440 \end{cases}$

   d. $\begin{cases} x + y = 440 \\ 8x + 5y = 3130 \end{cases}$

2. Consider the valid system(s) from Question 1. How would you solve each valid system: by graphing or by substitution? Explain your reasoning.

ACTIVITY 4.1

Comparing Two Fee Schedules

The activities director of the Community Center is planning a skating event for all the students at the local middle school. There are several skating rinks in the area, but the director does not know which one to use. At a previous event at Skate Park the director initially paid $230 for a party of 10, but when 20 students attended she ended up paying $260. For a different event at Roller Rama, she paid $125 for 25 students, but ended up paying $200 when 40 students attended.

Assume that the skating rinks have not changed their rates for skating parties.

1. Define variables to represent the total cost and the number of students attending the event.

2. Write and interpret an equation for the total cost of using Skate Park in terms of the number of students attending.

3. Write and interpret an equation for the total cost of using Roller Rama in terms of the number of students attending.

4. Suppose the activities director anticipates that 50 students will attend.

   a. Calculate the total cost of using Skate Park.

   b. Calculate the total cost of using Roller Rama.

5. Suppose the activities director has $650 to spend on the skating event.

   a. Determine the number of students who can attend if the event is held at Skate Park.

   b. Determine the number of students who can attend if the event is held at Roller Rama.

6. Write a system of equations to represent this problem situation.

7. Solve this system using each strategy. Interpret the meaning of the solution in the context of the problem situation.

You can use a variety of strategies and representations to solve a system of linear equations.

- inspection
- table
- graph
- substitution

Table

Number of Students	Skate Park	Roller Rama

Graph

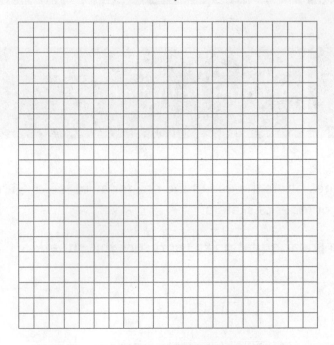

Substitution

8. Which skating rink would you recommend to the activities director? Explain your reasoning.

9. Explain the advantages and disadvantages of using each strategy.

      table   graph   substitution

ACTIVITY 4.2

A Third Equation

Super Skates offers the use of the rink for a flat fee of $1000 for an unlimited number of skaters.

1. Write a linear equation to represent this situation.

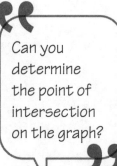

"Can you determine the point of intersection on the graph?"

2. Add a column to the table in the previous activity for Super Skates. Also, graph the equation for Super Skates on the grid in the previous activity.

3. Use substitution to determine when Super Skates is the same price as Skate Park and Roller Rama. In which case did you need to use substitution to determine the solution?

4. Describe when going to Super Skates is a better option than going to Skate Park or Roller Rama. Explain your reasoning.

5. Explain under what conditions you would recommend each skating rink to the director of the Community Center based solely on the cost to rent each skating rink.

ACTIVITY
4.3   Analyzing Structure

> Look at the structure of each system before you choose your solution strategy.

Solve each linear system. State what elements of each system led to your chosen solution strategy.

1. $\begin{cases} y = 5x + 12 \\ y = 9x - 4 \end{cases}$

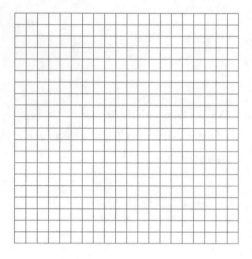

2. $\begin{cases} 8x + 3y = 30 \\ 8x + 3y = 16 \end{cases}$

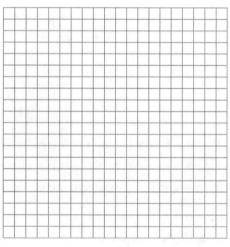

3. $\begin{cases} 4y = 11 - 3x \\ 3x + 2y = -5 \end{cases}$

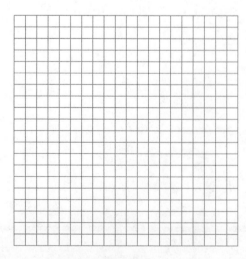

4. $\begin{cases} 15x + 28y = 420 \\ 30x + 24y = 720 \end{cases}$

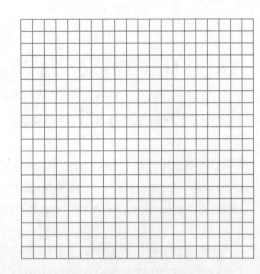

5. $\begin{cases} 3x + 2y = 6 \\ 1.5x + y = 3 \end{cases}$

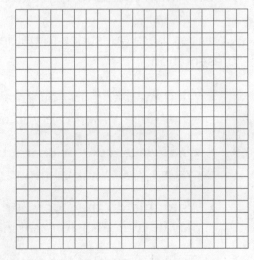

6. $\begin{cases} 4x + 3y = 27 \\ \frac{1}{3}x = 2y + 1 \end{cases}$

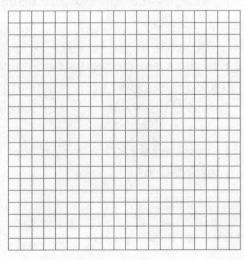

TALK the TALK 💬

How Do You Choose?

Throughout this topic, you have solved systems of linear equations through inspection of the equations, graphing, and substitution. How do you decide when each method is most efficient?

Create a presentation or a poster to illustrate your decision-making process when you solve a system of linear equations.

Consider these questions to guide the content of your presentation.

- **What methods do you know for solving systems of linear equations? When can you use each one?**

- **What visual cues or characteristics of the equations in the system of linear equations guide your decision?**

- **What role do the slope and *y*-intercept of the equations play in your decision-making?**

- **Does the form of the equations in the system affect your choice?**

Use the systems of linear equations you solved throughout this lesson to support your reasoning and as examples of when you would choose each solution method.

List at least three key points that you want to include in your presentation.

1.

2.

3.

Assignment

Write

Explain why you may need to use substitution to solve a system of linear equations if you already solved the system by graphing.

Remember

To most efficiently solve a system of linear equations, look at the equations in the system. The coefficients and constants in the equations can help you choose the best solution method.

Practice

1. Rent-A-Wreck rents cars for $50 a day, plus $0.25 per mile. Drive-A-Lemon rents cars for $40 a day, plus $0.30 per mile.

   a. Write a system of equations that best models the cost of renting a car from each business. Let x represent the number of miles, and let y represent the cost per day.

   b. Solve the system using your chosen method.

   c. Interpret the solution of the linear system in terms of the problem situation.

   d. In what situations would you recommend renting a car from Rent-A-Wreck?

2. Rika works in the perfume department at Hoover's Department Store. She is giving away samples of a new fragrance and a new scented hand lotion to customers that pass by her station. She is required to hand out a total of 114 samples during her shift. She has already handed out 36 samples, which represents $\frac{1}{3}$ of the number of fragrance samples and $\frac{1}{4}$ of the number of hand lotion samples that she must hand out.

   a. Write a system of equations for this problem situation. Let x represent the number of fragrance samples, and let y represent the number of hand lotion samples.

   b. Solve the system using your chosen method.

   c. Interpret the solution of the linear system in terms of the problem situation.

3. Belinda works in the kitchen department of Hoover's Department Store. As part of the store's effort to reward their customers, Belinda is handing out coupons for two different types of silverware packages. The first coupon is for the classic set, and the second coupon is for the modern set. On one particular day, she has handed out a total of 144 coupons, which represents $\frac{1}{2}$ of the number of classic coupons and $\frac{3}{4}$ of the number of modern coupons. She handed out twice as many coupons for the modern set as she did for the classic set.

   a. Write a system of equations for this problem situation. Let x represent the number of coupons for the classic set, and let y represent the number of coupons for the modern set.

   b. Solve the system using your chosen method.

   c. Interpret the solution of the linear system in terms of the problem situation.

4. Ms. Jupino is the leader of her daughter's Girl Scout troop, which has 15 members. The troop would like to take an end-of-year field trip to an amusement park, but they need to raise money for the trip. They have researched different fundraising companies and have narrowed their search down to two. Both companies have fundraising opportunities that involve selling coupon booklets. The first company, Great Ideas, will donate $50 if the troop uses their company, plus the girls will make $10 for every booklet that they sell. The second company, Paper and Things, will donate $275 if the troop uses their company, plus the girls will make $7 for every booklet that they sell.

   a. Write a system of equations that represents the problem situation. Define your variables.

   b. Solve the system using your chosen method.

   c. Interpret the solution of the linear system in terms of the problem situation.

   d. Which company would you recommend the girls use? Explain.

5. Solve each system using your chosen method.

   a. $\begin{cases} 3x - 2y = 9 \\ -3x + y = -12 \end{cases}$

   b. $\begin{cases} 5x - 3y = 30 \\ \frac{5}{3}x - 10 = y \end{cases}$

   c. $\begin{cases} 2x + 6y = 12 \\ x + 3y = 4 \end{cases}$

   d. $\begin{cases} 2x + 2y = 4 \\ 2y = x - 17 \end{cases}$

Stretch

You can also use inequalities to solve problems that involve systems. Suppose the Community Center director who was planning the skating party has a budget of $895.

Write and solve an inequality to determine the number of students who can be invited to each of the three locations. Then interpret each solution in terms of the problem situation.

Review

1. Write and solve each system using substitution.

   a. You want to make your grandmother's recipe for fudge. You have all the ingredients except sugar and chocolate. You have $10.50 to spend on the sugar and chocolate. Sugar costs $1.40 per pound, and chocolate costs $8.40 per pound. Your grandmother's recipe calls for 4 times as much sugar as chocolate. How much sugar and chocolate can you buy?

   b. Your piggy bank contains 68 coins, made up of quarters and dimes. The piggy bank gives a digital readout of the total amount of money that it contains. The display reads $13.10. How many quarters and dimes do you have?

2. Solve each equation.

   a. $4(2x + 1) - 3(x - 2) = 10 + 5x$

   b. $10(x - 2) + 15 = 8x + 7$

   c. $2(x + 3) + 2 = 2(x + 4)$

   d. $3(2x + 2) = 6(x + 6)$

Systems of Linear Equations Summary

KEY TERMS

- point of intersection
- break-even point
- system of linear equations
- solution of a linear system

- consistent system
- inconsistent system
- standard form of a linear equation
- substitution method

LESSON 1 | **Crossing Paths**

The **point of intersection** is the point at which two lines cross on a coordinate plane. When one line represents the cost of an item and the other line represents the income from selling the item, the point of intersection is called the **break-even point**.

The point where two linear graphs intersect represents the solution to both of the equations that describe the graphs.

For example, Jenna plans to sell hats that she knits at the local craft fair. The cost for a booth at the fair is $100 and each hat costs her $5 to make. She plans to sell each hat for $25. Jenna's total cost for selling the hats can be represented by the equation $y = 100 + 5x$, while her income can be represented by the equation $y = 25x$. The graph of each equation is shown. The point of intersection is (5, 125). This point represents the break-even point because it will cost Jenna $125 to make 5 hats, and her income from selling 5 hats is $125.

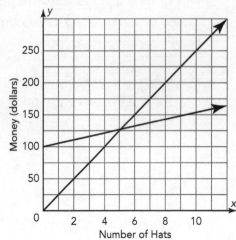

The Road Less Traveled

When two or more linear equations define a relationship between quantities, they form a **system of linear equations**. The **solution of a linear system** is an ordered pair (x, y) that is a solution to both equations in the system. Graphically, the solution is the point of intersection, the point at which two or more lines cross.

A system of linear equations is written with a brace as shown:

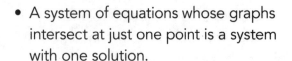

$$\begin{cases} y = x + 5 \\ y = -2x + 8 \end{cases}$$

You can determine the solution to this system by graphing the equations. The point of intersection is the solution to the system.

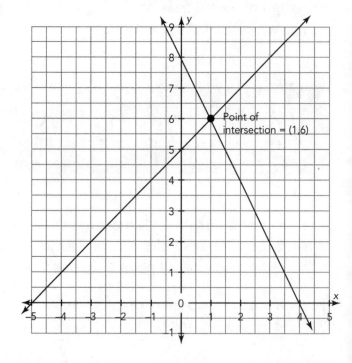

Point of intersection = (1,6)

- A system of equations whose graphs intersect at just one point is a system with one solution.

- A system of equations that has parallel line graphs is a system with no solutions. These equations will have equal slopes, but different y-intercepts.

- A system of equations that has identical graphs is a system with infinitely many solutions.

The **standard form of a linear equation** can be written as $ax + by = c$, where a, b, and c are constants, and a and b are not both zero.

Sometimes a system of equations may not be accurately solved using graphs. There is an algebraic method that can be used called the substitution method. The **substitution method** is a process of solving a system of equations by substituting a variable in one equation with an equivalent expression.

For example, consider the system of equations.

$$\begin{cases} 1.25x + 1.05y = 30 \\ \qquad\quad y = 8x \end{cases}$$

Step 1:   To use the substitution method, begin by choosing one equation and isolating the variable. This will be considered the first equation. Because $y = 8x$ is in slope-intercept form, use this as the first equation.

Step 2:   Now, substitute the expression equal to the isolated variable into the second equation. Substitute $8x$ for y in the equation $1.25x + 1.05y = 30$. Write the new equation: $1.25x + 1.05(8x) = 30$.

Step 3:   Solve the new equation.

$$1.25x + 8.40x = 30$$
$$9.65x = 30$$
$$x \approx 3.1$$

Now, substitute the value for x into $y = 8x$ to determine the value for y.

$$y \approx 8(3.1) \approx 24.8$$

Step 4:   Check your solution by substituting the values for both variables into the original system to show that they make both equations true.

When a system has no solution, the equation resulting from the substitution step has no solution. When a system has infinite solutions, the equation resulting from the substitution step has infinite solutions.

Rockin' Roller Rinks

To most efficiently solve a system of linear equations, look at the equations in the system. The coefficients and constants in the equations can help you choose the best solution method—either through inspection of the equations, graphing, or substitution.

For example, both of the equations in this system are written in standard form, so you may choose to solve the system of equations using substitution:

$$\begin{cases} x + y = 440 \\ 5x + 8y = 3130 \end{cases}$$

However, suppose you are solving this other system of equations.

$$\begin{cases} y = 2x + 2 \\ y = x - 1 \end{cases}$$

Because both of the equations are written in slope-intercept form, you may choose to solve this system of equation using graphing.

EXPANDING NUMBER SYSTEMS

The lessons in this module connect number, equations, and geometry. You will explore the properties that define the number systems that you are familiar with and then learn about a new system. You will develop an understanding of the Pythagorean Theorem and its converse and then apply those theorems to solve real-world problems.

The Real Number System

Pi is probably one of the most famous numbers in all of history. As a decimal, it goes on and on forever without repeating.

Module 4: Expanding Number Systems

TOPIC 1: THE REAL NUMBER SYSTEM

In this topic, students build onto their knowledge of number systems to include the set of irrational numbers. Students will review writing fractions as decimals and then write repeating decimals in fractional form. They learn that numbers that are not rational are called irrational; the decimal form of irrational numbers does not terminate or repeat. Students also use square root and cube root symbols to express the solutions to equations of the form $x^2 = p$ and $x^3 = p$, where p is a positive rational number.

Where have we been?

The first lesson of this topic provides students the opportunity to recall number sets they should already know before learning about properties of each set and about irrational numbers. Students also review additive identity, additive inverse, multiplicative identity, and multiplicative inverse.

Where are we going?

This topic prepares students to solve problems with non-perfect squares in the next topic, *Pythagorean Theorem*. Students need to understand that mathematics is not arbitrary; every new number system they learn results from a need for a number that is not in the current known number systems. Studying identities, inverses, and closure helps students understand that each number system has unique properties.

Using Perfect Squares to Estimate Square Roots

The square root of a number can be estimated using the square roots of perfect squares. For example, $\sqrt{10}$ is between $\sqrt{9}$, which is 3, and $\sqrt{16}$, which is 4. So, $3 < \sqrt{10} < 4$.

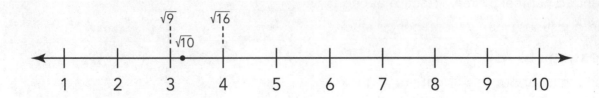

Myth: Cramming for an exam is just as good as spaced practice for long-term retention.

Everyone has been there. You have a big test tomorrow, but you've been so busy that you haven't had time to study. So you had to learn it all in one night. You may have gotten a decent grade on the test. However, did you to remember the material a week, month, or year later?

The honest answer is, "probably not." That's because long-term memory is designed to retain useful information. How does your brain know if a memory is "useful" or not? One way is the frequency in which you encounter a piece of information. If you only see something once (like during cramming), then your brain doesn't deem those memories as important. However, if you sporadically come across the same information over time, then it's probably important. To optimize retention, encourage your student to periodically study the same information over expanding intervals of time.

#mathmythbusted

Talking Points

You can further support your student's learning by resisting the urge, as long as possible, to get to the answer in a problem that your student is working on. Students are encountering irrational numbers formally for the first time in this topic. They will need time and space to struggle with all the implications of working with this expanded number system. Practice asking good questions when your student is stuck.

Questions to Ask

- Let's think about this. What are all the things you know?
- What do you need to find out?
- How can you model this problem?

Key Terms

irrational numbers
Decimals that represent irrational numbers cannot be written as fractions in the form $\frac{a}{b}$, where a and b are integers and b is not equal to 0.

real numbers
Combining the set of rational numbers and the set of irrational numbers produces the set of real numbers.

So Many Numbers, So Little Time

Number Sort

1

WARM UP

Represent each number as a fraction, decimal, and percent.

1. $\frac{5}{8}$
2. 105%
3. 0.55

LEARNING GOALS

- Review and analyze numbers.
- Determine similarities and differences among various numbers.
- Sort numbers by their similarities and rationalize the differences between groups of numbers.

You have been using numbers to count and perform calculations for nearly your entire life. If someone were to ask you to define the word *number*, could you do it? How can you identify and organize different types of numbers?

Gimme, Gimme, Gimme!

1. List three numbers that are positive numbers.

2. List three numbers that are between 0 and 1.

3. Give one example of a percent.

4. Give one example of a fraction.

5. Give one example of a mixed number.

Searching for patterns and sorting objects into different groups can provide valuable insights.

1. Cut out the 30 number cards located at the end of the lesson. Then, analyze and sort the numbers into different groups. You may group the numbers in any way you feel is appropriate. However, you must sort the numbers into more than one group.

   In the space provided, record the information for each of your groups.

   - Name each group of numbers.
   - List the numbers in each group.
   - Provide a rationale for why you created each group.

> Are any of the types of numbers shared among your groups? Or are they unique to each group?

2. Compare your groupings with your classmates' groupings. Create a list of the different types of numbers you noticed.

ACTIVITY 1.2 Taking a Closer Look at the Number Sort

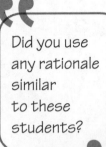

> Did you use any rationale similar to these students?

In this activity, you will analyze the ways in which other students grouped the numbers and their rationale.

1. Lauren grouped these numbers together.

   $0.\overline{91}$, $-\frac{2}{3}$, $\frac{100}{11}$, $1.523232323...$, $-0.\overline{3}$

   Why do you think Lauren put these numbers in the same group?

2. Zane and Tanya provided the same rationale for one of their groups of numbers. However, the numbers in their groups were different.

   Zane

   $|-3|$, $\sqrt{100}$, $627{,}513$, 3.21×10^{12}, 4^2, $|2|$

   When I simplify each number, it is a positive integer.

   Tanya

   20%, $\sqrt{100}$, $627{,}513$, 3.21×10^{12}, 4^2, $|2|$, 212%

   Each of these numbers represents a positive integer.

   Who is correct? Explain your reasoning.

3. Tim grouped these numbers together.

   $-\frac{3}{8}$, -101, -6.41, $-\frac{2}{3}$, $-\sqrt{9}$, -1, $-0.\overline{3}$

   What rationale could Tim provide?

4. Isaac grouped all the numbers between 0 and 1.

   Identify all of the numbers that satisfy Isaac's reasoning.

Clip all your numbers together and keep them. You'll need them later in this topic.

5. Lezlee grouped these numbers together.

   -6.41, $\frac{100}{11}$, $1.523232323...$, 212%, $6\frac{1}{4}$

   What could Lezlee name the group? Explain your reasoning.

TALK the TALK

Match 'Em Up

Match each group of numbers with the appropriate group name.
Explain your reasoning for each.

1. 1.5, $\frac{5}{3}$, −212.2, 16.12, $-\frac{6}{5}$

   A. Negative Numbers

2. $-\frac{6}{3}$, −200, −0.5, −50.313..., −1

   B. Integers

3. −0.75, 20%, 3.5%, −0.005, $\frac{1}{5}$, $-\frac{1}{2}$

   C. Improper Fractions

4. −10, 50, 2100, 10^2, 5^3, 400%, 0

   D. Numbers Between −1 and 1

π	0.25	$-\dfrac{3}{8}$
-101	20%	$\lvert -3 \rvert$
-6.41	$0.\overline{91}$	$\sqrt{100}$
627,513	0.001	$-\dfrac{2}{3}$
0	$\sqrt{2}$	3.21×10^{12}
1,000,872.0245	4^2	0.5%
$-\sqrt{9}$	$\lvert 2 \rvert$	$\dfrac{100}{11}$
$-\sqrt{2}$	1.523232323…	-1
$-0.\overline{3}$	1.0205×10^{-23}	$\sqrt{\dfrac{9}{16}}$
212%	$6\dfrac{1}{4}$	$\sqrt{0.25}$

Assignment

Write

Describe the characteristics that you look for in numbers when you are grouping them.

Remember

Numbers can be grouped in a variety of ways according to their characteristics. Sometimes, a number may fit into multiple groupings.

Practice

Ling's teacher gives her students the list of numbers to sort.

$$5\%, \ -3^3, \ \sqrt{0.36}, \ 2.14, \ |-6|, \ \tfrac{12}{18}, \ 15, \ \overline{4}, \ -\tfrac{16}{3}, \ \pi, \ \sqrt{\tfrac{4}{10}}, \ 8003.876, \ 0.2\%, \ -\sqrt{25}, \ 3\tfrac{1}{3}$$

1. Ling groups the following numbers together with the rationale that they are all repeating decimals.

$$\tfrac{12}{18}, \ -\tfrac{16}{3}, \ 3\tfrac{1}{3}$$

   Do you agree with Ling's grouping? Explain your reasoning.

2. Ling groups the following numbers together with the rationale that they are all positive numbers.

$$5\%, \ \sqrt{0.36}, \ 2.14, \ |-6|, \ \tfrac{12}{18}, \ 15, \ \sqrt{4}, \ \pi, \ \sqrt{\tfrac{4}{10}}, \ 8003.876, \ 0.2\%, \ 3\tfrac{1}{3}$$

   Do you agree with Ling's grouping? Explain your reasoning.

3. Ling groups the following numbers together with the rationale they are all rational numbers.

$$\tfrac{12}{18}, \ 15, \ \sqrt{4}, \ -\tfrac{16}{3}, \ 3\tfrac{1}{3}$$

   Do you agree with Ling's grouping? Explain your reasoning.

Stretch

What is so interesting about the fraction $\frac{16}{64}$? This fraction is called a *digit-canceling fraction*, since you can cross out the common digit in the numerator and denominator and the value of the fraction remains the same.

$$\frac{1\cancel{6}}{\cancel{6}4} = \frac{1}{4}$$

There are exactly four digit-canceling fractions with two-digit numerators and two-digit denominators that are less than one, not counting examples such as $\frac{30}{50}$, where you cross out the zeros. Research these special fractions and identify the other three.

Review

1. A company makes and sells flags with various seasonal themes. It costs $12 to manufacture each flag, and there is a set-up cost of $200 for a new design. The company sells the flags to home improvement stores for $20 per flag.

   a. Write a system of equations to represent this situation.

   b. What is the break-even point for making and selling flags? Show your work.

2. The school dance team is raising money by charging admission to the spring ballet. They charge $2 for each student ticket and $5 for each adult ticket, with a goal to raise $510 from ticket sales.

   a. If they sell 50 student tickets, how many adult tickets do they need to sell to reach their goal?

   b. If they sell 30 adult tickets, how many student tickets to they need to sell to reach their goal?

3. Solve each equation.

   a. $3(n - 5) = 7 - 2(n + 1)$

   b. $2(5k + 8) = 4(k + 4)$

Rational Decisions

2

Rational and Irrational Numbers

WARM UP

1. Place $\frac{5}{8}$ and $\frac{6}{25}$ on the number line.

2. Rewrite $\frac{5}{8}$ as a decimal.

3. Rewrite $\frac{6}{25}$ as a decimal.

4. Place the decimal equivalents of $\frac{5}{8}$ and $\frac{6}{25}$ on the number line.

5. Are your strategies to plot fractions the same or different than your strategies to plot decimals?

LEARNING GOALS

- Determine under which operations (addition, subtraction, multiplication, and division) number sets are closed.
- Recognize that all numbers can be written as decimals and that rational numbers can be written as terminating or repeating decimals.
- Write repeating decimals as fractions.
- Identify numbers that are not rational as irrational numbers.

KEY TERMS

- natural numbers
- whole numbers
- integers
- closed
- rational numbers
- irrational numbers
- terminating decimal
- repeating decimal
- bar notation

You have learned about rational numbers. How are they different from other number sets?

A Science Experiment

A science class is conducting an experiment to see how the weight of a paper airplane affects the distance that it can fly. The class is divided into two groups. Group 1 measures the distance the airplane flew in feet. Group 2 measures the distance in meters, and then converts those measurements to feet. The results of the experiment are shown in the table.

Because paper is typically sold in 500-sheet quantities, a paper's weight is determined by the weight of 500 sheets of the paper.

Type of Paper	Group 1 Measurements	Group 2 Converted Measurements
20-pound paper	$13\frac{7}{8}$ feet	13.9 feet
28-pound paper	$14\frac{3}{8}$ feet	14.4 feet

1. The science class needs to compare the measurements between the two groups for each type of paper.

   a. Write $13\frac{7}{8}$ as a decimal.   b.   Write $14\frac{3}{8}$ as a decimal.

2. On the number line shown, graph the Group 1 measurements written as decimals and the Group 2 converted measurements.

3. Use the number line to determine which group's paper airplane traveled farther for the 20-pound paper and for the 28-pound paper. Write your answers using complete sentences.

The first set of numbers that you learned when you were very young was the set of *counting numbers*, or *natural numbers*. **Natural numbers** consists of the numbers that you use to count objects: {1, 2, 3, …}.

In the set {1, 2, 3, …}, the dots at the end of the list mean that the list of numbers goes on without end.

1. Consider the set of natural numbers.

   a. Why do you think this set of numbers is sometimes referred to as the set of counting numbers?

   b. How many natural numbers are there?

   c. Does it make sense to ask which natural number is the greatest? Explain why or why not.

You have also used the set of *whole numbers*. **Whole numbers** are made up of the set of natural numbers and the number 0, the additive identity.

2. Why is zero the additive identity?

3. Explain why having zero makes the set of whole numbers more useful than the set of natural numbers.

Another set of numbers is the set of **integers**, which is a set that includes all of the whole numbers and their additive inverses.

4. **What is the additive inverse of a number?**

5. **Represent the set of integers. Use set notation and remember to use three dots to show that the numbers go on without end in both directions.**

6. **Does it make sense to ask which integer is the least or which integer is the greatest? Explain why or why not.**

When you perform an operation such as addition or multiplication on the numbers in a set, the operation could produce a defined value that is also in the set. When this happens, the set is said to be **closed** under the operation.

The set of integers is said to be closed under the operation of addition. This means that for every two integers a and b, the sum $a + b$ is also an integer.

7. **Determine if each set of numbers is closed under the given operation. Provide an example to support your response.**

   a. **Are the natural numbers closed under addition?**

   b. **Are the whole numbers closed under addition?**

c. Are the natural numbers closed under subtraction?

d. Are the whole numbers closed under subtraction?

e. Are the integers closed under subtraction?

f. Are any of these sets closed under multiplication?

g. Are any of these sets closed under division?

Is the product of two natural numbers always a natural number? What about their quotient?

In previous courses, you have learned about the additive inverse, the multiplicative inverse, the additive identity, and the multiplicative identity.

8. Consider each set of numbers and determine if the set has an additive identity, additive inverse, multiplicative identity, or a multiplicative inverse. Explain your reasoning for each.

a. the set of natural numbers

A set of numbers must include an identity to also include the related inverse.

b. the set of whole numbers

c. the set of integers.

ACTIVITY 2.2 | Rational Numbers

New number systems arise out of a need to create new types of numbers. If you divide two integers, what type of number have you created? You've created a *rational number*.

A **rational number** is a number that can be written in the form $\frac{a}{b}$, where *a* and *b* are both integers and *b* is not equal to 0.

1. Consider how each set of numbers is related. Answer each question and provide an example to support your response.

   a. Does the set of rational numbers include the set of whole numbers?

   b. Does the set of rational numbers include the set of integers?

   c. Does the set of rational numbers include all fractions?

   d. Does the set of rational numbers include all decimals?

2. Determine if the set of rational numbers is closed under the given operation. Provide an example to support your response.

   a. addition

   b. subtraction

   c. multiplication

   d. division

3. Determine whether the set of rational numbers contains the identity or inverse given. Provide an example to support your response.

   a. additive identity

   b. multiplicative identity

   c. additive inverse

   d. multiplicative inverse

ACTIVITY
2.3

Converting Repeated
Decimals to Fractions

You have seen some numbers such as π that are not rational numbers. There are other numbers that are not rational numbers. For example, $\sqrt{2}$ and $\sqrt{5}$, which are called square roots, cannot be written in the form $\frac{a}{b}$, where a and b are both integers.

As you will see in the next lesson, even though you often approximate square roots using a decimal, most square roots are *irrational numbers*. Because all rational numbers can be written as $\frac{a}{b}$, where a and b are integers, they can be written as *terminating decimals* (e.g., $\frac{1}{4} = 0.25$) or *repeating decimals* (e.g., $\frac{1}{6} = 0.1666...$).

All other decimals are **irrational numbers,** because these decimals cannot be written as fractions in the form $\frac{a}{b}$, where a and b are integers and b is not equal to 0.

1. **Convert the fraction to a decimal by dividing the numerator by the denominator. Continue to divide until you see a pattern. Describe the pattern.**

    $\frac{1}{3} = 3\overline{)1}$

Does "repeating decimal" mean that only one digit repeats?

2. Order the fractions from least to greatest. Then, convert each fraction to a decimal by dividing the numerator by the denominator. Continue to divide until you see a pattern.

a. $\frac{5}{6} = 6\overline{)5}$

b. $\frac{2}{9} = 9\overline{)2}$

c. $\frac{9}{11} = 11\overline{)9}$

d. $\frac{3}{22} = 22\overline{)3}$

3. Explain why these decimal representations are called repeating decimals.

A **terminating decimal** is a decimal that has a finite number of non-zero digits. For instance, the decimal 0.125 is a terminating decimal, because it has three non-zero digits. 0.125 is the decimal equivalent of $\frac{1}{8}$, because 1 divided by 8 is equal to 0.125.

A **repeating decimal** is a decimal with digits that repeat in sets of one or more. You can use two different notations to represent repeating decimals. One notation shows one set of digits that repeats with a bar over the repeating digits. This is called **bar notation**.

$$\frac{1}{3} = 0.\overline{3} \qquad\qquad \frac{7}{22} = 0.3\overline{18}$$

Another notation shows two sets of the digits that repeat with dots to indicate repetition. You saw these dots as well when describing the number sets in the previous lesson.

$$\frac{1}{3} = 0.33\ldots \qquad\qquad \frac{7}{22} = 0.31818\ldots$$

Do you write $\frac{7}{22}$ as 0.318... or as 0.3181...?

4. Write each repeating decimal from **Question 2** using both notations.

   a. $\frac{5}{6}$

   b. $\frac{2}{9}$

   c. $\frac{9}{11}$

   d. $\frac{3}{22}$

Some repeating decimals represent common fractions, such as $\frac{1}{3}$, $\frac{2}{3}$, and $\frac{1}{6}$, and are used often enough that you can recognize the fraction by its decimal representation. For most repeating decimals, though, you cannot recognize the fraction that the decimal represents. For example, can you tell which fraction is represented by the repeating decimal 0.44… or $0.\overline{09}$? In these cases, you need a method for converting from a repeating decimal to a fraction.

WORKED EXAMPLE

You can use algebra to determine the fraction that is represented by the repeating decimal 0.44... . First, write an equation by setting the decimal equal to a variable that will represent the fraction.

$$w = 0.44...$$

Next, write another equation by multiplying both sides of the equation by a power of 10. The exponent on the power of 10 is equal to the number of decimal places until the decimal begins to repeat. In this case, the decimal begins repeating after 1 decimal place, so the exponent on the power of 10 is 1. Because $10^1 = 10$, multiply both sides by 10.

$$10w = 4.4...$$

Then, subtract the equations.

$$10w = 4.44...$$
$$\underline{-w = 0.44...}$$
$$9w = 4$$

Finally, solve the equation by dividing both sides by 9.

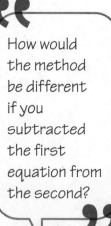

How would the method be different if you subtracted the first equation from the second?

5. Identify the fraction represented by the repeating decimal 0.44....

6. Use this method to write the fraction that represents each repeating decimal.

   a. 0.55...

   b. 0.0505...

   c. $0.\overline{12}$

   d. $0.\overline{36}$

TALK the TALK

Closing Time

Complete the table to summarize the number sets you have learned about and reviewed in this lesson. Provide examples for each number set to address the four operations of addition, subtraction, multiplication, and division.

Number Set	Description	Closed under these operations. Provide examples.	Not closed under these operations. Provide examples.
Natural Numbers			
Whole Numbers			
Integers			
Rational Numbers			

Assignment

Write

Match each term with the number that best represents that term.

1. Irrational number
2. Terminating decimal
3. Repeating decimal
4. Bar notation

a. $\frac{1}{2} = 0.5$
b. $0.\overline{3}$
c. π
d. $\frac{5}{9} = 0.555...$

Remember

All rational numbers can be written as terminating or repeating decimals. A repeating decimal is a decimal in which one or more digits repeat indefinitely. A terminating decimal is a decimal that has a finite number of non-zero digits.

Practice

1. Marcy Green is the manager for her high school softball team. She is in charge of equipment, as well as recording statistics for each player on the team. The table shows some batting statistics for the four infielders on the team during the first eight games of the season.

Player	At Bats	Hits
Brynn Thomas	36	16
Hailey Smith	32	12
Serena Rodrigez	33	11
Kata Lee	35	14

a. In order to compare the batting averages of the players, Marcy must convert all of the ratios of hits to at-bats to decimal form. Determine the batting averagev for each player, and continue to divide until you see a pattern. Write your answers using both dots and bar notation for repeating decimals.

b. Write the batting averages of the players in order from lowest to highest. Who has the best batting average so far?

c. Marcy keeps track of how many home runs each infielder hits on the high school softball team. For each player, the fraction of home runs per at-bats is given in decimal form. Determine how many home runs each player has had so far.
   - Brynn: $0.0\overline{5}$
   - Hailey: 0.15625
   - Serena: $0.\overline{12}$
   - Kata: 0.2

2. Tell whether the numbers in each problem are natural numbers, whole numbers, integers, or rational numbers, and state whether those numbers are closed under the operation used.

   a. $-12 \div (-5)$ b. $\frac{3}{7} + (-\frac{3}{8})$

3. Convert each fraction to a decimal. State whether the fraction is equivalent to a terminating or repeating decimal.

a. $1\frac{2}{5}$

b. $\frac{5}{12}$

c. $\frac{5}{8}$

d. $\frac{8}{11}$

4. Write each repeating decimal as a fraction.

a. $0.\overline{8}$

b. 0.5454...

c. 0.0777...

d. $0.\overline{185}$

Stretch

Numbers can be operated on using operations other than addition, subtraction, multiplication, and division. Let's define a new operation called $\bigstar$, where $2 \bigstar 4 = 2^2 \div 4$ and $6 \bigstar 3 = 6^6 \div 3$. Is the set of whole numbers closed under the operation $\bigstar$? That is, does $a \bigstar b$, where a and b are whole numbers, always result in a whole number? Justify your claim.

Review

1. Provide a rationale for each grouping of numbers.

a. $3, \frac{75}{5}, -18, -\frac{30}{3}$

b. $25\%, \frac{7}{11}, 0.912912..., 0.5\%$

2. Write and solve a system of equations for each problem situation. Interpret the solution in terms of the context.

a. Pedro has 97 athlete cards. In his collection, he has 39 more baseball player cards than football player cards. How many of each type of card does Pedro have?

b. The Ryans are researching venues for their family reunion. The Picnic Place charges $150 to reserve a picnic shelter and $20 per hour to use the shelter. Totally Tents charges $300 for the rental and setup of a tent and $10 per hour to use their land. When would the cost be the same at both The Picnic Place and Totally Tents? What is that cost?

3. Solve each equation.

a. $6(x + 3) = 3(2x + 5) - 3$

b. $-5(x + 4) = 2(x - 10)$

What Are Those?!

The Real Numbers

3

Warm Up

Rewrite each fraction as a decimal.

1. $\frac{1}{2}$

2. $\frac{1}{4}$

3. $\frac{1}{3}$

4. $\frac{1}{9}$

5. How are the decimals of the first two fractions different from the decimals of the second two fractions?

LEARNING GOALS

- Identify irrational numbers.
- Identify the square roots of numbers that are not perfect squares and the cube roots of numbers that are not perfect cubes as irrational numbers.
- Use rational approximations of irrational numbers to compare the size of irrational numbers.
- Locate irrational numbers on a number line and estimate their values.
- Classify numbers within the set of real numbers.

KEY TERMS

- perfect cube
- cube root
- index
- real numbers
- Venn diagram

You have learned about rational numbers and about irrational numbers. In this lesson, you will learn about some special irrationals. Putting the set of rational numbers and the set of irrational numbers together forms the set of real numbers.

An Irrational Assignment?

1. Write an irrational number.

2. Have a classmate verify whether or not your number is an irrational number. Explain why your number is or is not an irrational number.

Understanding Square Roots

Recall that a square root is one of two equal factors of a given number. Every positive number has two square roots: a positive square root and a negative square root.

For instance, 5 is a square root of 25 because (5)(5) = 25. Also, −5 is a square root of 25 because (−5)(−5) = 25. The positive square root is called the principal square root. In this course, you will only use the principal square root.

The symbol $\sqrt{}$ is called a radical, and it is used to indicate square roots. The radicand is the quantity under a radical.

radical

radicand

$\sqrt{25}$

This is read as "the square root of 25," or as "radical 25."

Remember that a perfect square is a number that is equal to the product of a distinct factor multiplied by itself. In the example above, 25 is a perfect square because it is equal to the product of 5 multiplied by itself.

1. **Write the square root for each perfect square.**

   a. $\sqrt{1}$ = _____

   b. $\sqrt{4}$ = _____

   c. $\sqrt{9}$ = _____

   d. $\sqrt{16}$ = _____

   e. $\sqrt{25}$ = _____

   f. $\sqrt{36}$ = _____

   g. $\sqrt{49}$ = _____

   h. $\sqrt{64}$ = _____

   i. $\sqrt{81}$ = _____

   j. $\sqrt{100}$ = _____

   k. $\sqrt{121}$ = _____

   l. $\sqrt{144}$ _____

   m. $\sqrt{169}$ = _____

   n. $\sqrt{196}$ _____

   o. $\sqrt{225}$ _____

2. What is the value of $\sqrt{0}$? Explain your reasoning.

3. Notice that the square root of each expression in Question 1 resulted in a rational number. Do you think that the square root of every number will result in a rational number? Explain your reasoning.

4. Use a calculator to evaluate each square root. Show each answer to the hundred-thousandth.

a. $\sqrt{25}$ = _____   b. $\sqrt{0.25}$ = _____   c. $\sqrt{250}$ = _____

d. $\sqrt{5}$ = _____   e. $\sqrt{-25}$ = _____   f. $\sqrt{2.5}$ = _____

g. $\sqrt{2500}$ = _____   h. $\sqrt{676}$ = _____   i. $\sqrt{6760}$ = _____

j. $\sqrt{6.76}$ = _____   k. $\sqrt{67.6}$ = _____   l. $\sqrt{-6.76}$ = _____

5. What do you notice about the square roots of rational numbers? Justify your response.

6. Is the square root of a whole number always a rational number? Justify your response.

7. Is the square root of a decimal always an irrational number?

8. Consider Penelope and Martin's statements and reasoning.

Penelope

I know that 144 is a perfect square. Therefore, $\sqrt{144}$ is a rational number. I can move the decimal point to the left, and $\sqrt{14.4}$ and $\sqrt{1.44}$ will also be rational numbers.

Likewise, I can move the decimal point to the right, so $\sqrt{1440}$ and $\sqrt{14,400}$ will also be rational numbers.

Martin

I know that 144 is a perfect square. Therefore, $\sqrt{144}$ is a rational number. I can move the decimal point two places to the right or left to get another perfect square rational number. In other words, $\sqrt{1.44}$ and $\sqrt{14,400}$ will also be rational numbers.

Moving the decimal point two places at a time is like multiplying or dividing by 100. The square root of 100 is 10, which is also a rational number.

Who is correct? Explain your reasoning.

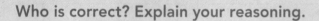

Estimating with Square Roots

The square root of most numbers is not an integer. You can *estimate* the square root of a number that is not a perfect square. Begin by determining the two perfect squares closest to the radicand so that one perfect square is less than the radicand, and one perfect square is greater than the radicand. Then consider the location of the expression on a number line and use approximation to estimate the value.

WORKED EXAMPLE

To estimate $\sqrt{10}$ to the nearest tenth, identify the closest perfect square less than 10 and the closest perfect square greater than 10.

The closest perfect square less than 10:	The square root you are estimating:	The closest perfect square greater than 10:
9	$\sqrt{10}$	16

You know:

$$\sqrt{9} = 3 \qquad\qquad\qquad \sqrt{16} = 4$$

This means that the estimate of $\sqrt{10}$ is between 3 and 4.

Locate each square root on a number line. The approximate location of $\sqrt{10}$ is closer to 3 than to 4 when plotted.

Think about the location of $\sqrt{10}$ in relation to the values of 3 and 4.

Therefore, $\sqrt{10} \approx 3.2$.

The symbol $\approx$ means approximately equal to.

---

1. **Calculate the square of 3.2 to determine if it is a good estimation of $\sqrt{10}$. Adjust the estimated value if necessary.**

2. Consider each expression.

$\sqrt{8}$　　　$\sqrt{91}$　　　$\sqrt{70}$　　　$\sqrt{45}$

To locate the approximation of a square root on a number line, identify the two closest perfect squares, one greater than the radicand and one less than the radicand.

a. Order the expressions from least to greatest.

b. Locate the approximation of each expression on the number line. Explain the strategy you used to plot each value.

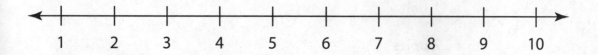

c. Estimate the value of each expression to the nearest tenth. Then, calculate the square of each approximation to determine if it is a good estimation. Adjust the estimated value, if necessary.

3. Solve each equation. Round your answer to the nearest tenth.

If $x^2 = 4$, then $x = \sqrt{4}$. Use this fact to show the solution to each equation.

a. $x^2 = 25$

b. $a^2 = 13$

c. $c^2 = 80$

d. $g^2 = 53$

In the previous activity, you investigated squares and square roots. Now, let's consider cubes and cube roots.

1. **Use unit cubes to build three different cubes with the given side lengths. Then complete the table.**

   a. **1 unit**

   b. **2 units**

   c. **3 units**

Dimensions of Each Cube	Total Number of Unit Cubes
$4 \times 4 \times 4$	

The formula for the volume of a cube is $V = s \times s \times s$, which can be written as $V = s^3$.

You just calculated the volume of 3 cubes whose side lengths were the first 3 counting numbers, $1^3 = 1$, $2^3 = 8$, and $3^3 = 27$. The numbers 1, 8, and 27 are called *perfect cubes*. A perfect cube is the cube of a whole number. For example, 64 is a perfect cube since 4 is a whole number, and $4 \times 4 \times 4 = 64$. To calculate the cube of a number, you multiply the number by itself 3 times.

2. Calculate the cubes of the first 10 whole numbers.

$1^3 =$ _____ $2^3 =$ _____

$3^3 =$ _____ $4^3 =$ _____

$5^3 =$ _____ $6^3 =$ _____

$7^3 =$ _____ $8^3 =$ _____

$9^3 =$ _____ $10^3 =$ _____

If you know the volume of a cube, you can work backwards to calculate the side lengths of the cube. For example, to determine the side lengths of a cube that has a volume of 125, you need to determine what number used as a factor 3 times will equal 125. Since 5 × 5 × 5 = 125, a side length of the cube is 5, and 5 is called the *cube root* of 125. A **cube root** is one of 3 equal factors of a number. As with the square root, the cube root also uses a radical symbol but has a 3 as an *index*: $\sqrt[3]{1}$. The **index** is the number placed above and to the left of the radical to indicate what root is being calculated.

The cube root of a number that is not a perfect cube is often an irrational number.

3. Write the cube root for each perfect cube.

$\sqrt[3]{1} =$ _____ $\sqrt[3]{8} =$ _____

$\sqrt[3]{27} =$ _____ $\sqrt[3]{64} =$ _____

$\sqrt[3]{125} =$ _____ $\sqrt[3]{216} =$ _____

$\sqrt[3]{343} =$ _____ $\sqrt[3]{512} =$ _____

$\sqrt[3]{729} =$ _____ $\sqrt[3]{1000} =$ _____

4. **What is the side length of the largest cube you can create with 729 cubes?**

5. **Will the cube root of a number always be a whole number? If not, provide an example of a cube root that is not an integer.**

Remember, the radicand is under the $\sqrt{}$.

Most numbers do not have whole numbers for their cube root. Let's estimate the cube root of a number using the same method used to estimate the square root of a number.

WORKED EXAMPLE

To estimate $\sqrt[3]{33}$ to the nearest tenth, first identify the two perfect cubes closest to the radicand. One of the perfect cubes must be less than the radicand, and the other must be greater than the radicand. Then consider the location of the expression on a number line and use approximation to estimate the value.

The closest perfect cube less than 33:	The cube root you are estimating:	The closest perfect cube greater than 33:
27	$\sqrt[3]{33}$	64

You know:
$\sqrt[3]{27} = 3$ $\sqrt[3]{64} = 4$

This means that the estimate of $\sqrt[3]{33}$ is between 3 and 4.

Locate the approximate value of $\sqrt[3]{33}$ on a number line

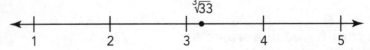

Next, choose decimals between 3 and 4, and calculate the cube of each decimal to determine which one is the best estimate.

Consider: $(3.2)(3.2)(3.2) = 32.768$
$(3.3)(3.3)(3.3) = 35.937$

Therefore, $\sqrt[3]{33} \approx 3.2$.

6. Identify the two closest perfect cubes, one greater than the radicand and one less than the radicand. Then locate the approximation of each expression on a number line. Finally, estimate each cube root to the nearest tenth.

a. $\sqrt[3]{100}$

b. $\sqrt[3]{175}$

c. $\sqrt[3]{256}$

7. Solve each equation. Round to the nearest tenth.

a. $x^3 = 27$

b. $a^3 = 31$

c. $c^3 = 512$

-101 -6.41

$-\sqrt{9}$ $-\sqrt{2}$

-1 $-\dfrac{2}{3}$

$-\dfrac{3}{8}$ -0.3

0 $|2|$

1.0205×10^{-23}

0.001 0.5%

20% 0.25

$\sqrt{0.25}$ $\sqrt{\dfrac{9}{16}}$

$0.\overline{91}$ $\sqrt{2}$

$1.523232323\ldots$

212% $|-3|$

π $6\dfrac{1}{4}$

$\dfrac{100}{11}$ $\sqrt{100}$

4^2 $627{,}513$

$1{,}000{,}872.0245$

3.21×10^{12}

TALK the TALK

Venn Diagrams and Real Numbers

Combining the set of rational numbers and the set of irrational numbers produces the set of **real numbers**. You can use a **Venn diagram** to represent how the sets within the set of real numbers are related.

1. The Venn diagram shows the relationship between the six sets of numbers shown. Write each of the 30 numbers in the appropriate section of the Venn diagram.

Real Numbers

Rational Numbers	Irrational Numbers
Integers	
Whole Numbers	
Natural Numbers	

2. Use your Venn diagram to decide whether each statement is true or false. Explain your reasoning.

   a. A whole number is sometimes an irrational number.

   b. A real number is sometimes a rational number.

   c. A whole number is always an integer.

Assignment

Write

In your own words, write a definition for *irrational number*. Use examples to help illustrate your definition.

Remember

The set of real numbers includes the set of rational numbers and the set of irrational numbers.

Practice

1. Identify each number as rational or irrational.
   a. π
   b. $\sqrt{4}$
   c. $\sqrt{18}$
   d. $\sqrt[3]{27}$
   e. $\sqrt[3]{30}$
   f. $\frac{\sqrt{1}}{\sqrt{49}}$

2. Indicate whether each real number shown is a rational number, an irrational number, an integer, a whole number, a natural number, or some combination.
   a. 35
   b. $\sqrt{17}$
   c. -6
   d. 5.25
   e. $\sqrt{81}$
   f. $-\frac{2}{3}$

3. Consider the expressions $\sqrt{15}$, $\sqrt{97}$, and $\sqrt{40}$. Locate the approximate value of each on a number line. Then, estimate each square root to the nearest tenth.

Stretch

A number called the Champernowne constant is an irrational number formed by placing the digits of successive integers together, like this:

$$0.12345678910111213141516\ldots$$

What is the 100th digit of the Champernowne constant, not including the beginning zero?

Review

1. Write each repeating decimal as a fraction.
   a. 0.888…
   b. 0.272727…

2. Tell whether the system of equations has one solution, no solutions, or infinite solutions.
   a. $\begin{cases} y = 2x - 1 \\ y = 10 + 2x \end{cases}$
   b. $\begin{cases} 3x - y = -4 \\ y = 2(1.5x + 2) \end{cases}$

3. Solve each system of equations.
   a. $\begin{cases} 4x - 3y = 26 \\ x = 5y + 15 \end{cases}$
   b. $\begin{cases} 7x - 3y = -22 \\ 5x - 3y = -14 \end{cases}$

The Real Number System Summary

KEY TERMS

- natural numbers
- whole numbers
- integers
- closed
- rational numbers
- irrational numbers
- terminating decimal
- repeating decimal
- bar notation
- perfect cube
- cube root
- index
- real numbers
- Venn diagram

LESSON 1

So Many Numbers, So Little Time

Numbers can be grouped in a variety of ways according to their characteristics. Sometimes, a number may fit into multiple groupings. For example, $-\frac{3}{4}$ is both a fraction and a negative number. The number 27 can be grouped with whole numbers and with integers.

LESSON 2

Rational Decisions

The set of **natural numbers**, consists of the numbers that you use to count objects: {1, 2, 3, 4, 5, …}. The set of **whole numbers** is made up of the set of natural numbers and the number 0, the additive identity. Another set of numbers is the set of **integers**, which is a set that includes all of the whole numbers and their additive inverses:
{…, −3, −2, −1, 0, 1, 2, 3, …}

When you perform an operation such as addition or multiplication on the numbers in a set, the operation could produce a defined value that is also in the set. When this happens, the set is said to be **closed** under the operation. The set of integers is said to be closed under the operation of addition. This means that for every two integers a and b, the sum $a + b$ is also an integer.

A **rational number** is a number that can be written in the form $\frac{a}{b}$, where a and b are both integers and b is not equal to 0. A rational number can be written as either a terminating or repeating decimal. All other decimals are **irrational numbers**, because these decimals cannot be written as fractions in the form $\frac{a}{b}$, where a and b are integers and b is not equal to 0.

A **terminating decimal** is a decimal that has a finite number of non-zero digits $\left(\text{e.g.,} \frac{1}{8} = 0.125\right)$. A **repeating decimal** is a decimal with digits that repeat in sets of one or more. You can use two different notations to represent repeating decimals. One notation is **bar notation**, which shows one set of digits that repeats with a bar over the repeating digits $\left(\text{e.g.,} \frac{1}{3} = 0.\overline{3}\right)$. Another notation shows two sets of digits that repeat with dots to indicate repetition $\left(\text{e.g.,} \frac{1}{3} = 0.33...\right)$.

You can use algebra to determine the fraction that is represented by a repeating decimal.

For example, write the decimal 0.44... as a fraction.

$w = 0.44...$ First, write an equation by setting the decimal equal to a variable that will represent the fraction.

$10w = 4.4...$ Next, write another equation by multiplying both sides of the equation by a power of 10. The exponent on the power of 10 is equal to the number of decimal places until the decimal begins to repeat.

$\begin{aligned} 10w &= 4.44... \\ -w &= 0.44... \\ \hline 9w &= 4 \end{aligned}$ Then, subtract the equations.

$w = \frac{4}{9}$ Finally, solve the equation by dividing both sides by 9.

What Are Those?!

A square root is one of two equal factors of a given number. Every positive number has two square roots: a positive square root and a negative square root. The positive square root is called the principal square root.

The symbol $\sqrt{10}$ is called a radical. The radicand is the quantity under a radical. For example, the expression shown is read as "the square root of 25," or as "radical 25."

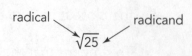

A perfect square is a number that is equal to the product of a distinct factor multiplied by itself. In the example above, 25 is a perfect square because it is equal to the product of 5 multiplied by itself.

The square roots of most numbers are not integers. You can estimate the square root of a number that is not a perfect square.

For example, to estimate $\sqrt{10}$ to the nearest tenth, identify the closest perfect square less than 10 and the closest perfect square greater than 10.

$$\sqrt{9} < \sqrt{10} < \sqrt{16}$$

This means that the estimate of $\sqrt{10}$ is between 3 and 4. Locate each square root on a number line. The approximate location of $\sqrt{10}$ is closer to 3 than to 4 when plotted.

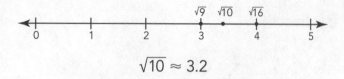

$$\sqrt{10} \approx 3.2$$

You can check your estimate by calculating the squares of values between 3 and 4.

$$(3.1)(3.1) = 9.61$$
$$(3.2)(3.2) = 10.24$$
$$(3.3)(3.3) = 10.89$$

A **perfect cube** is the cube of a whole number. For example, 64 is a perfect cube since 4 is a whole number and $4 \times 4 \times 4 = 64$. A **cube root** is one of 3 equal factors of a number. As with the square root, the cube root also uses a radical symbol but has a 3 as an index: $\sqrt[3]{1}$. The **index** is the number placed above and to the left of the radical to indicate what root is being calculated.

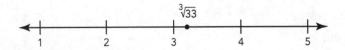

$$\sqrt[3]{27} < \sqrt[3]{33} < \sqrt[3]{64}$$

You can use the same method used to estimate the square root of a number to estimate the cube root of a number.

To estimate $\sqrt[3]{33}$ to the nearest tenth, identify the closest perfect cube less than 33 and the closest perfect cube greater than 33.

This means that the estimate of $\sqrt[3]{33}$ is between 3 and 4. Locate the approximate value of $\sqrt[3]{33}$ on a number line.

Next, choose decimals between 3 and 4, and calculate the cube of each decimal to determine which one is the best estimate.

Consider: $(3.2)(3.2)(3.2) = 32.768$
               $(3.3)(3.3)(3.3) = 35.937$

Therefore, $\sqrt[3]{33} \approx 3.2$.

TOPIC 2
Pythagorean Theorem

James Abram Garfield was the 20th President of the United States. Garfield also discovered a unique proof of the Pythagorean Theorem.

Module 4: Expanding Number Systems

TOPIC 2: THE PYTHAGOREAN THEOREM

In this topic, students explore the Pythagorean Theorem and its converse. They learn that in the case of right triangles, knowing two side lengths allows them to determine the third side length, therefore forming a unique triangle. Students practice applying the theorem to determine unknown side lengths in right triangles and apply the converse of the theorem: if three side lengths are given, determine if the triangle is a right triangle. Students apply the Pythagorean Theorem to real-world and mathematical problems.

Where have we been?

Students learned about right angles and right triangles in grade 4 and evaluated numerical expressions with whole-number exponents in grade 6, and they have continued to use these skills in subsequent courses.

Where are we going?

In high school, students will use right triangles and similarity to define ratios of sides, the trigonometric ratios. These new ratios, along with the Pythagorean Theorem, will be used to solve application problems. Students will use the Pythagorean Theorem in the study of analytic geometry when they use coordinates to prove geometric theorems algebraically, including deriving the Distance Formula.

Studying Visual Proofs of the Pythagorean Theorem

The triangles on the left, with leg lengths a and b and hypotenuse length c, can be rearranged as shown on the right. The space not occupied by the triangles in each figure is equal to $a^2 + b^2$ (on the left) and c^2 (on the right), proving that $a^2 + b^2 = c^2$, which is the Pythagorean Theorem.

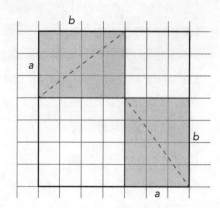
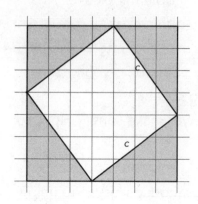

Myth: "I'm not smart."

The word "smart" is tricky because it means different things to different people. For example, would you say a baby is "smart"? On the one hand, a baby is helpless and doesn't know anything. But on the other hand, a baby is exceptionally smart because they are constantly learning new things every day.

This example is meant to demonstrate that "smart" can have two meanings. It can mean "the knowledge that you have," or it can mean, "the capacity to learn from experience." When someone says they are "not smart," are they saying they do not have lots of knowledge, or are they saying they lack the capacity to learn? If it's the first definition, then none of us are smart until we acquire that information. If it's the second definition, then we know that is completely untrue because everyone has the capacity to grow as a result of new experiences.

So, if your student doesn't think that they are smart, encourage them to be patient. They have the capacity to learn new facts and skills. It might not be easy, and it will take some time and effort. But the brain is automatically wired to learn. Smart should not refer only to how much knowledge you currently have.

#mathmythbusted

Talking Points

You can further support your student's learning by asking questions about the work they do in class or at home. Your student is learning about the Pythagorean Theorem.

Questions to Ask

- How does this problem look like something you did in class?
- Can you show me the strategy you used to solve this problem? Do you know another way to solve it?
- Does your answer make sense? How do you know?
- Is there anything you don't understand? How can you use today's lesson to help?

Key Terms

hypotenuse
The side opposite the right angle in a right triangle is called the hypotenuse. The other two sides are called legs of the right triangle.

Pythagorean Theorem
The special relationship that exists between the squares of the lengths of the sides of a right triangle is known as the Pythagorean Theorem. The sum of the squares of the lengths of the legs of a right triangle equals the square of the length of the hypotenuse: $a^2 + b^2 = c^2$.

Pythagorean triple
Any set of three positive integers a, b, and c that satisfies the equation $a^2 + b^2 = c^2$ is a Pythagorean triple.

The Right Triangle Connection

1

The Pythagorean Theorem

WARM UP

Solve for x.

1. $8^2 + 3^2 = x^2$

2. $36 + x^2 = 85$

3. $3^2 + 4^2 = x^2$

4. $6^2 + 8^2 = x^2$

LEARNING GOALS

- Make and prove a conjecture about the relationship between the lengths of the sides of right triangles.
- Explain a proof of the Pythagorean Theorem.
- Use the Pythagorean Theorem to determine the unknown side lengths in right triangles.

KEY TERMS

- hypotenuse
- legs
- Pythagorean Theorem
- proof
- diagonal of a square

You know the sum of two side lengths of any triangle is greater than the length of the third side. Are there other relationships between the side lengths of a triangle? What special relationships exist between the side lengths of a right triangle?

Searching for the Right Pattern

The triangles are not drawn to scale.

A right triangle is a triangle with a right angle. A right angle has a measure of 90° and is indicated by a square drawn at the corner formed by the angle.

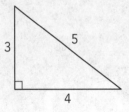 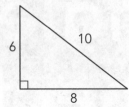 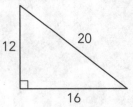

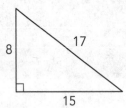 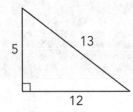 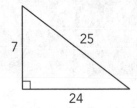

If you square the length of each side of the first triangle, you get

$$3^2 = 9 \qquad 4^2 = 16 \qquad 5^2 = 25.$$

If you repeat this process with the second triangle, you get

$$6^2 = 36 \qquad 8^2 = 64 \qquad 10^2 = 100.$$

1. **Repeat this process with the remaining triangles. Do you see a pattern in the squares of the side lengths of a right triangle? If so, describe it.**

Introducing the Pythagorean Theorem

In the right triangle shown, the lengths of the sides are *a*, *b*, and *c*.

1. Using the pattern you discovered in the previous activity, what statement can you make about the relationship among a^2, b^2, and c^2?

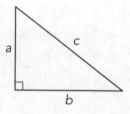

2. Consider the relative lengths of the sides of the triangle.

   a. Which side length must be the longest: *a*, *b*, or *c*? Explain how you know.

   b. Describe the relationship between the side lengths of any triangle.

The side opposite the right angle in a right triangle is called the **hypotenuse**. The other two sides are called **legs** of the right triangle. In the figure, the sides with lengths *a* and *b* are the legs, and the side with length *c* is the hypotenuse.

3. Label the legs and the hypotenuse in the right triangle shown.

The special relationship that exists between the squares of the lengths of the sides of a right triangle is known as the *Pythagorean Theorem*. The **Pythagorean Theorem** states that the sum of the squares of the lengths of the legs of a right triangle equals the square of the length of the hypotenuse.

$$a^2 + b^2 = c^2$$

The Pythagorean Theorem is one of the earliest known theorems to ancient civilization and one of the most famous. This theorem was named after Pythagoras (580 to 496 B.C.), a Greek mathematician and and philosopher who was the first to prove the theorem.

You can verify that the Pythagorean Theorem holds true for the triangles in the previous activity.

> **WORKED EXAMPLE**
>
> The first right triangle has sides of length 3 units, 4 units, and 5 units, where the sides of length 3 units and 4 units are the legs and the side with length 5 units is the hypotenuse.
>
> The sum of the squares of the
> lengths of the legs: $3^2 + 4^2 = 9 + 16$
> $$= 25$$
> The square of the hypotenuse: $5^2 = 25$
>
> Therefore $3^2 + 4^2 = 5^2$, which verifies the Pythagorean Theorem, holds true.

The sum of the lengths of two sides of a triangle must be greater than the length of the third side.

4. **Verify that the Pythagorean Theorem holds true for two additional triangles.**

   a. right triangle with side lengths 8, 15, and 17

   b. right triangle with side lengths 7, 24, and 25

5. **Use the Pythagorean Theorem to determine the length of the hypotenuse in each right triangle. Round your answer to the nearest tenth, if necessary.**

   a.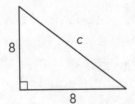

   b.

Proving the Pythagorean Theorem

You verified the Pythagorean Theorem for select triangles, but how do you know that it holds for *all* right triangles? In this activity, you will create a geometric *proof* of the theorem.

A **proof** is a line of reasoning used to validate a theorem.

1. Complete the geometric proof assigned to you. The cut-outs for proofs are located at the end of the lesson. Then record your findings on the graphic organizer and prepare to share your results with your classmates.

Proof 1
An isosceles right triangle is drawn on the grid.

a. A square on the hypotenuse has been drawn for you. Use a straightedge to draw squares on the other two sides of the triangle. Then use different colored pencils to shade each small square.

b. Draw two diagonals in each of the two smaller squares.

c. Cut out the two smaller squares along the legs. Then, cut those squares into fourths along the diagonals you drew.

A **diagonal of a square** is a line segment connecting opposite vertices of the square.

d. Redraw your original figure and the squares on the grid on the graphic organizer at the end of the activity. Shade the smaller squares again.

e. Arrange the pieces that you cut out to fit inside the larger square on the graphic organizer. Then, tape the triangles on top of the larger square.

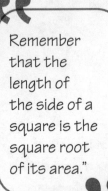

> Remember that the length of the side of a square is the square root of its area."

Proof 2

A right triangle has one leg 4 units in length and the other leg 3 units in length.

a. Use a straightedge to draw squares on each side of the triangle. Use different colored pencils to shade each square along the legs.

b. Cut out the two smaller squares along the legs.

c. Cut the two squares into strips that are either 4 units by 1 unit or 3 units by 1 unit.

d. Redraw your original figure and the squares on the grid on the graphic organizer at the end of the activity. Shade the smaller squares again.

e. Arrange the strips and squares you cut out on top of the square along the hypotenuse on the graphic organizer. You may need to make additional cuts to the strips to create individual squares that are 1 unit by 1 unit. Then, tape the strips on top of the square you drew on the hypotenuse.

Proof 3

A right triangle has one leg 2 units in length and the other leg 4 units in length.

a. Use a straightedge to draw squares on each side of the triangle. Use different colored pencils to shade each square along the legs.

b. Cut out the two smaller squares.

c. Draw four congruent right triangles on the square with side lengths of 4 units. Then, cut out the four congruent right triangles you drew.

d. Redraw your original figure and the squares on the grid on the graphic organizer at the end of the activity. Shade the smaller squares again.

e. Arrange and tape the small square and the 4 congruent triangles you cut out over the square that has one of its sides as the hypotenuse.

Description of Right Triangle in Proof

What do you notice?

Describe the relationship among the areas of the squares.

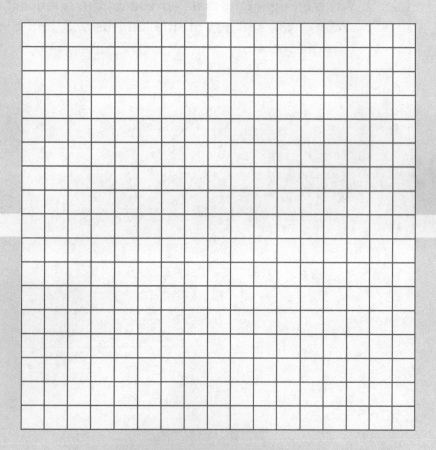

Determine the length of the hypotenuse.

Share your proof and graphic organizer with your classmates.

2. Compare the descriptions of the relationship among the areas of the squares from each proof. What do you notice?

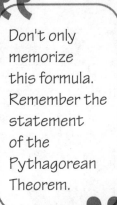

Don't only memorize this formula. Remember the statement of the Pythagorean Theorem.

3. Write an equation that represents the relationship among the areas of the squares of side lengths *a*, *b*, and *c* in the right triangle shown.

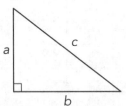

Determining the Length of the Hypotenuse

The Pythagorean Theorem can be used to determine unknown side lengths in a right triangle. Evan and Sophi are using the theorem to determine the length of the hypotenuse, c, with leg lengths of 2 and 4. Examine their work.

Evan

$$c^2 = 2^2 + 4^2$$
$$c^2 = 6^2$$
$$c = 6$$

The length of the hypotenuse is 6 units.

Sophi

$$c^2 = 2^2 + 4^2$$
$$c^2 = 4 + 16 = 20$$
$$c = \sqrt{20} \approx 4.5$$

The length of the hypotenuse is approximately 4.5 units.

---

1. Explain the algebraic error in Evan's work.

Mitch maintains the Magnolia Middle School campus. Use the Pythagorean Theorem to help Mitch with some of his jobs.

2. Mitch needs to wash the windows on the second floor of a building. He knows the windows are 12 feet above the ground. Because of dense shrubbery, he has to put the base of the ladder 5 feet from the building. What ladder length does he need?

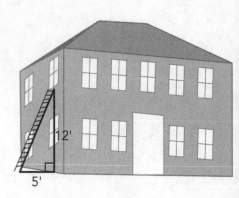

3. The gym teacher, Ms. Fisher, asked Mitch to put up the badminton net. Ms. Fisher said that the top of the net must be 5 feet above the ground. She knows that Mitch will need to put stakes in the ground for rope supports. She asked that the stakes be placed 6 feet from the base of the poles. Mitch has two pieces of rope, one that is 7 feet long and a second that is 8 feet long. Will these two pieces of rope be enough to secure the badminton poles? Explain your reasoning.

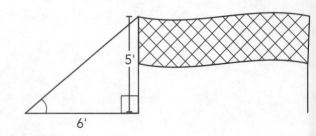

4. Mitch stopped by the baseball field to watch the team practice. The first baseman caught a line drive right on the base. He touched first base for one out and quickly threw the ball to third base to get another out. How far did he throw the ball?

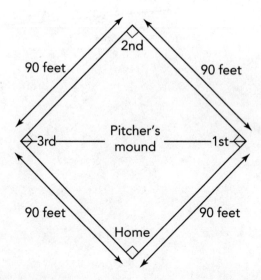

5. The skate ramp on the playground of a neighboring park is going to be replaced. Mitch needs to determine how long the ramp is to get estimates on the cost of a new skate ramp. He knows the measurements shown in the figure. How long is the existing skate ramp?

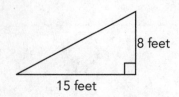

6. A wheelchair ramp that is constructed to rise 1 foot off the ground must extend 12 feet along the ground. How long will the wheelchair ramp be?

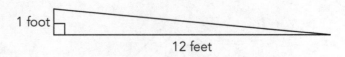

1 foot

12 feet

7. The school's new industrial-size refrigerator is 7 feet tall and 5 feet wide. The refrigerator is lying on its side. Mitch and the movers want to tilt the refrigerator upright, but they are worried that the refrigerator might hit the 8-foot ceiling. Will the refrigerator hit the ceiling when it is tilted upright?

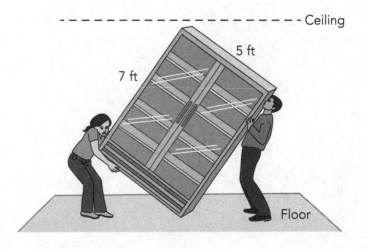

Ceiling

5 ft

7 ft

Floor

Determining the Length of a Leg

Use the Pythagorean Theorem to solve each problem.

1. Write an equation to determine each unknown length. Then, solve the equation. Round your answer to the nearest tenth, if necessary.

a.

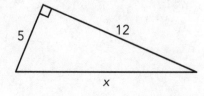

b.

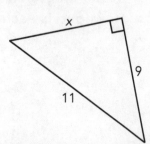

c.

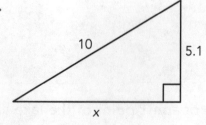

d.

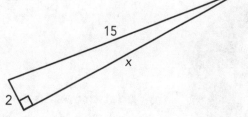

Would it help to draw a picture?

2. Chandra has a ladder that is 20 feet long. If the top of the ladder reaches 16 feet up the side of a building, how far from the building is the base of the ladder?

3. The length of the hypotenuse of a right triangle is 40 centimeters. The legs of the triangle are the same length. How long is each leg of the triangle?

What path will the plane take to reach the runway?

4. A plane is 5 miles directly above a house and 42 miles from the runway at the nearest airport. How far is the house from the airport?

5. A boat drops an anchor at the deepest point of the lake and spends the day drifting along the lake. If the lake is 75 feet deep and the chain on the anchor is 200 feet, determine the greatest distance the boat can drift from where it dropped anchor.

TALK the TALK

Another Proof!

While it is called the Pythagorean Theorem, the mathematical knowledge was used by the Babylonians 1000 years before Pythagoras. Many proofs followed that of Pythagoras, including ones proved by Euclid, Socrates, and even the twentieth President of the United States, President James A. Garfield.

Let's use the figures shown to prove the Pythagorean Theorem another way. Each figure includes four right triangles with leg lengths a and b and hypotenuse of length c.

Figure 1

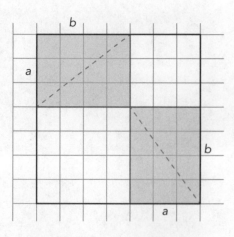

Figure 2

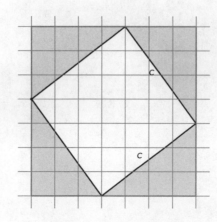

1. Write an expression for the total area of the non-shaded region of Figure 1, in terms of a and b.

2. Explain how to use transformations to transform Figure 1 onto Figure 2.

3. Write an expression for the non-shaded region of Figure 2, in terms of c.

4. Explain why these figures prove the Pythagorean Theorem.

Proof Cutouts   Proof 1

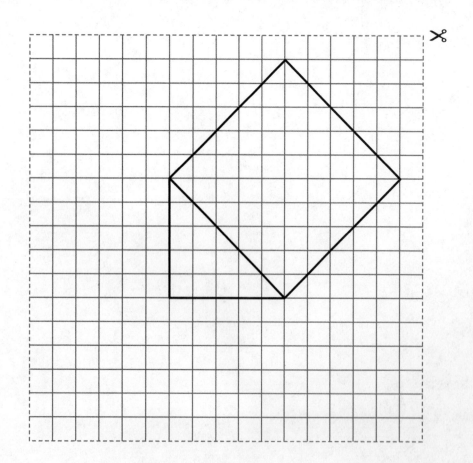

Proof 2

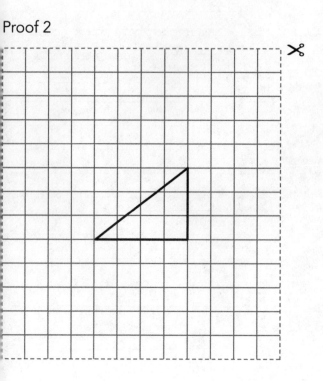

Proof 3

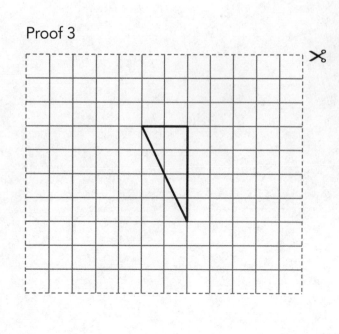

Assignment

Write

Describe the relationship between the areas of the squares on the sides of right triangles.

Remember

The Pythagorean Theorem is used to determine unknown lengths in right triangles in mathematical and contextual problems.

Practice

Determine the unknown in each situation. Round your answers to the nearest tenth.

1. Lamar goes shopping for a new flat-panel television. A television is usually described by the length of the screen's diagonal. He finds a great deal on a 42-inch display model.
   a. If the screen's height is 21 inches, what is the width of the screen?
   b. The border around the screen is 2 inches. What are the dimensions of the television, including the border?
   c. How long is the diagonal of the television, including the border?
2. Lamar sells his old television in his neighborhood's garage sale. It has a rectangular screen with a diagonal measure of 27 inches. A potential buyer is concerned about the television fitting in the 24-inch square opening of his entertainment center.

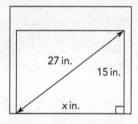

27 in.
15 in.
x in.

   a. What is the width of the television's screen?
   b. Will the television fit in the buyer's entertainment center? Explain your reasoning.
3. Clayton is responsible for changing the broken light bulb in a streetlamp. The streetlamp is 12 feet high. Clayton places the base of his ladder 4 feet from the base of the streetlamp. Clayton can extend his ladder from 10 feet to 14 feet. How long must his ladder be to reach the top of the streetlamp?
4. A scaffold has a diagonal support beam to strengthen it. If the scaffold is 15 feet high and 5 feet wide, how long must the support beam be?
5. A rectangular swimming pool is 24 meters by 10 meters. Jane said she could swim diagonally from one corner to another without taking a breath. Carli said she could swim much farther than Jane and still swim diagonally from one corner to another. Determine the distances Jane and Carli may have swum.

Determine the unknown side length in each right triangle. Round your answers to the nearest tenth.

6.

7.

8.

9.

10.

11.

Stretch

Examine President Garfield's proof of the Pythagorean Theorem.

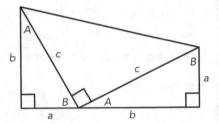

In the figure, an arbitrary right triangle with sides of length a and b and hypotenuse of length c was drawn and copied so that a ∥ b. Then, an additional segment was drawn to form a trapezoid.

1. Determine the area of the trapezoid using the formula, $A = \frac{1}{2}(b_1 + b_2)h$, where b_1 and b_2 are the lengths of the parallel bases and h is the perpendicular distance between the bases.
2. Determine the area of each triangle inside the trapezoid. Sum the areas.
3. How do these area calculations prove the Pythagorean Theorem? (Hint: $(a + b)^2 = a^2 + 2ab + b^2$.)

Review

1. Estimate each radical to the nearest tenth.
   a. $\sqrt{38}$ b. $\sqrt{14}$
2. Name all number sets to which each number belongs.
   a. $\frac{2}{3}$ b. 5
3. Solve each equation.
   a. $4x + 3x + 12 = 2(15 + 2x)$ b. $3(2c + 5) = 12 + 3(c + 4)$

Can That Be Right?

2

The Converse of the Pythagorean Theorem

WARM UP

A bird leaves its nest and flies 3 miles due south, 2 miles due east, 5 miles due south, and 1 mile due east to visit a friend's nest.

1. Draw a model of the situation.
2. Determine the distance between the nests.

LEARNING GOALS

- Determine if three side lengths form a right triangle.
- Generate side lengths of right triangles.
- Use the Pythagorean Theorem and the Converse of the Pythagorean Theorem to determine unknown side lengths in right triangles.

KEY TERMS

- converse
- Converse of the Pythagorean Theorem
- Pythagorean triple

You know that the Pythagorean Theorem can be used to solve for unknown lengths in a right triangle. How can you use the theorem to prove that a triangle is a right triangle?

Is It Right?

Often, geometry diagrams are not drawn to scale, and even if a triangle looks like a right triangle, it may not be. A square is used to indicate the presence of the right angle, but what if that symbol is missing? How do you know if a triangle is a right triangle?

1. **Use a protractor to determine which triangles are right triangles.**

   a.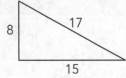

   b.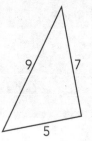

   c.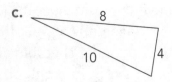

   d.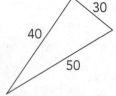

Does a non-right triangle have a hypotenuse?

2. **What do you notice about the squares of the lengths of the sides of the triangle of the non-right triangles versus the right triangles?**

The Pythagorean Theorem can be used to solve many problems involving right triangles, squares, and rectangles. The Pythagorean Theorem states that, if a triangle is a right triangle, then the square of the hypotenuse length equals the sum of the squares of the leg lengths. Have you wondered if the *converse* is true?

The **Converse of the Pythagorean Theorem** states that if the sum of the squares of the two shorter sides of a triangle equals the square of the longest side, then the triangle is a right triangle.

In other words, if the lengths of the sides of a triangle satisfy the equation $a^2 + b^2 = c^2$, then the triangle is a right triangle.

> The **converse** of a theorem is created when the if-then parts of that theorem are exchanged.

1. Determine whether the triangle with the given side lengths is a right triangle.

   a. 9, 12, 15   b. 24, 45, 51

   c. 25, 16, 9   d. 8, 8, 11

> Think about which measures would represent legs of the right triangle and which measure would represent the hypotenuse.

You may have noticed that each of the right triangles in Question 1 had side lengths that were integers. Any set of three positive integers a, b, and c that satisfies the equation $a^2 + b^2 = c^2$ is a **Pythagorean triple**. For example, the integers 3, 4, and 5 form a Pythagorean triple because $3^2 + 4^2 = 5^2$.

Given a Pythagorean triple, you can identify other right triangles by multiplying each side length by the same factor.

2. Complete the table to identify more Pythagorean triples.

	a	b	c	Check: $a^2 + b^2 = c^2$
Pythagorean Triple	3	4	5	$9 + 16 = 25$
Multiply by 2				
Multiply by 3				
Multiply by 5				

What if I multiplied 3, 4, and 5 each by a decimal, such as 2.2? Would those side lengths form a right triangle?

3. Determine a new Pythagorean triple not used in Question 2, and complete the table.

	a	b	c	Check: $a^2 + b^2 = c^2$
Pythagorean Triple				
Multiply by 2				
Multiply by 3				
Multiply by 5				

4. Record other Pythagorean triples that your classmates determined.

Proving the Converse

Because the Converse of the Pythagorean Theorem is, itself, a theorem, you can prove it.

Step 1: Assume you are given $\triangle ABC$ such that the sum of the squares of the lengths of two sides equals the square of the length of the third side, or $a^2 + b^2 = c^2$.

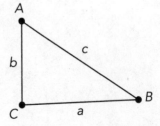

1. Do you have enough information to determine if the triangle is a right triangle without using the Converse of the Pythagorean Theorem? Why can't you use the converse to answer this question?

Step 2: Now, construct a right triangle, $\triangle DEF$, using the side lengths a and b from Triangle ABC. By the Pythagorean Theorem, $a^2 + b^2 = x^2$, where x is the hypotenuse of $\triangle DEF$.

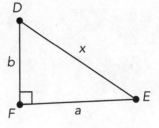

2. Why can you apply the Pythagorean Theorem to the side lengths of $\triangle DEF$?

Step 3: If $a^2 + b^2 = c^2$ and $a^2 + b^2 = x^2$, then $c^2 = x^2$ and $c = x$.

3. Explain why $c^2 = x^2$.

Recall that three sides of a triangle create a unique triangle. Therefore, all triangles with those side lengths are congruent.

Step 4: $\triangle ABC \cong \triangle DEF$ because all of their corresponding side lengths are equal.

4. If the triangles are congruent and $\triangle DEF$ is a right triangle, what must be true about $\triangle ABC$?

You have proven the Converse of the Pythagorean Theorem. If the sum of the squares of the lengths of two sides of a triangle equals the square of the length of the third side, then the triangle is a right triangle.

Use your knowledge of the Pythagorean Theorem and its converse to solve each.

1. A carpenter attaches a brace to a rectangular picture frame. If the dimensions of the picture frame are 30 inches by 40 inches, what is the length of the brace?

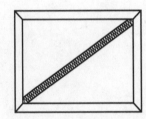

2. Bill is staking out a location to build a rectangular deck that will be 8 feet wide and 15 feet long. Tyrone is helping Bill with the deck. Tyrone has two boards, one that is 8 feet long and one that is 7 feet long. He puts the two boards together, end to end, and lays them on the diagonal of the deck area, where they just fit. What should he tell Bill?

3. A television is identified by the diagonal measurement of the screen. A television has a 36-inch screen, whose height is 22 inches. What is the width of the television screen? Round your answer to the nearest inch.

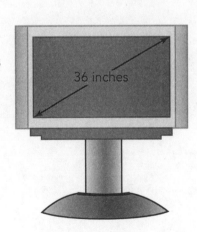

36 inches

4. Orville and Jerri want to put a custom-made, round table in their dining room. The table top is made of glass with a diameter of 85 inches. The front door is 36 inches wide and 80 inches tall. Orville thinks the table top will fit through the door, but Jerri does not. Who is correct and why?

5. Sherie makes a canvas frame for a painting using stretcher bars. The rectangular painting will be 12 inches long and 9 inches wide. How can she use a ruler to make sure that the corners of the frame will be right angles?

6. A 10-foot ladder is placed 4 feet from the edge of a building. How far up the building does the ladder reach? Round your answer to the nearest tenth of a foot.

7. Chris has a tent that is 64 inches wide with a slant height of 68 inches on each side. What is the height of the center pole needed to prop up the tent?

8. A ship left shore and sailed 240 kilometers east, turned due north, and then sailed another 70 kilometers. How many kilometers is the ship from shore by the most direct path?

9. Danielle walks 88 feet due east to the library from her house. From the library, she walks 187 feet northwest to the corner store. Finally, she walks approximately 139 feet from the corner store back home. Does she live directly south of the corner store? Justify your answer.

10. What is the diagonal length of a square that has a side length of 10 cm?

TALK the TALK 💬

Triple Play

Create a Pythagorean triple that contains each length or lengths. Verify that the side lengths form a right triangle.

1. 9 and 41

2. 21 and 29

3. 12

4. 15

5. Can any integer be used to create a Pythagorean triple? Why or why not?

6. Are the side lengths of a right triangle always integers? Why or why not?

Assignment

Write

Complete each statement:

1. The Converse of the Pythagorean Theorem states that if the sum of the squares of two sides of a triangle equals the square of the third side, then the triangle is a _____.

2. The converse of a theorem is created when the if-then parts of the theorem are _____.

3. A Pythagorean triple is a set of three _____ _____ a, b, and c that satisfy the equation $a^2 + b^2 = c^2$.

Practice

1. Determine whether each triangle with the given side lengths is a right triangle.

   a. 6, 9, 14

   b. 2, 3.75, 4.25

   c.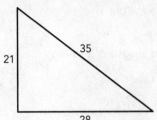

   d.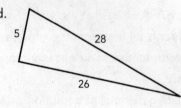

2. Elena has received grant money to open a local community center. She wants to save as much of the money as possible for programs. She will be doing many of the improvements herself to the old building she has rented. While touring the building to make her project list, she uses a tape measure to check whether floors, doorways, and walls are square, meaning that they meet at right angles.

   a. Elena measures the lobby of the building for new laminate flooring. The length is 30 feet, the width is 16 feet, and the diagonal is 34 feet. Is the room square?

   b. Can Elena use the edges of the room as a guide to start laying the boards of laminate flooring? Explain your reasoning.

   c. The landing outside the main entrance of the building does not have a railing. Elena wants to install railing around the landing to make it safer. The length of the landing is 12 feet, the width is 9 feet, and the diagonal is 14 feet. Is the landing square?

   d. Elena needs to order a new door for her office. The width of the door frame is 3 feet, the height is 8 feet, and the diagonal is $8\frac{5}{8}$ feet. Is the door frame square?

   e. The sign that will be mounted to the outside of the building is a rectangle that is 9 feet by 12 feet. The largest doorway into the building is 4 feet wide and 8 feet high. What is the diagonal measurement of the doorway?

   f. Does Elena have to mount the sign the day it is delivered or can she store it inside the building until she is ready? Explain your answer.

3. Given the Pythagorean triple 21-220-221, generate an additional triple and verify that the side lengths form a right triangle.

Stretch

Euclid developed a formula for generating Pythagorean triples given any integers m and n with $m > n > 0$: $a = m^2 - n^2$, $b = 2mn$, and $c = m^2 + n^2$.

It can be proven that there are exactly eight Pythagorean triples for a right triangle with a perimeter of 840 units.

Use Euclid's formula, your knowledge of perimeter and algebra, and number sense to find as many of the eight Pythagorean triples with a perimeter of 840 units as you can.

Review

1. A carpenter props a ladder against the wall of a building. The base of the ladder is 10 feet from the wall. The top of the ladder is 24 feet from the ground. How long is the ladder?

2. The length of the hypotenuse of a right triangle is 50 inches. Determine the length of the legs if each leg is the same length.

3. Rewrite each repeating decimal as a fraction.

   a. 0.191919...   b. $0.\overline{5}$

4. Solve each system of equations.

   a. $\begin{cases} y = 4x + 3 \\ y = 2x + 5 \end{cases}$ b. $\begin{cases} 3x + y = 14 \\ y = 5x - 2 \end{cases}$

Pythagoras Meets Descartes

Distances in a Coordinate System

3

WARM UP

Use the coordinate plane shown to answer each question.

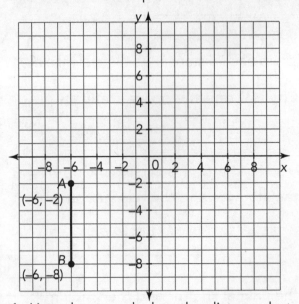

LEARNING GOALS

- Apply the Pythagorean Theorem to determine the distance between two points on a coordinate plane.
- Use square roots to represent solutions to equations.

1. How do you calculate the distance between points *A* and *B*?

2. What is the distance between points *A* and *B*?

3. How do the negative coordinates affect the distance between points A and B?

You have learned about the Pythagorean Theorem and the Converse of the Pythagorean Theorem. How can you apply the Pythagorean Theorem to determine distances on a coordinate plane?

As the Crow Flies

The map shows certain locations within a city. Each unit on the map represents 1 block.

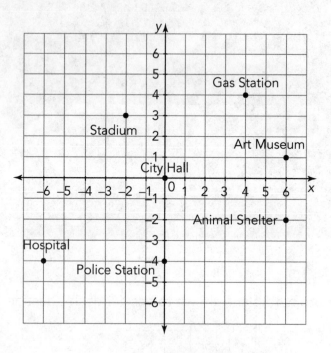

The phrase *as the crow flies* means "the straight-line distance" between two points.

Describe how you could express each distance "as the crow flies."

1. the distance between City Hall and the police station

2. the distance between the stadium and the gas station

3. the distance between the animal shelter and the stadium

Right Triangles on the Coordinate Plane

Two friends, Shawn and Tamara, live in a city in which the streets are laid out in a grid system.

Shawn lives on Descartes Avenue and Tamara lives on Pythagoras Street, as shown.

1. The two friends often meet at the bookstore. Each grid square represents one city block.

   a. How many blocks does Shawn walk to get to the bookstore?

   b. How many blocks does Tamara walk to get to the bookstore?

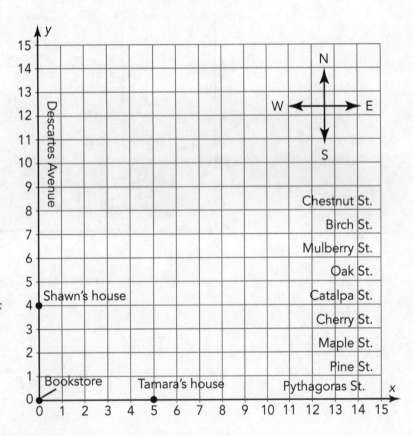

   c. Determine the distance, in blocks, Tamara would walk if she traveled from her house to the bookstore and then to Shawn's house.

   d. Determine the distance, in blocks, Tamara would walk if she traveled in a straight line from her house to Shawn's house. Explain your calculation. Round your answer to the nearest tenth of a block.

2. **Don, a friend of Shawn and Tamara, lives three blocks east of Descartes Avenue and five blocks north of Pythagoras Street. Freda, another friend, lives seven blocks east of Descartes Avenue and two blocks north of Pythagoras Street. Plot the location of Don's house and Freda's house on the grid. Label each location and label the coordinates of each location.**

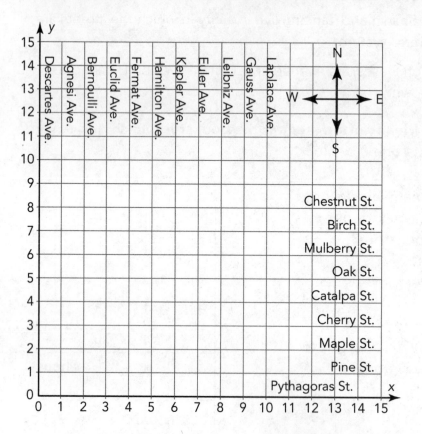

a. Name the streets that Don lives on.

b. Name the streets that Freda lives on.

3. Another friend, Bert, lives at the intersection of the avenue that Don lives on and the street that Freda lives on. Plot the location of Bert's house on the grid in Question 2 and label the coordinates. Describe the location of Bert's house with respect to Descartes Avenue and Pythagoras Street.

4. How do the coordinates of Bert's house compare to the coordinates of Don's house and Freda's house?

5. Use ordered pairs to write and evaluate an expression that represents the distance between Don's and Bert's houses.

6. How far, in blocks, does Don have to walk to get to Bert's house?

7. Use ordered pairs to write an expression that represents the distance between Bert's and Freda's houses.

8. How far, in blocks, does Bert have to walk to get to Freda's house?

9. All three friends meet at Don's house to study geometry. Freda walks to Bert's house, and then they walk together to Don's house. Use the coordinates to write and evaluate an expression that represents the distance from Freda's house to Bert's house, and from Bert's house to Don's house.

10. How far, in blocks, does Freda walk altogether?

11. Draw the direct path from Don's house to Freda's house on the coordinate plane in Question 2. If Freda walks to Don's house on this path, how far, in blocks, does she walk? Explain how you determined your answer.

Applying the Pythagorean Theorem to Determine Distances on the Coordinate Plane

The points (1, 2) and (3, 7) are shown on the coordinate plane. You can calculate the distance between these two points by drawing a right triangle. When you think about this line segment as the hypotenuse of the right triangle, you can use the Pythagorean Theorem.

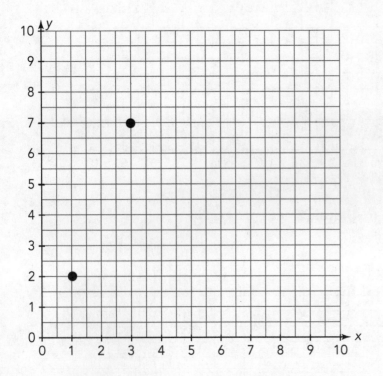

1. Calculate the distance between the two points shown.

   a. Connect the points with a line segment. Draw a right triangle with this line segment as the hypotenuse.

   b. Determine the lengths of each leg of the right triangle. Then use the Pythagorean Theorem to determine the length of the hypotenuse. Round your answer to the nearest tenth.

> Therefore, if you think of the distance between two points as a hypotenuse, you can draw a right triangle and then use the Pythagorean Theorem to calculate its length.

2. **Determine the distance between each pair of points. Round your answer to the nearest tenth.**

   a. (3, 4) and (6, 8)

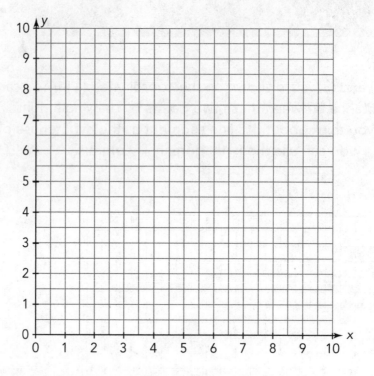

   b. (−6, 4) and (2, −8)

> Make sure to pay attention to the intervals shown on the axes.

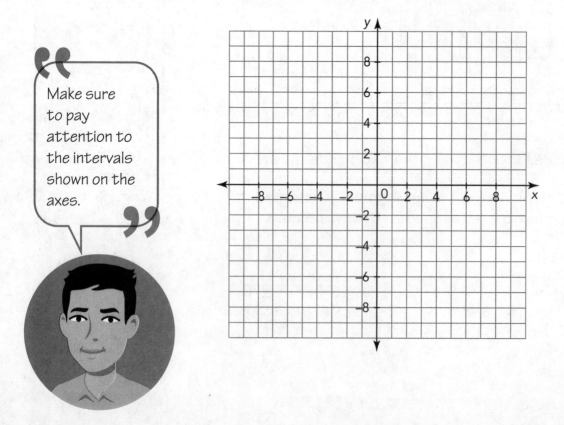

c. (−5, 2) and (−6, 10)

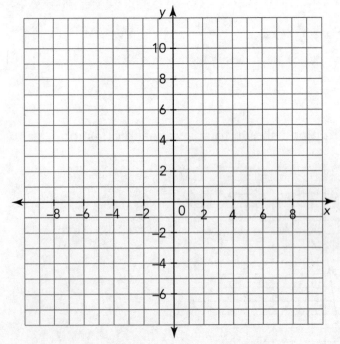

d. (−1, −4) and (−3, −6)

TALK the TALK

Exit Ticket

Use the coordinate plane shown to answer each question.

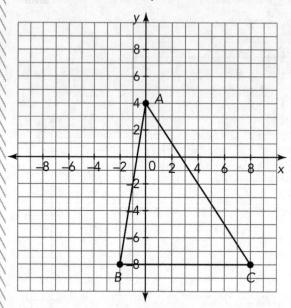

1. What are the coordinates of the vertices of △ABC?

2. What is a strategy for determining the length of side AC?

3. Determine the length of side AC.

4. Can the same strategy be used to determine the length of side AB?

5. Determine the length of side AB.

Assignment

Write

In your own words, explain how to determine the distance between two points on a coordinate plane when the points:

(a) have the same y-coordinate.

(b) have the same x-coordinate.

(c) have different x- and y-coordinates.

Remember

The distance between two points on a coordinate plane is always a positive number.

Practice

1. Ben is playing soccer with his friends Abby and Clay. The grid shows their locations on the soccer field. Each grid square represents a square that is 2 meters long and 2 meters wide. How far does Ben have to kick the ball to reach Clay?

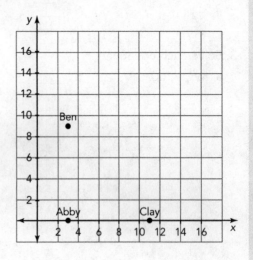

2. Graph and connect each pair of points on a coordinate plane. Then calculate the distance between each pair of points.

   a. (−8, 3) and (−8, 9)

   b. (−6, 8) and (−1, 8)

   c. (8, −7) and (−4, −7)

   d. (8, 8) and (8, −2)

3. Calculate the distances between the points.

   a. (4, 1), (2, 1), and (4, 4)

   b. (1, −4), (1, 1), and (−2, −4)

Stretch
What right triangles can be drawn, given the coordinates of the endpoints of the hypotenuse (−1, 1) and (2, 5)?

Review
1. Determine whether the triangle with the given side lengths is a right triangle.

   a. 105, 175, 140

   b. 36, 49, 64

2. Determine whether each number is rational or irrational.

   a. $-\frac{1}{6}$

   b. $\sqrt{81}$

   c. $\sqrt[3]{19}$

   d. $\sqrt[3]{100}$

3. Solve each equation.

   a. $4x^2 = 100$

   b. $x^3 - 10 = -2$

Catty Corner

Side Lengths in Two and Three Dimensions

4

WARM UP

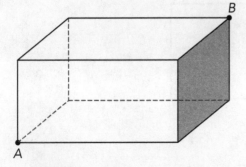

1. Imagine that the rectangular solid is a room. An ant is on the floor situated at point A. Describe the shortest path the ant can crawl to get to point B in the corner of the ceiling.

2. Suppose it isn't really an ant at all—it's a fly! Describe the shortest path the fly can fly to get from point A to point B.

3. If the ant's path and the fly's path were connected, what figure would they form?

LEARNING GOALS

- Apply the Pythagorean Theorem to determine unknown side lengths of right triangles in mathematical and real-world problems.
- Apply the Pythagorean Theorem to determine the lengths of diagonals of two- and three-dimensional figures.

KEY TERM

- diagonal

You have learned about the Pythagorean Theorem and its converse. How can you apply the Pythagorean Theorem to determine lengths in geometric figures?

Diagonally

Draw all of the sides you cannot see in each rectangular solid using dotted lines. Then draw a three-dimensional diagonal using a solid line.

1.

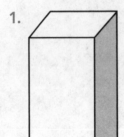

How many three-dimensional diagonals can be drawn in each figure?

2.

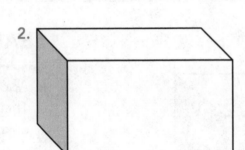

ACTIVITY 4.1

Determining the Lengths of Diagonals of Rectangles and Trapezoids

Previously, you have drawn or created many right triangles and used the Pythagorean Theorem to determine side lengths. In this lesson, you will explore the diagonals of various shapes.

1. Rectangle *ABCD* is shown.

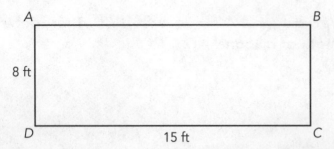

A ————————————— B

8 ft

D ————— 15 ft ————— C

a. Draw diagonal *AC* in Rectangle *ABCD*. Then, determine the length of diagonal *AC*.

Be on the lookout for right triangles.

b. Draw diagonal *BD* in Rectangle *ABCD*. Then, determine the length of diagonal *BD*.

c. What can you conclude about the diagonals of this rectangle?

2. Square *ABCD* is shown.

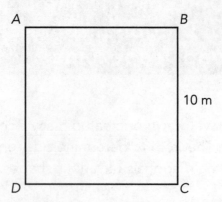

a. Draw diagonal *AC* in Square *ABCD*. Then, determine the length of diagonal *AC*.

b. Draw diagonal *BD* in Square *ABCD*. Then, determine the length of diagonal *BD*.

All squares are also rectangles, so does your conclusion make sense?

c. What can you conclude about the diagonals of this square?

3. Graph and label the coordinates of the vertices of
   Trapezoid *ABCD*: *A* (1, 2), *B* (7, 2), *C* (7, 5), *D* (3, 5).

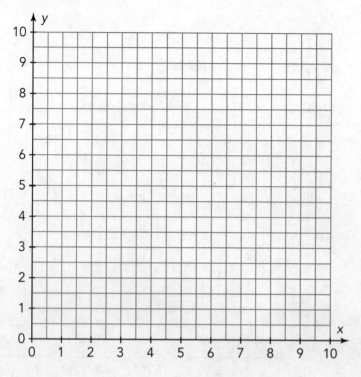

a. Draw diagonal *AC* in Trapezoid *ABCD*.

b. What right triangle can be used to determine the length of
   diagonal *AC*?

c. Determine the length of diagonal *AC*.

d. Draw diagonal *BD* in Trapezoid *ABCD*.

e. What right triangle can be used to determine the length of
   diagonal *BD*?

f. Determine the length of diagonal *BD*.

g. What can you conclude about the diagonals of this trapezoid?

4. Graph and label the coordinates of the vertices of isosceles Trapezoid *ABCD*: *A* (1, 2), *B* (9, 2), *C* (7, 5), *D* (3, 5).

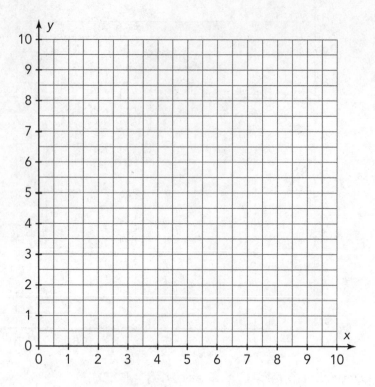

How is this trapezoid different from the first trapezoid you drew?

a. Draw diagonal *AC* in Trapezoid *ABCD*.

b. What right triangle can be used to determine the length of diagonal *AC*?

c. Determine the length of diagonal *AC*.

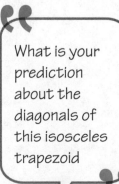

What is your prediction about the diagonals of this isosceles trapezoid

d. Draw diagonal *BD* in Trapezoid *ABCD*.

e. What right triangle can be used to determine the length of diagonal *BD*?

f. Determine the length of diagonal *BD*.

g. What can you conclude about the diagonals of this isosceles trapezoid?

Use your knowledge of right triangles, the Pythagorean Theorem, and area formulas.

1. Determine the area of each shaded region. Use 3.14 for π and round to the nearest tenth.

   a. A rectangle is inscribed in a circle as shown.

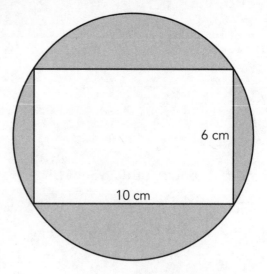

6 cm

10 cm

   b. The figure is composed of a right triangle and a semi-circle.

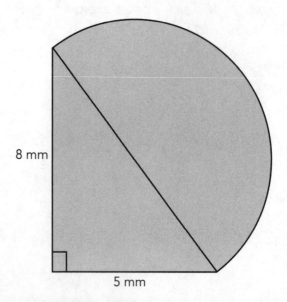

8 mm

5 mm

A rectangular box of long-stem roses is 18 inches in length, 6 inches in width, and 4 inches in height.

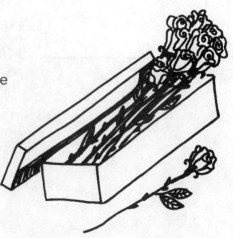

Without bending a long-stem rose, you are to determine the maximum length of a rose that will fit into the box.

1. **What makes this problem different from all of the previous applications of the Pythagorean Theorem?**

2. **Compare a two-dimensional diagonal to a three-dimensional diagonal. Describe the similarities and differences.**

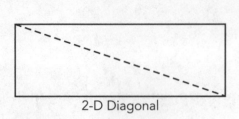

2-D Diagonal

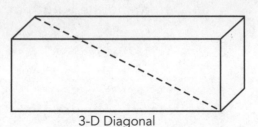

3-D Diagonal

3. **Which diagonal represents the maximum length of a rose that can fit into a box?**

4. Consider the rectangular solid shown.

   a. Draw all of the sides in the rectangular solid you cannot see using dotted lines.

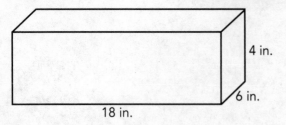

4 in.

6 in.

18 in.

   b. Draw a three-dimensional diagonal in the rectangular solid.

   c. Let's consider that the three-dimensional diagonal you drew in the rectangular solid is also the hypotenuse of a right triangle. If a vertical edge is one of the legs of that right triangle, where is the second leg of that same right triangle?

   d. Draw the second leg using a dotted line. Then lightly shade the right triangle.

   e. Determine the length of the second leg you drew.

   f. Determine the length of the three-dimensional diagonal.

   g. What does the length of the three-dimensional diagonal represent in terms of this problem situation?

5. Describe how the Pythagorean Theorem was used to solve this problem.

Determine the length of the diagonal of each rectangular solid.

1.

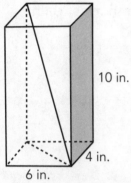

10 in.

4 in.

6 in.

2.

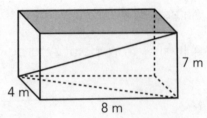

7 m

4 m

8 m

3.

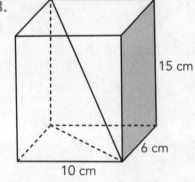

15 cm

6 cm

10 cm

4.

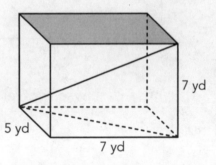

7 yd

5 yd

7 yd

5.

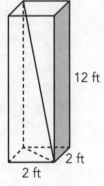

12 ft

2 ft

2 ft

6.

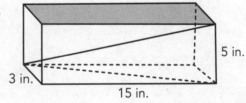

5 in.

3 in.

15 in.

TALK the TALK

The Ant and the Fly Again

A rectangular room is 10 ft × 16 ft × 8 ft.

An ant crawls from point A to point B taking the shortest path.

A fly flies from point A to point B taking the shortest path.

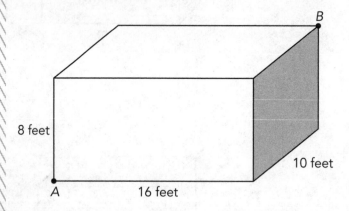

1. Whose path was shorter?

2. How much shorter is the shorter path?

Assignment

Write

In your own words, explain how you can determine a diagonal length inside a rectangular prism. Use an example to illustrate your explanation.

Remember

You can use the Pythagorean Theorem to determine the length of a diagonal in a two- or three-dimensional figure.

Practice

1. Determine the length of the diagonals in each given quadrilateral.

   a. The figure is a square with side lengths of 15 feet.

   b. The figure is a rectangle with a length of 18 inches and a height of 10 inches.

   c.

   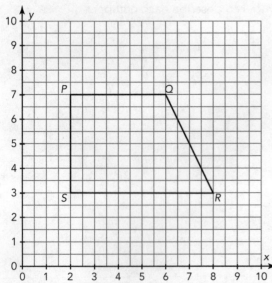

   d.

   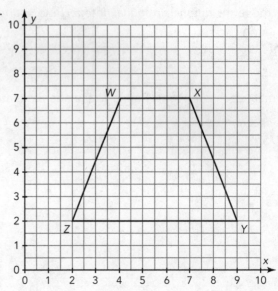

2. A packing company is in the planning stages of creating a box that includes a three-dimensional diagonal support inside the box. The box has a width of 5 feet, a length of 6 feet, and a height of 8 feet. How long will the diagonal support need to be?

3. A plumber needs to transport a 12-foot pipe to a jobsite. The interior of his van is 90 inches in length, 40 inches in width, and 40 inches in height. Will the pipe fit inside his van?

4. George is landscaping the flower beds in his front yard. He chooses to plant a tree that measures 5 feet from the root ball to the top. The interior of his car is 60 inches in length, 45 inches in width, and 40 inches in height. Will the tree fit inside George's car?

Stretch

Norton thought he knew a shortcut to determine the length of a three-dimensional diagonal. He said, "All you have to do is calculate the sum of the squares of the rectangular solid's three perpendicular edges (the length, the width, and the height), and that sum would be equivalent to the square of the three-dimensional diagonal." Does this work? Explain your reasoning.

Review

Determine the distance between each pair of points.

1. $(-9, -5)$, $(3, 12)$
2. $(5, 5)$, $(1, -10)$

Use the terms *rational, irrational, integer,* and *counting number* to describe each number.

3. $-\sqrt{100}$
4. $\frac{75}{4}$

Estimate each cube root. Round to the nearest tenth.

5. $\sqrt[3]{36}$
6. $\sqrt[3]{75}$

Pythagorean Theorem Summary

KEY TERMS

- hypotenuse
- legs
- Pythagorean Theorem
- proof
- diagonal of a square

- converse
- Converse of the Pythagorean Theorem
- Pythagorean triple
- diagonal

The Right Triangle Connection

LESSON 1

In the right triangle shown, the lengths of the sides are *a*, *b*, and *c*.

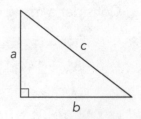

The side opposite the right angle is called the **hypotenuse**. The other two sides are called **legs** of the right triangle. In the figure, the sides with lengths *a* and *b* are the legs, and the side with length *c* is the hypotenuse.

The special relationship that exists among the squares of the lengths of the sides of a right triangle is known as the Pythagorean Theorem. The **Pythagorean Theorem** states that the sum of the squares of the lengths of the legs of a right triangle equals the square of the length of the hypotenuse: $a^2 + b^2 = c^2$.

There are different ways to prove that the Pythagorean Theorem holds true for all right triangles. A **proof** is a line of reasoning used to validate a theorem. In some proofs, you need to draw the diagonal of a square. A **diagonal of a square** is a line segment connecting opposite vertices of the square.

The Pythagorean Theorem can be used to determine unknown side lengths in a right triangle if you know two of the other side lengths.

For example, suppose you want to determine the length of the hypotenuse of the right triangle with leg lengths of 2 and 4.

$$c^2 = 2^2 + 4^2$$
$$c^2 = 4 + 16 = 20$$
$$c = \sqrt{20} \approx 4.5$$

The length of the hypotenuse is approximately 4.5 units.

LESSON

2   Can That Be Right?

The **converse** of a theorem is created when the if-then parts of that theorem are exchanged. The **Converse of the Pythagorean Theorem** states that if the sum of the squares of the two shorter sides of a triangle equals the square of the longest side, then the triangle is a right triangle.

Consider a triangle with the side lengths 9, 12, and 15.

$$9^2 + 12^2 \overset{?}{=} 15^2$$
$$81 + 144 \overset{?}{=} 225$$
$$225 = 225$$

This is a right triangle according to the Converse of the Pythagorean Theorem.

Any set of three positive integers a, b, and c that satisfies the equation $a^2 + b^2 = c^2$ is a **Pythagorean triple**. The integers 3, 4, and 5 form a Pythagorean triple because $3^2 + 4^2 = 5^2$. Given a Pythagorean triple, you can identify other right triangles by multiplying each side length by the same factor.

Pythagoras Meets Descartes

You can calculate the distance between two points on the coordinate plane by drawing a right triangle. When you think about this line segment as the hypotenuse of the right triangle, you can use the Pythagorean Theorem.

For example, consider the points (−5, 2) and (−8, 8). You can calculate the distance between these two points by first determining the length of each leg of a right triangle formed using that line segment as the hypotenuse. One leg measures 3 units, and the other leg measures 6 units.

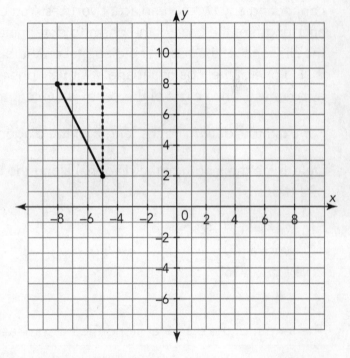

$$3^2 + 6^2 = c^2$$
$$9 + 36 = c^2$$
$$45 = c^2$$
$$c = \sqrt{45}$$

The distance between points (−5, 2) and (−8, 8) is $\sqrt{45}$ units.

The distance between two points on a coordinate plane is always a positive number.

You can use the Pythagorean Theorem to determine the length of a diagonal in a two- or three-dimensional figure.

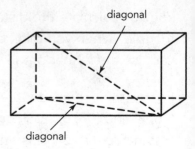

diagonal

diagonal

In a three-dimensional figure, a **diagonal** is a line segment connecting any two non-adjacent vertices. You can use the width and length of the base of the prism to determine the measure of the diagonal of the base. The diagonal on the base of the prism is also one of the legs of a triangle with an inner-diagonal as the hypotenuse. The height of the prism is the length of the other leg.

For example, determine the length of the diagonal of the rectangular prism shown.

Determine the length of the diagonal along the bottom face of the prism.

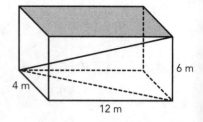

6 m

4 m

12 m

$$c^2 = 4^2 + 12^2$$
$$c^2 = 160$$
$$\sqrt{c^2} = \sqrt{160}$$
$$c \approx 12.6$$

The length of the diagonal along the bottom face is approximately 12.6 m.

Determine the length of the 3-D diagonal.

$$c^2 = 6^2 + 12.6^2$$
$$c^2 = 194.76$$
$$\sqrt{c^2} = \sqrt{194.76}$$
$$c \approx 13.96$$

The length of the 3-D diagonal is approximately 13.96 m.

MODULE 5

APPLYING POWERS

The lessons in this module build on your knowledge of exponents to develop new rules for operating with integer exponents. You will learn how to write, recognize, compare, and operate with numbers expressed in scientific notation. You will build on your prior experiences with the volume of prisms and pyramids to develop formulas for the volume of cylinders, cones, and spheres.

TOPIC 1

Exponents and Scientific Notation

The Pinwheel Galaxy, also known as Messier 101, is a spiral galaxy that is 21 million light-years away from earth in the constellation Ursa Major. For huge distances and tiny distances, you'll want to use scientific notation.

Module 5: Applying Powers

TOPIC 1: EXPONENTS AND SCIENTIFIC NOTATION

In this topic, students learn and apply properties of integer exponents. Students then explore a specific application of exponents and the exponent rules: scientific notation. They learn to express numbers in standard form in scientific notation and those in scientific notation in standard form. Throughout the conversion activities, students attend to the reasonableness of their answers. Once students understand scientific notation, they multiply, divide, add, and subtract numbers expressed in scientific notation, making connections to the exponent rules learned earlier in the topic.

Where have we been?

Students have been working with exponents since grade 5. They have learned to write and evaluate numerical and algebraic expressions with whole number exponents. In this topic, students expand on that knowledge.

Where are we going?

In high school, students will evaluate rational number exponents. Therefore, this topic provides a bridge between students' first formal use of exponents and a more rigorous and abstract exposure in high school. Scientific notation, an application of exponents, will arise in students' science courses in middle school and high school, particularly in the study of chemistry.

Using Tree Diagrams to Study Exponential Growth

A tree diagram can show exponential growth. This tree diagram is actually a family tree—for a dog. Rickson represents 2^0, or 1, dog. His parents in Generation 1 are 2^1, or 2, dogs. Generation 2 has 2^2, or 4, dogs, and Generation 3 shows 2^3, or 8, dogs.

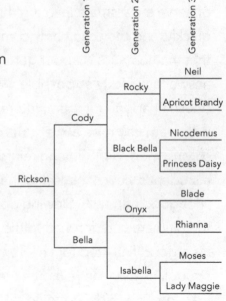

Myth: Faster = smarter.

In most cases, speed has nothing to do with how smart you are. Why is that? Because it largely depends on how familiar you are with a topic. For example, a bike mechanic can look at a bike for about 8 seconds and tell you details about the bike that you probably didn't even notice (e.g., the front tire is on backwards). Is that person smart? Sure! Suppose, instead, you show the same bike mechanic a car. Will **they** be able to recall the same amount of detail as for the bike? No!

It's easy to confuse speed with understanding. Speed is associated with the memorization of facts. Understanding, on the other hand, is a methodical, time-consuming process. Understanding is the result of asking lots of questions and seeing connections between different ideas. Many mathematicians who won the Fields Medal (i.e., the Nobel prize for mathematics) describe themselves as extremely slow thinkers. That's because mathematical thinking requires understanding over memorization.

#mathmythbusted

Talking Points

You can support your student's learning by approaching problems slowly. Students may observe a classmate learning things very quickly, and they can easily come to believe that mathematics is about getting the right answer as quickly as possible. When this doesn't happen for them, future encounters with math can raise anxiety, making problem solving more difficult, and reinforcing a student's view of himself or herself as "not good at math." Slowing down is not the ultimate cure for math difficulties. But it's a good first step for children who are struggling. You can reinforce the view that learning with understanding takes time, and that slow, deliberate work is the rule, not the exception.

Key Terms

base
The base of a power is the factor that is multiplied repeatedly in the power.

exponent
The exponent of a power is the number of times the base is used as a factor.

scientific notation
In general terms, $a \times 10^n$ is a number written in scientific notation, where a is greater than or equal to 1 and less than 10, and n is any integer. The number a is called the mantissa, and n is the called the characteristic.

It's a Generational Thing

Properties of Powers with Integer Exponents

1

WARM UP

Simplify each expression.

1. $(-10)(-10)(-10)$

2. $(-10)(-10)(-10)(-10)$

3. $(-1)(2)(-3)(4)(-5)$

4. $(-2)(-3)(-4)(-5)$

LEARNING GOALS

- Expand a power into a product.
- Write a product as a power.
- Simplify numeric expressions containing integer exponents.
- Develop rules to simplify a product of powers, a power of a power, and a quotient of powers.
- Apply the properties of integer exponents to create equivalent expressions.

KEY TERMS

- power
- base
- exponent

You have learned how to evaluate numeric expressions involving whole-number exponents. In this lesson, you will develop the properties of integer exponents to generate equivalent numeric expressions.

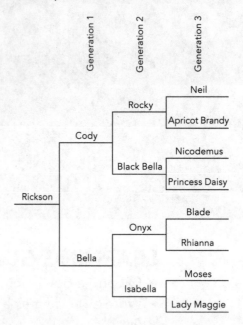

Three Generations

Jake adopted an English Mastiff puppy that he named Rickson. The breeder provided documentation that verified Rickson's lineage for three generations, as shown.

A dog's lineage is similar to a person's family tree. It shows a dog's parents, grandparents, and great-grandparents.

1. **How many parents does Rickson have? What are his parents' names?**

2. **How many grandparents does Rickson have?**

3. **How many great-grandparents does Rickson have?**

4. **What pattern is there in the number of dogs in each generation?**

Review of Powers and Exponents

Jake wants to trace Rickson's lineage back seven generations. How many sires (male parents) and dams (female parents) are there in seven generations of Rickson's lineage?

1. **Complete the second column of the table, Number of Sires and Dams, to show the total number of dogs in each generation.**

	Number of Sires and Dams		
Generation 1			
Generation 2			
Generation 3			
Generation 4			
Generation 5			
Generation 6			
Generation 7			

An expression used to represent the product of a repeated multiplication is a *power*. A **power** has a *base* and an *exponent*. The **base** of a power is the expression that is used as a factor in the repeated multiplication. The **exponent** of a power is the number of times that the base is used as a factor in the repeated multiplication.

WORKED EXAMPLE

You can write a power as a product by writing out the repeated multiplication.

$$2^7 = (2)(2)(2)(2)(2)(2)(2)$$

The power 2^7 can be read as:
- "two to the seventh power."
- "the seventh power of two."
- "two raised to the seventh power."

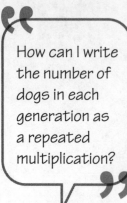

How can I write the number of dogs in each generation as a repeated multiplication?

2. Label the third column Expanded Notation. Then write each generation total as a product.

3. Label the fourth column of the table Power. Then write each generation total as a power.

4. How many dogs are in Rickson's lineage in the 12th generation back? Write your answer as a power, and then use a calculator to determine the total number of dogs.

5. How many total sires and dams are there in all three generations shown in Rickson's lineage? Explain your calculation.

In this activity, you will investigate the role of parentheses in expressions containing exponents.

1. Identify the base(s) and exponent(s) in each. Then, write each power as a product. Finally, evaluate the power.

   a. 5^3

   b. $(-9)^5$

   c. -11^3

   d. $(4)^5(3)^6$

2. Write each as a product. Then, calculate the product.

   a. -1^2 b. -1^3 c. -1^4 d. -1^5

   e. $(-1)^2$ f. $(-1)^3$ g. $(-1)^4$ h. $(-1)^5$

When the negative sign is not in parentheses, it's not part of the base.

3. What conclusion can you draw about a negative number raised to an odd power?

4. What conclusion can you draw about a negative number raised to an even power?

ACTIVITY 1.3
Multiplying and Dividing Powers

1 gigabyte =
1024 megabytes

1 megabyte =
1024 kilobytes

1 kilobyte =
1024 bytes

File sizes of eBooks, podcasts, and song downloads depend on the complexity of the content and the number of images.

WORKED EXAMPLE

Suppose that a medium-sized eBook contains about 1 megabyte (MB) of information.

Since 1 megabyte is 1024 kilobytes (kB), and 1 kilobyte is 1024 bytes (B), you can multiply to determine the number of bytes in the eBook:

$$1 \text{ MB} = (1024 \text{ kB}) \left(\frac{1024 \text{ B}}{1 \text{ kB}} \right) = 1{,}048{,}576 \text{ B}$$

There are 1,048,576 bytes in the eBook.

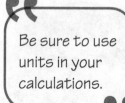

Be sure to use units in your calculations.

1. One model of an eBook can store up to 256 MB of data. A USB jump drive can hold 2 GB of storage. Use the method shown in the worked example to calculate each.

   a. Calculate the number of bytes the eBook can store.

   256 MB × _____ × _____

   b. A USB jump drive can hold 2 GB of storage. How many bytes can the USB jump drive hold?

   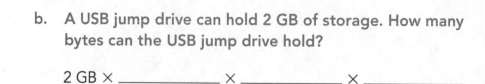
   2 GB × _____ × _____ × _____

   c. How many times more storage space does the jump drive have than the eBook? Show your work.

   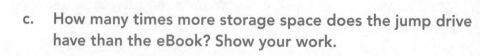
   $$\frac{2 \times \times \times}{256 \times \times }$$

WORKED EXAMPLE

Computers use binary math, or the base-2 system, instead of the base-10 system.

Base 10

$10^1 = 10$

$10^2 = (10)(10) = 100$

$10^3 = (10)(10)(10) = 1000$

Base 2

$2^1 = 2$

$2^2 = (2)(2) = 4$

$2^3 = (2)(2)(2) = 8$

2. Revisit Question 1, parts (a) through (c), by rewriting each factor and either your product or quotient as a power of 2.

   a.

   b.

   c.

3. Analyze your answers to Question 2. What do you notice about all the bases in Question 2?

4. In parts (a) and (b), how does the exponent in each product relate to the exponents in the factors?

5. In part (c), how does the exponent in the quotient relate to the exponents in the numerator and denominator?

Product of Powers

In this activity, you will explore different expressions to develop rules to evaluate powers.

1. Rewrite each expression as a product using expanded notation. Then identify the base or bases and record the number of times the base is used as a factor.

   a. $2^4 \cdot 2^3$

   b. $(-3)^3(-3)^3$

   c. $(4)(4^5)$

   d. $(5^2)(6^2)(5^3)(6)$

   e. $(9^3)(4^2)(9^2)(4^5)$

2. Rewrite each of your answers from Question 1 as a power or a product of powers.

3. What relationship do you notice between the exponents in the original expression and the number of factors?

4. Write a rule that you can use to multiply powers.

A power can also be raised to a power.

WORKED EXAMPLE

The exponential expression $(4^2)^3$ is a power to a power. It can be written as two repeated multiplication expressions using the definition of a power.

$(4^2)^3 = (4^2)(4^2)(4^2)$

$\quad\quad = (4)(4)(4)(4)(4)(4)$

There are 6 factors of 4.

5. Use the definition of a power to write repeated multiplication expressions for each power to a power, as modeled in the worked example. Then, record the number of factors.

   a. $(8^2)^3$

   b. $(5^4)^2$

   c. $-(6^1)^6$

   d. $((-6)^2)^2$

6. What relationship do you notice between the exponents in each expression in Question 5 and the number of factors? Write each expression as a single power.

7. Write a rule that you can use to raise a power to a power.

8. Simplify each expression using the rules that you wrote.

a. $6^4 \cdot 6^3$

b. $9^7 \cdot 9^8$

c. $(4^3)^5$

d. $(2)(3)(8)^5$

e. $5^5 \cdot 5^2 \cdot 5$

f. $((2)(3))^4$

9. Ramon says that $2^6 = 12$. Randy says that $2^6 = 64$. Who is correct? Explain your reasoning.

10. Isabel says that $2^2 + 2^3 = 2^5$, and Elizabeth says that $2^2 + 2^3 \neq 2^5$. Who is correct? Explain your reasoning.

ACTIVITY
1.5

Quotient of Powers

NOTES

Now, let's investigate what happens when you divide powers with like bases.

1. Write each numerator and denominator as a product. Then, simplify each expression and write the simplified expression using exponents.

   a. $\dfrac{9^5}{9^2}$ b. $\dfrac{5^6}{5^3}$ c. $\dfrac{10^8}{10^6}$ d. $\dfrac{10^2}{10}$

2. What relationship do you notice between the exponents in the numerator and denominator and the exponents in the simplified expression?

3. Write a rule that you can use to divide with powers.

4. Simplify each expression using the rule that you wrote for a quotient of powers.

   a. $\dfrac{6^8}{6^3}$ b. $-\dfrac{9^7}{9^5}$ c. $\dfrac{2^3}{3^2}$

You know that any number divided by itself is 1. How can you use that knowledge to develop another rule to evaluate powers?

Consider each representation of 1.

$$\frac{4}{4} = 1 \qquad\qquad \frac{9}{9} = 1 \qquad\qquad \frac{25}{25} = 1$$

1. Rewrite the numerator and denominator of each fraction as a power. Do not simplify.

2. Next, simplify the fractions you just wrote using the Quotient Rule of Powers. Leave your answer as a power. What do you notice?

An exception is that 0^0 is not equal to 1, because that would mean that using zero as a factor zero times would give you 1, and that's not possible.

3. Write a rule that you can use when raising any base to the zero power.

Let's determine how to use powers to represent numbers that are less than 1.

You know that you can use powers to represent numbers that are greater than or equal to 1.

4. Let's start with 1 and multiply by 10 three times.

a. Complete the representation. Write each as a power.

$$1 \quad = \quad 10^0$$

Multiply by 10 = ⟶ _____ = _____

Multiply by 10 = ⟶ _____ = _____

Multiply by 10 = ⟶ _____ = _____

b. Describe what happens to the exponents as the number becomes greater.

5. Now, let's start with 1 and divide by 10 three times.

a. Complete the representation. Write the division as a fraction, and then rewrite using the definition of powers. Next, apply the Quotient Rule of Powers, and finally, simplify each expression.

$$1 \quad = \quad \frac{10^0}{10^0} \quad = \quad 10^{0-0} \quad = \quad 10^0$$

Divide by 10 = ⟶ $\dfrac{1}{10}$ = $\dfrac{10^0}{10^1}$ = 10^{0-1} = 10^{-1}

Divide by 10 = ⟶ ____ = ____ = ____ = ____

Divide by 10 = ⟶ ____ = ____ = ____ = ____

b. Describe what happens to the exponents as the number becomes less.

c. Write each of the powers as a decimal.

6. Rewrite each sequence of numbers using the definition of powers.

   a. $\frac{1}{8}, \frac{1}{4}, \frac{1}{2}, 1, 2, 4, 8$

   b. $\frac{1}{27}, \frac{1}{9}, \frac{1}{3}, 1, 3, 9, 27$

   c. Describe the exponents in the sequence.

7. Simplify each expression using the Quotient Rule of Powers. Then, write each as a decimal.

   a. $\frac{10^0}{10^3}$

   b. $\frac{10^0}{10^5}$

   c. $\frac{10^0}{10^4}$

8. Complete the table shown.

Unit	Number of Grams	Number of Grams as an Expression with a Positive Exponent	Number of Grams as an Expression with a Negative Exponent
Milligram	$\frac{1}{1000}$		10^{-3}
Microgram		$\frac{1}{10^6}$	
Nanogram	$\frac{1}{1,000,000,000}$		10^{-9}
Picogram		$\frac{1}{10^{12}}$	

9. Rewrite the power so that the exponent is positive.

   a. 8^{-4}

   b. 5^{-6}

   c. 7^{-5}

   d. $(4^{-2})(3^{-3})$

10. Complete the table shown.

Given Expression	Expression with a Positive Exponent	Value of Expression
$\dfrac{1}{3^{-2}}$		
$\dfrac{1}{4^{-2}}$		
$\dfrac{1}{5^{-2}}$		
$\dfrac{2^{-2}}{1}$	$\dfrac{1}{2^{2}}$	$\dfrac{1}{4}$
$\dfrac{3^{-2}}{1}$		
$\dfrac{5^{-2}}{1}$		

11. Describe how to rewrite any expression with a negative exponent in the numerator.

12. Describe how to rewrite any expression with a negative exponent in the denominator.

TALK the TALK 💬

Simplifying

In this lesson, you have developed rules for operating with powers. A summary of these rules is shown in the table.

Properties of Powers	Words	Rule
Product Rule of Powers	To multiply powers with the same base, keep the base and add the exponents.	$a^m \cdot a^n = a^{m+n}$
Power to a Power Rule	To simplify a power to a power, keep the base and multiply the exponents.	$(a^m)^n = a^{mn}$
Quotient Rule of Powers	To divide powers with the same base, keep the base and subtract the exponents.	$\frac{a^m}{a^n} = a^{m-n}$, if $a \neq 0$
Zero Power	The zero power of any number expect for 0 is 1.	$a^0 = 1$, if $a \neq 0$
Negative Exponents in the Numerator	An expression with a negative exponent in the numerator and a 1 in the denominator equals 1 divided by the power with its opposite exponent placed in the denominator.	$a^{-m} = \frac{1}{a^m}$, if $a \neq 0$ and $m > 0$
Negative Exponents in the Denominator	An expression with a negative exponent in the denominator and a 1 in the numerator equals the power with its opposite exponent.	$\frac{1}{a^{-m}} = a^m$, if $a \neq 0$ and $m > 0$

Simplify each expression using the properties of powers.

1. $2a^8 \cdot 2a^6$

2. $4b^2 \cdot 8b^9$

3. $-3c \cdot 5c^3 \cdot 2c^9$

4. $(3d^2)^3$

5. $(10ef^3)^5$

6. $\dfrac{f^8}{f^3}$

7. $\dfrac{10g^4}{5g^6}$

8. $\dfrac{30h^8}{15h^2}$

9. $\dfrac{35i^7j^3}{7i^2j^3}$

10. $\left(\dfrac{a^2}{a^5}\right)^0$

11. $\dfrac{2^2}{2^6}$

12. $(4x^2)(3x^5)$

13. $(9^4)(9^{-5})$

14. $(8^0)(8^{-2})$

15. $\dfrac{3^{-3}}{3^{-3}}$

16. $\dfrac{4^{-2}}{4^{-3}}$

17. $\dfrac{(-3)^2}{(-3)^4}$

18. $\dfrac{h^3}{h^5}$

19. $\dfrac{x^4}{x^5}$

20. $\dfrac{m^2 p^{-2}}{m^4 p^3}$

Assignment

Write

Use the term *base*, *power*, or *exponent* to complete each sentence.

1. The _____ of a power is the number of times that the factor is repeatedly multiplied.

2. An expression used to represent a factor as repeated multiplication is called a _____.

3. The _____ of a power is the repeated factor in a power.

Remember

Properties of Powers	Words	Rule
Product Rule of Powers	To multiply powers with the same base, keep the base and add the exponents.	$a^m \cdot a^n = a^{m+n}$
Power to a Power Rule	To simplify a power to a power, keep the base and multiply the exponents.	$(a^m)^n = a^{mn}$
Quotient Rule of Powers	To divide powers with the same base, keep the base and subtract the exponents.	$\dfrac{a^m}{a^n} = a^{m-n}$, if $a \neq 0$

Practice

1. As the principal of Hope Middle School, Mr. Williams is in charge of notifying his staff about school delays or cancellations due to weather, power outages, or other unexpected events. Mr. Williams starts a phone chain by calling three staff members. Each of these staff members then calls three more staff members, who each call three more staff members. This process completes the calling list.

   a. Excluding Mr. Williams, how many staff members are there at Hope Middle School? Explain your calculation.

   b. Complete the first three columns in the table.

	Round 1	Round 2	Round 3	Round 4
Number of calls made				
Expanded notation				
Power				

   c. Dr. Novella, superintendent of the school district, decides that she should start the phone chain instead of the school principals. She starts the calling list by calling each of the principals of the three schools in her district. The principals continue the phone chain as described previously. Explain why the table in part (b) can be used to represent Dr. Novella's phone chain.

   d. Complete the fourth column in the table to represent the fourth round of calls in Dr. Novella's phone chain.

   e. How many calls are made in the fourth round? Show your work.

   f. Excluding Dr. Novella, how many principals and staff members are there in the entire school district? Explain your calculation.

2. The *hertz* (Hz) is a unit of frequency that represents the number of complete cycles per second. is used to measure repeating events, both scientific and general. For instance, a clock ticks at 1 Hz. One scientific application is the electromagnetic spectrum, or the range of all possible frequencies of electromagnetic waves. The spectrum includes frequencies from everyday contexts, such as radio and TV signals, microwaves, light (infrared, visible, and ultraviolet), and X-rays.

Name	Frequency
1 kilohertz (kHz)	1000 Hz
1 megahertz (MHz)	1000 kHz
1 gigahertz (GHz)	1000 MHz
1 terahertz (THz)	1000 GHz

For each question, use powers to write a mathematical expression. Then evaluate each expression. Express your answer as a power.

a. How many hertz are in 1 gigahertz? 1 terahertz?

b. A television channel has a frequency of 60 megahertz. What is the channel's frequency in hertz?

c. The frequency of a microwave is 30 gigahertz. What is the microwave's frequency in hertz?

d. The frequency of a visible ray of light is 1000 terahertz. A radio station has a frequency of 100 megahertz. How many times greater is the frequency of the light than the frequency of the radio station?

3. Each expression has been simplified incorrectly. Explain the mistake that occurred, and then make the correction.

a. $(-2x)^3 = 8x^3$

b. $\frac{16x^5}{4x} = 12x^4$

c. $(x^2y^4)^3 = x^6y^7$.

d. $(x^5y^7)(x^2yz) = x^7y^7z$

4. When you take a picture, the camera shutter controls how much light reaches the film or the digital image sensor. The shutter speed is the amount of time, in seconds, that the shutter stays open. Write each shutter speed as a power with a negative exponent.

a. $\frac{1}{4}$ second

b. $\frac{1}{8}$ second

c. $\frac{1}{125}$ second

d. $\frac{1}{1000}$ second

5. True or False: A number raised to a negative power is always a negative number. Give an example to support your answer.

6. Give an example of a number raised to a negative exponent that is a negative number.

7. Simplify each expression using the properties of powers. Show your work.

a. $\frac{10^2}{10^5}$

b. $\frac{3^{-5}}{3^{-5}}$

c. $(6x^4)(2x^{-2})$

d. $(7^{-6})(7^4)$

e. $(4^0)(4^{-3})$

f. $\frac{5^2}{5^{-2}}$

g. $\frac{4^{-1}}{4^2}$

h. $\frac{p^4}{p^9}$

i. $\frac{m^{-2}}{m^{-6}}$

j. $\frac{q^{-2}\,r^{-3}}{q^6\,r^{-4}}$

Stretch

Exponents can be stacked as high as you like. Some mathematicians have used double arrows to represent repeated exponents. For example, $3 \uparrow \uparrow 3$ represents $3^{3^{3}}$, or 3^{27}.

Write different numbers using double-arrow notation. How can you write 10 billion using this notation?

Review

Use the Pythagorean Theorem and its converse to answer each question.

1. You are making a picture frame in the craft cabin. The frame measures 9 inches by 12 inches. You measure the diagonal and it is 17 inches. Is the frame rectangular?

2. On the third day at camp, you go canoeing on the camp lake. You paddle from the dock due north for 500 yards and then due west for 475 yards. How far are you from the dock? Round your answer to the nearest whole number.

3. Complete the table of Pythagorean Triples.

Leg 1	Leg 2	Hypotenuse
3 feet	4 feet	
6 feet	8 feet	
9 feet	12 feet	
12 feet	16 feet	
15 feet	20 feet	

4. Use what you know about approximating square roots to answer each question.
   a. Explain how you know that the value of $\sqrt{12}$ is between 3 and 4.
   b. Shade between two values to show where $\sqrt{12}$ lies on the number line.

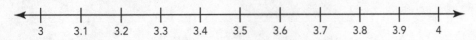

Show What You Know

2

Analyzing Properties of Powers

Warm Up

Simplify each expression.

1. $\frac{1}{3^2}$

2. $-(2^5)^2$

3. $\frac{2}{5} \cdot 10$

4. $\frac{32 + 8}{80 \div 2}$

LEARNING GOALS

- Review the Product Rule of Powers.
- Review the Power to a Power Property.
- Review the Quotient Rule of Powers Property.
- Generate equivalent expressions by applying properties of integer exponents.

You have learned about the properties of powers with integer exponents. How can you use these properties to justify your reasoning when solving problems?

Are They Equal?

The symbol for "is equal to" is =. The symbol for "is not equal to" is ≠. Write the appropriate symbol in each box to compare the two expressions. Explain your reasoning.

1. 2^3 ☐ 2^{-3}

2. $\dfrac{1}{2^3}$ ☐ 2^{-3}

3. $\dfrac{1}{2^{-3}}$ ☐ 2^3

4. $\dfrac{1}{2^{-3}}$ ☐ 2^{-3}

Using Properties of Powers to Justify Steps in Simplifying

Analyze the worked example.

WORKED EXAMPLE

$$\left(\frac{2^5}{2^4}\right)^3 =$$

$$= (2^1)^3 \quad \text{Quotient Rule of Powers}$$

$$= 2^3 \quad \text{Power to a Power Rule}$$

1. Identify the rule that justifies each step to simplify the expression.

   a. $2^4 \cdot (-4^1)^3$

   $= 2^4 \cdot (-4^3)$ _____

   $= (16)(-64)$ _____

   b. $\dfrac{(3 \cdot 5^3)^2}{(2 \cdot 5^4)^2}$

   $= \dfrac{(3^2 \cdot 5^6)}{(2^2 \cdot 5^8)}$ _____

   $= \dfrac{3^2}{(2^2 \cdot 5^2)}$ _____

   $= \dfrac{9}{4 \cdot 25}$ _____

   $= \dfrac{9}{100}$ _____

2. Simplify each expression using the properties of powers. Express your answers using only positive exponents.

a. $\dfrac{2(6)^3(4)^5}{4(6)^3(4)^2}$

b. $\dfrac{(4(1)^2(3)^3)^4}{(2(1)^3(3)^2)^3}$

c. $\dfrac{(-3(5)^2(8)^4)^8}{(-3(5)^2(8)^4)^8}$

d. $\dfrac{(10^5 \cdot 10^5)}{10^6}$

Analyzing Errors in Applying Properties of Powers

Determine which student(s) used the properties of powers correctly.
Explain why the other expressions are not correct.

1. $\dfrac{5^7 4^4}{5^3 4^9}$

   Adam wrote $5^{10}4^{13}$.

   Nic wrote $\dfrac{5^4}{4^5}$.

   Shane wrote $5^4 4^5$.

   Who is correct?

2. $\dfrac{2(3)^{-4}}{5^{-2}}$

   Adam wrote $\dfrac{2(5)^2}{3^4}$.

   Nic wrote $\dfrac{5^2}{2(3)^4}$.

   Shane wrote $\dfrac{2(3)^4}{5^2}$.

   Who is correct?

3. Each expression has been simplified incorrectly. Explain the mistake that occurred, and then make the correction.

a. $(-2 \cdot 7)^3 = 8 \cdot 7^3$

b. $\dfrac{16 \cdot 7^5}{4 \cdot 7} = 12 \cdot 7^4$

c. $(7^2 10^4)^3 = 7^6 10^7$

d. $(7^5 10^7)(7^2 10 \cdot 2) = 7^7 10^7 2$

TALK the TALK

Organize the Properties

1. Create graphic organizers for each.

   Product Rule of Powers

   Quotient Rule of Powers

   Power of a Power Rule

   Zero Power Rule

   Negative Exponent Rule

As you are creating your representations, consider the following:

Definition in your own words:	How would you describe this property to a friend?
Facts/Characteristics:	Are there specific characteristics if the numbers are positive or negative? Does this property work the same for variables and numbers?
Examples:	Include examples with variables and different types of numbers (e.g., positive, negative, and fractions).
General Rule:	Use variables. Be mindful of when a variable cannot be zero.

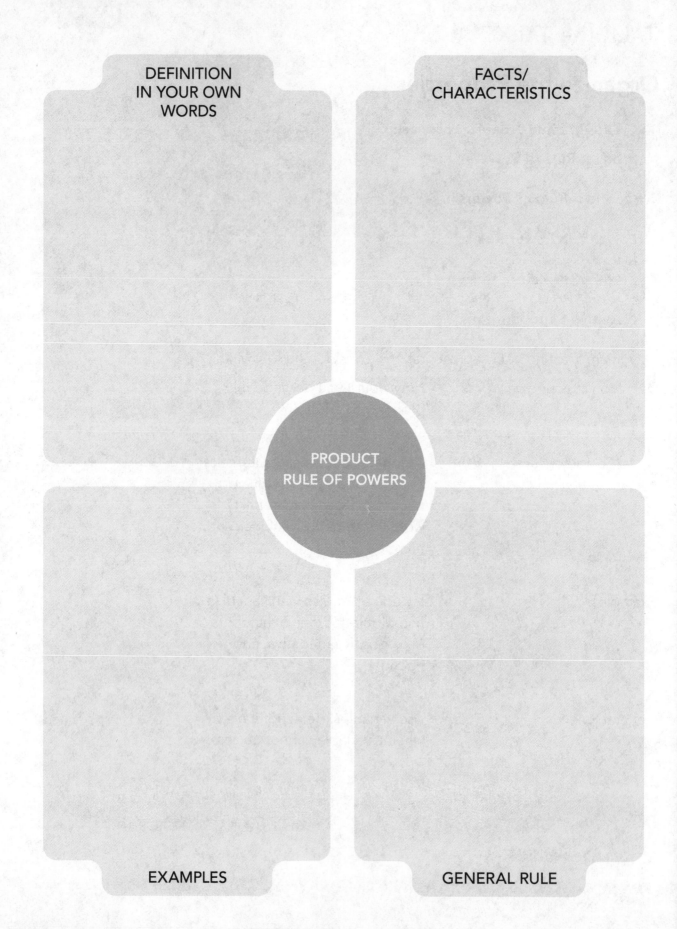

DEFINITION
IN YOUR OWN
WORDS

FACTS/
CHARACTERISTICS

PRODUCT
RULE OF POWERS

EXAMPLES

GENERAL RULE

DEFINITION
IN YOUR OWN
WORDS

FACTS/
CHARACTERISTICS

QUOTIENT
RULE OF POWERS

EXAMPLES

GENERAL RULE

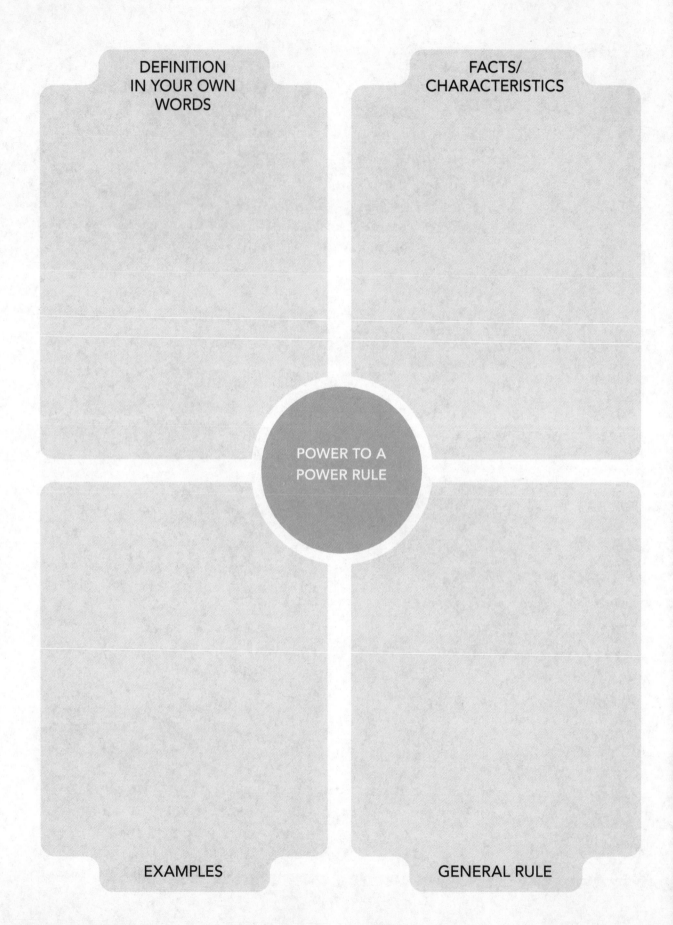

DEFINITION
IN YOUR OWN
WORDS

FACTS/
CHARACTERISTICS

POWER TO A
POWER RULE

EXAMPLES

GENERAL RULE

DEFINITION
IN YOUR OWN
WORDS

FACTS/
CHARACTERISTICS

ZERO POWER RULE

EXAMPLES

GENERAL RULE

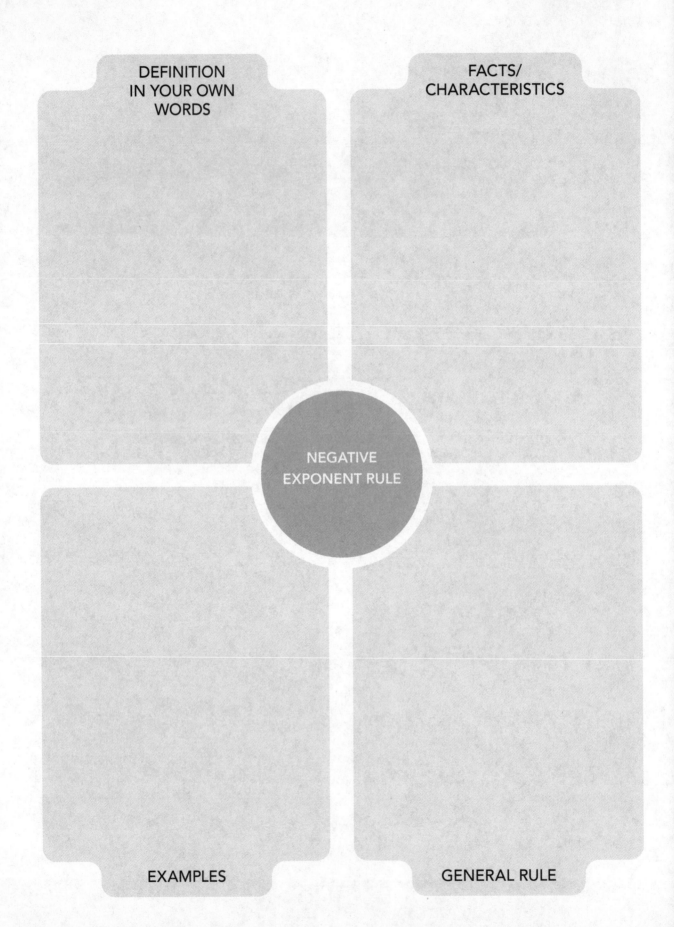

DEFINITION
IN YOUR OWN
WORDS

FACTS/
CHARACTERISTICS

NEGATIVE
EXPONENT RULE

EXAMPLES

GENERAL RULE

Assignment

Write

In your own words write the Quotient Rule, Product Rule, and Power to a Power Rule. Use examples to illustrate your descriptions.

Remember

Negative exponents in the numerator can be moved to the denominator and become positive, $a^{-m} = \frac{1}{a^m}$, if $a \neq 0$ and $m > 0$.

The zero power of any number except for 0 is 1.

Practice

Justify each step to simplify each expression. Choose the properties from the box.

Product Rule of Powers	Power to a Power Rule	Negative Exponent Rule	Quotient Rule of Powers
Zero Power Rule	Simplify Powers	Identity Property of Multiplication	Commutative Property of Multiplication

1. $4x^5 \cdot 6x^2y^6 \cdot xy$

2. $3a^2b^3 \cdot 7ab^5 \cdot b^2$

3. $(4m^2n^5)^3$

4. $(-3x^7y^3)^5$

5. $\frac{27y^8z^5}{-3y^4z^2}$

6. $\frac{-96m^9n^2}{8m^2n^6}$

7. $-2x^5y^3 \cdot 8x^2y^{-5} \cdot x^{-9}y^2$

8. $\frac{42m^5n^3 \cdot m^4n^2}{6m^6n^5}$

Stretch

Three positive integers have a sum of 10. How can you place the integers in the square brackets to form the greatest number possible?

$([\quad]) \cdot ([\quad])^{[]}$

Review

1. Simplify each expression using the properties of powers.

   a. $10^4 \cdot 10^{-5}$

   b. $2^{-6} \div 2^{-2}$

2. Plot and connect the points on a coordinate plane. Use the Pythagorean theorem to determine the length of the hypotenuse.

   a. A (0, 1), B (0, 7), C (8, 1)

   b. E (1, 4), F (1, 0), G (8, 4)

3. In each set of numbers, determine which value(s) are irrational numbers.

   a. $2\frac{2}{3}, \frac{5}{11}, \pi, \sqrt{9}, \sqrt{8}$

   b. $5.333, 0.\overline{33}, 4.25, 4.\overline{23}, 4.232425\ldots$

The Big and Small of It

3

Scientific Notation

WARM UP

Complete each statement to make it true.

1. $15 \cdot$ _____ $= 15{,}000$

2. $2.13 \cdot$ _____ $= 21{,}300{,}000$

3. $1.435 \cdot 0.1 =$ _____

4. _____ $\cdot \, 0.001 = 0.00576$

LEARNING GOALS

- Express numbers in scientific notation.
- Express numbers in standard form.
- Compare numbers written in scientific notation.
- Interpret scientific notation that has been generated by technology.

KEY TERMS

- scientific notation
- mantissa
- characteristic
- order of magnitude

You have used properties of powers to rewrite expressions with various bases and integer exponents. How can you use powers of 10 to represent and compare very large and very small numbers?

In the Blink of an Eye

"Your childhood will be gone in the blink of an eye!"

Has anyone ever told you not to grow up too fast? Or have you heard something similar?

Have you ever thought about how short a blink is? Or how many times you blink in an hour? In a day? In a year?

1. If the average person blinks once every 3 seconds, how many times have you blinked in your lifetime?

Kanye, Corinne, and Brock wanted to know how many times their
entire class has blinked in their lifetimes. Each student used a
different technology device: Kanye used a basic calculator, Corinne
used the calculator on her phone, and Brock used a graphing
calculator. There are 25 students in the class. Kanye, Corinne, and
Brock decided that, on average, the students each had blinked
98,112,000 times.

Corinne could
also rotate
her phone to
see a display
similar to the
display on
the graphing
calculator.

1. Analyze the display on each calculator.

2.4528e9

```
98112000*25
      2452800000
```

a. What was the total number of blinks for the entire class?
    Which display did you use to determine the total number?

b. Use the total number of blinks to interpret each of the
    remaining displays. How are the displays similar?
    How are they different?

Scientific notation is a tool to help you read and think about extremely large or small positive numbers.

The numbers on the smaller displays represented the large number of blinks in *scientific notation*.

Scientific notation is a notation used to express a very large or a very small number as the product of two numbers:

- a number that is greater than or equal to 1 and less than 10, and
- a power of 10.

In general terms, $a \times 10^n$ is a number written in scientific notation, where a is greater than or equal to 1 and less than 10, and n is any integer. The number a is called the **mantissa**, and n is the called the **characteristic**.

Scientific notation makes it much easier to tell at a glance the *order of magnitude*. The **order of magnitude** is an estimate of size expressed as a power of ten. For example, Earth's mass has an order of magnitude of 10^{24} kilograms.

2. Write the number of blinks from the calculator displays in scientific notation. Identify the mantissa and characteristic. What do you think the e in the displays means?

3. Use your graphing or scientific calculator to explore extremely large and extremely small numbers.

   a. Enter each given number into your calculator and complete the table.

Given Number	Calculator Display	What Does the Calculator Display Mean?
35,400,000,000		
60,000,000,000,000		
0.0000007		
0.000008935		

   b. Describe the characteristics for extremely large numbers.

   c. Describe the characteristics for extremely small numbers.

   d. Describe the mantissa in each.

4. Kanye, Corinne, Brock, and Daniel each tried to write the number 16,000,000,000 in scientific notation. Analyze each student's reasoning.

Kanye's Method

I start with 1.6, a number that is less than 10 and greater than 1. Next, I need a power of 10. If I multiply 1.6 by 10, I get 16. Then, if I multiply by 10 again, I get 160. Multiply by 10 again, and I get 1600. So, I can just keep multiplying by 10 until I get back to the original number. I have to multiply by 10 ten times, so my power of 10 is 10^{10}. So, 16,000,000,000 in scientific notation is 1.6×10^{10}.

Brock's Method

I have to write a number greater than 1 and less than 10 multiplied by a power of 10. So, I have to multiply 1.6 by a power of 10. Since there are 9 zeros, my power of 10 will be 10^9. So, 16,000,000,000 is 1.6×10^9.

Daniel's Method

Well, that number is 16 billion. And 16 billion is 16 times 1 billion. One billion has 9 zeros, so 16,000,000,000 in scientific notation is 16×10^9.

CORINNE'S METHOD

WELL, THAT NUMBER IS 16 BILLION. AND 16 BILLION IS 16 TIMES 1 BILLION. 16 X 1 IS THE SAME AS 1.6 X 10, SO 16 TIMES 1 BILLION IS THE SAME AS 1.6 TIMES 10 BILLION. I HAVE TO MULTIPLY 10 TEN TIMES TO GET 10 BILLION, SO MY POWER OF 10 IS 10^{10}. THAT MEANS THAT 16 BILLION IN SCIENTIFIC NOTATION IS 1.6×10^{10}.

a. Compare Brock's and Daniel's methods.

b. Compare Kanye's and Brock's methods.

c. Compare Daniel's and Corinne's methods.

d. Of the correct methods, which method do you prefer? Why?

Scientific Notation and Large Numbers

In this activity, you will practice writing large numbers in either scientific notation or standard notation.

1. Write each number in the notation that is not given.

   a. There are approximately 3.34×10^{22} molecules in a gram of water.

   b. There are 2.5×10^{13} red blood cells in the human body.

   c. One light year is 5,880,000,000,000 miles.

   d. The speed of light is 186,000 miles per second.

2. The estimated populations, as of December 2016, of several countries are shown. Decide whether the number is written in scientific notation or standard notation. If the number is not in scientific notation, explain how you know it is not. Then, write the number in scientific notation.

   a. People's Republic of China: 1.382×10^9 people

   b. Pitcairn Islands: 50 people

   c. Australia: 24.3×10^6 people

   d. United States: 3.24×10^8 people

3. List the countries from Question 2 in order of population from least to greatest. Explain your strategy.

4. The primary U.S. currency note dispensed at an automated teller machine (ATM) is the 20-dollar bill. There are approximately 6 billion 20-dollar bills in circulation.

   a. Write the approximate number of 20-dollar bills in circulation in standard notation.

   b. Write the number of bills in scientific notation.

   c. Calculate the value of all the 20-dollar bills in circulation.

   d. Write the value you calculated in part (c) in scientific notation.

ACTIVITY 3.3

Scientific Notation and Small Numbers

Now, let's explore writing very small numbers using scientific notation.

1. A water molecule has an approximate length of 0.1 nanometer. One nanometer is $\frac{1}{10^7}$ of a centimeter. Complete the statements and answer the question. Write your answers as decimals.

   a. 1 nanometer = _____ centimeter

   b. 0.1 nanometer = _____ centimeter

   c. How many centimeters long is a string of 7 water molecules? Show your work.

Just as with large numbers, scientific notation can be used to express very small numbers in a more compact form that requires less counting of zeros. The value of the number does not change, only how it is written.

2. Each student tried to write the number 0.00065 in scientific notation. Analyze each student's reasoning.

Brock's Method

I can start with 6.5, which is less than 10 and greater than 1. If I divide by 10, I get 0.65. If I divide by 10 again, I get 0.065. I just keep dividing by 10 until I get to the original number.

I divided by 10 four times. So, 0.00065 = $\frac{6.5}{10^4}$. But in scientific notation, I have to use multiplication, not division. That's okay because $\frac{6.5}{10^4}$ is the same as 6.5 × $\frac{1}{10^4}$. And since $\frac{1}{10^4}$ is 10^{-4}, I can write 0.00065 in scientific notation as 6.5 × 10^{-4}.

CORINNE'S METHOD

I CAN WRITE 0.00065 AS A FRACTION LESS THAN 1. IN WORDS, THAT DECIMAL IS SIXTY-FIVE HUNDRED THOUSANDTHS, SO I COULD WRITE IT AS $\frac{65}{100,000}$.

IF I DIVIDE BOTH THE NUMERATOR AND DENOMINATOR BY 10, I GET $\frac{65 \div 10}{100000 \div 10} = \frac{6.5}{10,000}$. AS A POWER OF 10, THE NUMBER 10,000 IS WRITTEN AS 10^4. SO THAT'S $\frac{6.5}{10^4}$, WHICH IS THE SAME AS $6.5 \times \frac{1}{10^4}$, WHICH IS THE SAME AS 6.5×10^{-4}. THAT'S THE ANSWER.

Kanye's Method

I moved the decimal point in the number to the right until I made a number greater than 1 but less than 10. So, I moved the decimal point four times to make 6.5. And since I moved the decimal point four times to the right, that's the same as multiplying 10 x 10 x 10 x 10, or 10^4. So, the answer should be 6.5×10^4.

Daniel's Method

I don't like decimals, so I moved the decimal point all the way to the right until I had a whole number. Because I moved the decimal point five times to make 65, that's the same as dividing by 10 five times. So, the answer in scientific notation should be 65×10^{-5}.

a. Explain what is wrong with Kanye's reasoning.

b. Explain what is wrong with Daniel's method.

c. Of the correct methods, which method do you prefer? Why?

There are names given to measurements smaller than a meter (m). You are familiar with the centimeter, the millimeter, and now the nanometer. These statements show how some small measurements relate to a meter:

- 1 centimeter (cm) = $\frac{1}{10^2}$ meter
- 1 millimeter (mm) = $\frac{1}{10^3}$ meter
- 1 micrometer (μm) = $\frac{1}{10^6}$ meter
- 1 nanometer (nm) = $\frac{1}{10^9}$ meter
- 1 picometer (pm) = $\frac{1}{10^{12}}$ meter

3. Write each measurement as a power of 10. It is appropriate to have an expression with negative exponents in this question set.

a. 1 centimeter

b. 1 millimeter

c. 1 micrometer

d. 1 nanometer

e. 1 picometer

4. Write the radius of each type of blood vessel in standard form.

   a. The capillary is one of the minute blood vessels that connect arterioles and venules. The radius of a capillary is 5×10^{-3} mm.

   b. The venule is a small blood vessel that allows deoxygenated blood to return from the capillaries to the veins. The radius of a venule is 1×10^{-2} mm.

   c. The arteriole is a small blood vessel that extends and branches out from an artery and leads to capillaries. The radius of an arteriole is 5.0×10^{-1} mm.

5. Convert each measurement to meters, and then write the measurement in scientific notation.

   a. The diameter of a water molecule is 0.29 nanometers.

   b. The diameter of a red blood cell is 7 micrometers.

   c. The smallest microchip is 7 nanometers wide.

   d. A helium atom has a radius of 31 picometers.

6. Complete the table shown.

Object	Measurement	Measurement in Standard Form	Measurement in Scientific Notation
Earth	Radius in meters		6.38×10^6 m
Brachiosaurus	Mass in kilograms	77,100 kg	
Dust mite	Length in meters	0.00042 m	
Nucleus of an atom	Diameter in meters		1.6×10^{-15} m

ACTIVITY 3.4	Comparing Numbers in Scientific Notation

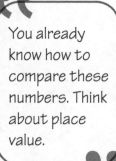

You already know how to compare these numbers. Think about place value.

Writing numbers in scientific notation is useful when comparing very large or very small numbers.

1. Compare each set of large numbers written in scientific notation using the appropriate symbol: <, >, or = .

a. 4.5×10^4 _____ 1.5×10^4

b. 7.6×10^{12} _____ 8.1×10^{12}

c. 4.5×10^4 _____ 4.5×10^7

d. 9.3×10^{15} _____ 9.3×10^{13}

e. 7.6×10^9 _____ 5.8×10^{12}

f. 1.9×10^8 _____ 3.2×10^4

2. Explain how to compare two large numbers using scientific notation.

3. Compare each set of small numbers written in scientific notation using the appropriate symbol: $<$, $>$, or $=$.

   a. 4.5×10^{-4} _____ 1.5×10^{-4}

   b. 7.6×10^{-12} _____ 8.1×10^{-12}

   c. 4.5×10^{-4} _____ 4.5×10^{-7}

   d. 9.3×10^{-15} _____ 9.3×10^{-13}

   e. 7.6×10^{-9} _____ 5.8×10^{-12}

   f. 1.9×10^{-8} _____ 3.2×10^{-4}

4. Explain how to compare two small numbers using scientific notation.

5. Describe the similarities and differences between the numbers 4.23×10^{5} and 4.23×10^{-5}.

TALK the TALK

A Rose by Any Other Name...

1. Complete the table to describe each notation.

Notation	Definition	Example
Scientific		
Standard		

Assignment

Write

Explain how to write a number expressed in standard form in scientific notation.

Remember

Scientific notation is a notation used to express a very large or very small number as the product of two numbers:

- the mantissa, which is a number greater than or equal to 1 and less than 10, and
- a power of 10, in which the exponent is called the characteristic.

Practice

1. Decide whether the number is written in scientific notation. If not, write the number in scientific notation. Explain your reasoning for each number.

   a 38.7×10^4

   b. 2.56×10^{-3}

   c. 0.025×10^{-6}

   d. 2.3^4

2. Complete the table.

Quantity	Measurement in Standard Form	Measurement in Scientific Notation
Approximate world population in number of people (December 2016)	7,433,000,000	
Time for a computer to perform an operation in seconds		3.0×10^{-10}
Average fingernail thickness in inches	0.015	
Gallons of fresh water used in the U.S. each year		2.5×10^{13}
Diameter of a very fine human hair in meters	0.000017	
Mass of Mars in tons		7.08×10^{20}
Diameter of bacteria in inches		8×10^{-6}

3. Write each number in scientific notation.

   a. There are over 29,000 grains of long-grain rice in a one-pound bag.

   b. The distance from Earth to the Moon is about 385,000,000 meters.

   c. The diameter of a red blood cell is about 0.00004 inch.

   d. A grain of salt weighs about 0.0000585 gram.

4. Write each number in standard form.

    a. There are about 1×10^5 strands of hair on the human head.

    b. The circumference of Earth at the equator is about 4.008×10^7 meters.

    c. An oxygen atom has a radius of about 4.8×10^{-11} meter.

5. Compare each set of numbers written in scientific notation using the appropriate symbol: $<$, $>$, or $=$.

    a. 6.7×10^{-8} _____ 9.5×10^{-8}

    b. 4.3×10^{12} _____ 1.3×10^{12}

    c. 3.1×10^{-4} _____ 3.1×10^{-7}

    d. 9.7×10^{15} _____ 9.7×10^{13}

    e. 2.9×10^{-11} _____ 6.8×10^{-12}

    f. 4.9×10^{-2} _____ 4.9×10^{2}

Stretch

Compare each set of numbers using the appropriate symbol: $<$, $>$, or $=$.

1. 2.478×10^4 _____ 2500

2. 2.478×10^{-4} _____ 0.00025

3. 10.5^3 _____ 5×10^3

4. 0.00012378 _____ 1.3×10^{-4}

Review

1. Simplify each expression using the properties of powers. Express your answers using only positive exponents.

    a. $\dfrac{(2^4)(2^7)(2^{-3})}{(2^{-1})(2^0)(2^8)}$
                 b. $\dfrac{(-3)^4(-3)^3(-3)^{-1}}{(-3)^5(-3)^{-2}}$

2. Use the Pythagorean Theorem to answer each question.

    a. Paul and Moriah are trying to find the shortest route to their favorite restaurant. They have narrowed their search to two routes which form a right triangle. The legs of the triangle are 8 miles and 10 miles. Would it be a shorter distance traveling the legs of the triangle or the hypotenuse? Justify your answer.

    b. Eric is designing a geometric statue for an arts festival. The base of the statue is a right triangle. If the lengths of the legs of the base are 13 inches and 84 inches, how long is the hypotenuse of the base?

3. Solve each equation.

    a. $x^2 + 8 = 17$
                 b. $2x^3 = 16$

How Much Larger?

Operations with Scientific Notation

WARM UP

Write each number in standard notation and in scientific notation.

1. seven thousand

2. 1.3 million

3. 2.34 billion

4. 6.85 trillion

LEARNING GOALS

- Perform operations using scientific notation.
- Compare relative sizes of numbers written in scientific notation.
- Choose units of appropriate size for measurements of very large or very small quantities.
- Interpret values in scientific notation to express how many times as much one value is than another.

You have learned about the properties of powers. How can you use these properties to perform operations with numbers expressed in scientific notation?

Eww... Eyelashes!

The average human has 90 to 150 eyelashes on each upper lid and 70–80 eyelashes on each lower lid. Each person loses approximately 1 to 4 eyelashes each day.

1. If the weight of one eyelash is approximately 0.00007 gram, approximately how many kilograms of eyelashes have you lost in your life?

ACTIVITY 4.1	Applying the Product Rules of Powers to Scientific Notation

Before a recent class trip to a lake, Vanessa said she wanted to bring back 3 million grains of sand for a classmate who could not go on the trip. If 1 grain of sand weighs approximately 6.7×10^{-7} kg, how heavy are 3 million grains of sand?

WORKED EXAMPLE

To calculate the total weight of 3,000,000 grains of sand, you would multiply the weight of 1 grain of sand by the total number of grains of sand, or $\dfrac{0.00000067 \text{ kilograms}}{1 \text{ grain of sand}}$ (3,000,000 grains of sand).

You can use scientific notation and the Product Rules of Powers to compute this product more efficiently.

Begin by writing the numbers in scientific notation.	$(6.7 \times 10^{-7})(3 \times 10^{6})$
Apply the Associative and Commutative Properties of Multiplication.	$(6.7 \times 3)(10^{-7} \times 10^{6})$
Apply the Product Rule of Powers to powers with the same base.	$(6.7 \times 3)(10^{-7+6})$
Simplify each factor of the product.	$(20.1)(10^{-1})$
Rewrite in standard form, if desired.	2.01 kg

Three million grains of sand weigh approximately 2.01 kilograms.

1. Suppose that a student has lost 15,000 eyelashes in his life. Use scientific notation to calculate the total weight, in kilograms, of his lost eyelashes. Write your answer in scientific notation.

2. An ecologist estimates that it takes approximately 196,000 pounds of buried plant matter to produce one gallon of gasoline. Some energy experts estimate that the United States consumed about 140.4 billion gallons of gasoline in 2015.

   Calculate the amount of buried plant matter needed to produce the amount of gasoline consumed in 2015. Write your answer in scientific notation.

3. An oil tanker is approximately 1400 feet long. How far would 9500 oil tankers span if they were placed end to end?

   a. Calculate the approximate length of 9500 oil tankers. Write your answer in scientific notation.

Remember: A number written in scientific notation has a mantissa greater than or equal to 1 and less than 10.

   b. What additional step is required to calculate the answer in Question 3, part (a) that was not required in Question 2?

4. Calculate each product. Express each product in scientific notation.

   a. $(3 \times 10^5)(2 \times 10^6)$ b. $(9 \times 10^4)(1 \times 10^7)$

   c. $(4.0 \times 10^8)(2.7 \times 10^4)$ d. $(5.6 \times 10^{-6})(3.5 \times 10^{15})$

5. Determine the unknown factors in each equation. Explain your reasoning.

   a. $(4 \times 10^7)(? \times ?) = 8 \times 10^{12}$ b. $(? \times ?)(5 \times 10^3) = 3.5 \times 10^8$

Applying the Quotient Rule of Powers to Scientific Notation

The Scoville scale measures the hotness of a chili pepper by the amount of capsaicin it contains. Capsaicin is the chemical that puts the "heat" in chili peppers. The number of Scoville heat units (SHU) indicates the amount of capsaicin present in the food. The table represents the Scoville rating for a variety of peppers.

Scoville Rating	Type
15,000,000 to 16,000,000	Pure Capsaicin
5,000,000 to 5,300,000	Law Enforcement Grade Pepper Spray
350,000 to 570,000	Red Savina Habanero
200,000 to 300,000	Habanero
70,000 to 80,000	Thai Pepper
30,000 to 50,000	Cayenne Pepper, Tabasco Pepper, some Chipotle Peppers
2500 to 8000	Jalapeño Peppers, Paprika (Hungarian)
500 to 2500	Anaheim Pepper (Mild Chile Pepper)
100 to 500	Pimento, Pepperoncini
0	No Heat, Bell Pepper

*Source: Mojave Pepper Farm's Pepper Scale

> I wonder how much hotter a habanero pepper is than a jalapeño pepper. How could you compare the peppers?

Use the values from the table to answer each question.

1. How many times hotter is the mildest law enforcement grade pepper spray than the hottest pepperoncini?

   a. First, write a ratio using the values in the table as they appear.

   b. Next, write your ratio in scientific notation.

   c. Finally, rewrite your expression using the Quotient Rule of Powers. Explain your reasoning.

   d. What does your result represent?

2. Answer each pepper heat comparison question.

   a. How many times hotter is the hottest Thai pepper than the hottest jalapeño pepper?

   b. How many times hotter is the mildest law enforcement grade pepper spray than the hottest cayenne pepper?

3. What do you notice about the results in Questions 1 and 2? Explain why this happened.

4. Answer each pepper heat comparison question.

   a. How many times hotter is the hottest red savina habanero than the mildest jalapeño pepper?

   b. How many times hotter is the hottest form of capsaicin than the mildest Anaheim pepper?

   c. How many times hotter is the hottest cayenne pepper than the mildest jalapeño pepper?

   d. How are these comparisons different from the comparisons in Questions 1 and 2?

5. Determine each quotient. Express the quotient in scientific notation.

   a. $\dfrac{(6 \times 10^8)}{(2 \times 10^3)}$

   b. $\dfrac{(9 \times 10^5)}{(3 \times 10^9)}$

   c. $\dfrac{(8 \times 10^{-4})}{(2 \times 10^3)}$

ACTIVITY 4.3

Adding and Subtracting Numbers in Scientific Notation

The table shows the average distance of each planet from the Sun.

Planet	Average Distance from the Sun, Written in Standard Notation (kilometers)	Average Distance from the Sun, Written in Scientific Notation (kilometers)
Mercury	58,000,000	
Venus	108,000,000	
Earth	149,600,000	
Mars	228,000,000	
Jupiter	778,500,000	
Saturn	1,430,000,000	
Uranus	2,880,000,000	
Neptune	4,500,000,000	

1. Write each distance in scientific notation in the table.

2. Compare the distances from Mars to the Sun and Venus to the Sun.

   a. Use the standard form of the distances to determine, on average, how much farther Mars is than Venus from the Sun.

   b. Write the answer from part (a) in scientific notation.

   c. Compare the characteristics for the distances from the Sun to Mars and from the Sun to Venus. Then look at the characteristic of your answer from part (b). What do you notice?

   d. Compare the mantissas for the distances from the Sun to Mars and from the Sun to Venus. Then look at the mantissa of your answer from part (b). What do you notice?

3. Describe how to calculate the difference of two numbers written in scientific notation that have the same characteristic.

4. Compare the distances from Mars to the Sun and from Mercury to the Sun.

a. Use the standard form of the distances to determine on average how much farther Mars is from the Sun than Mercury.

b. Carlos and Tonya used scientific notation to subtract: $2.28 \times 10^8 - 5.8 \times 10^7$.

How are their methods similar?
How are their methods different?

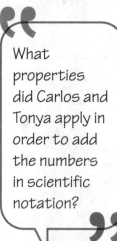

What properties did Carlos and Tonya apply in order to add the numbers in scientific notation?

Carlos

First, I rewrote 2.28×10^8 as 22.8×10^7. Then I subtracted.

$$2.28 \times 10^8 - 5.8 \times 10^7 = 22.8 \times 10^7 - 5.8 \times 10^7$$
$$= 17 \times 10^7$$
$$= 1.7 \times 10^8$$

Tonya

I rewrote 5.8×10^7 as 0.58×10^8, and then I subtracted.

$$2.28 \times 10^8 - 5.8 \times 10^7 = 2.28 \times 10^8 - 0.58 \times 10^8$$
$$= 1.7 \times 10^8$$

5. Describe how to calculate the sum or difference of two numbers written in scientific notation that have different characteristics.

6. Calculate each sum or difference using any method. Write your answer in scientific notation.

   a. $3.7 \times 10^5 + 2.1 \times 10^6$

   b. $2.9 \times 10^8 - 1.4 \times 10^4$

   c. $2.5 \times 10^4 - 3.1 \times 10^2$

   d. $9.1 \times 10^8 + 4.3 \times 10^7$

As you have seen, numbers can be written in a variety of forms. They are all just numbers, so you can operate on them once they are in similar forms. Because numbers can be written in many ways, you may need to decide what units to use when you express results of operations.

1. You are interested in determining how fast your hair grows.

   a. Which units do you think are most reasonable for this rate: nanometers per month, centimeters per month, or meters per month? Explain your reasoning.

   b. Your hairdresser says that your hair grows 6.35×10^{-6} kilometers per month. Determine how long your hair grows in 14 years. Express your answer in scientific notation, using the unit of length that you selected in part (a).

> As you work, your results may not be in scientific notation, but make sure your answer is!

2. Compare the speeds at which light and sound travel. Sound travels at a speed of 340.29 meters per second, and light travels at a speed of approximately 3×10^5 kilometers per second.

   a. Which units will you use to compare the two speeds? Explain your reasoning.

   b. How much faster is the speed of light than the speed of sound?

3. Calculate each sum, difference, product, or quotient. Write each answer in scientific notation.

a. $(2.35 \times 10^7) + 874{,}236$ b. $4.047 - (1.3 \times 10^{-2})$

c. $(792)(5.19 \times 10^{-5})$ d. $(6.02 \times 10^{23}) \div 12$

TALK the TALK

Operator, Operator

You have learned how to operate with numbers written in scientific notation. Can you generalize what you have learned?

1. Consider two numbers with the same characteristic: $a \times 10^n$ and $b \times 10^n$. In each case, a and b are at least 1 but less than 10, and n is an integer.

a. Determine the product of the numbers in terms of a, b, and n.

b. Determine the quotient of the numbers in terms of a, b, and n.

c. Determine the sum of the numbers in terms of a, b, and n.

d. Determine the difference of the numbers in terms of a, b, and n.

2. Consider two numbers with the same mantissa: $a \times 10^m$ and $a \times 10^n$.

   a. Determine the product of the numbers in terms of a, m, and n.

   b. Determine the quotient of the numbers in terms of a, m, and n.

   c. Explain how to determine the sum or difference of the numbers.

3. Consider any two numbers: $a \times 10^m$ and $b \times 10^n$.

   a. Determine the product of the numbers in terms of a, b, m, and n.

   b. Determine the quotient of the numbers in terms of a, b, m, and n.

   c. Explain how to determine the sum or difference of the numbers.

Assignment

Write

Explain how multiplying and dividing numbers in scientific notation is different from adding and subtracting numbers in scientific notation.

Remember

The properties of exponents apply to numbers expressed in scientific notation.

Practice

1. As the United States has developed over the last century, Americans have used increasing amounts of electricity. The total use of electricity is measured in kilowatt-hours (kWh) and is tracked by the Department of Energy.

   a. The total use of electricity in the United States in 1902 was about 6.03 billion kilowatt-hours. Electricity use was about 595 times greater by 2000. Calculate the total use of electricity in 2000. Use scientific notation.

   b. The total use of electricity in the United States was about 0.4 trillion kilowatt-hours in 1950 and about 2.8 trillion kilowatt-hours in 1990. How many times more electricity was used in 1990 than in 1950? Use scientific notation.

   c. The total use of electricity in the U.S. decreased by 51 billion kilowatt-hours from 2007 to 2008. The electricity usage in 2007 was 3.924 trillion kilowatt-hours. Calculate the percent of decrease in electricity use by dividing the amount of decrease by the usage in 2007. Use scientific notation.

   d. What do you think may have contributed to the decrease from 2007 to 2008?

2. Calculate each sum or difference. Express your answer in scientific notation.

   a. $2.45 \times 10^7 + 4.73 \times 10^8$

   b. $9.01 \times 10^{12} - 8.67 \times 10^{11}$

   c. $5.19 \times 10^{-5} + 6.8 \times 10^{-8}$

   d. $1.714 \times 10^{-10} - 3.23 \times 10^{-12}$

3. Calculate each product. Express the product in scientific notation.

   a. $(2 \times 10^{-3})(3 \times 10^8)$

   b. $(4.2 \times 10^{-4})(9.1 \times 10^{-6})$

   c. According to many scientists, Argentinosaurus is the heaviest known dinosaur. It weighed 220,000 pounds. How much would 1500 Argentinosaurus dinosaurs weigh? Use scientific notation to calculate the weight.

   d. The bee hummingbird is the world's smallest bird. It is about 0.05842 meter long. How far would 2,000,000 bee hummingbirds span if they were placed head to tail? Use scientific notation to calculate the length.

4. Calculate each quotient. Express the quotient in scientific notation.

a. $\dfrac{1.508 \times 10^7}{2.6 \times 10^3}$ b. $\dfrac{1.5 \times 10^{-7}}{5 \times 10^4}$ c. $\dfrac{8.82 \times 10^{-7}}{2.52 \times 10^{-2}}$

d. A football is about 280 millimeters long. A football field is about 100,000 millimeters long. How many footballs placed end to end would be needed to span the field? Use scientific notation to calculate the number of footballs.

Stretch

Calculate each power. Write your answer in scientific notation.

a. $(3 \times 10^2)^4$ b. $(1.7 \times 10^5)^3$

c. $(4.5 \times 10^3)^3$ d. $(1.2 \times 10^4)^6$

Review

1. Sylvia just completed a quiz on scientific notation. Score her quiz and provide her percent grade. Correct any errors.

Directions: Rewrite the numbers provided in either standard notation or scientific notation.

a. 3.4×10^8 = 3,400,000,000

b. 8.25×10^{-3} = 0.00825

c. 93,000,000 = 93 × 10⁶ 93×10^6

d. 4.0005×10^5 = 400,050

e. 0.000091   = 9.1 × 10⁵ 9.1×10^5

2. Use the Pythagorean theorem to determine unknown side length. Round your answer to the nearest tenth.

a.

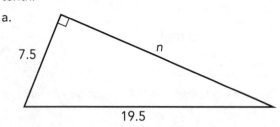

b. A right triangle has a hypotenuse with a length of 18 cm and a leg with length of 14 cm. Calculate the length of the third side.

3. Approximate each root to the nearest tenth.

a. $\sqrt{70}$ b. $\sqrt[3]{70}$

Exponents and Scientific Notation Summary

KEY TERMS

- power
- base
- exponent
- scientific notation

- mantissa
- characteristic
- order of magnitude

LESSON 1 It's a Generational Thing

An expression used to represent the product of a repeated multiplication is a power. A **power** has a base and an exponent. The **base** of a power is the expression that is used as a factor in the repeated multiplication. The **exponent** of a power is the number of times that the base is used as a factor in the repeated multiplication.

You can write a power as a product by writing out the repeated multiplication.

$$2^7 = (2)(2)(2)(2)(2)(2)(2)$$

The power 2^7 can be read as:

- "two to the seventh power."
- "the seventh power of two."
- "two raised to the seventh power."

Parentheses can change the value of expressions containing exponents. When the negative sign is not in parentheses, it's not part of the base. For example, $-1^2 = -1$, but $(-1)^2 = 1$.

Properties of Powers	Words	Rule
Product Rule of Powers	To multiply powers with the same base, keep the base and add the exponents.	$a^m \cdot a^n = a^{m+n}$
Power to a Power Rule	To simplify a power to a power, keep the base and multiply the exponents.	$(a^m)^n = a^{mn}$
Quotient Rule of Powers	To divide powers with the same base, keep the base and subtract the exponents.	$\dfrac{a^m}{a^n} = a^{m-n}$, if $a \neq 0$
Zero Power	The zero power of any number expect for 0 is 1.	$a^0 = 1$, if $a \neq 0$
Negative Exponents in the Numerator	An expression with a negative exponent in the numerator and a 1 in the denominator equals 1 divided by the power with its opposite exponent placed in the denominator.	$a^{-m} = \dfrac{1}{a^m}$, if $a \neq 0$ and $m > 0$
Negative Exponents in the Denominator	An expression with a negative exponent in the denominator and a 1 in the numerator equals the power with its opposite exponent.	$\dfrac{1}{a^{-m}} = a^m$, if $a \neq 0$ and $m > 0$

LESSON 2

Show What You Know

The properties of powers can be used to simplify numeric expressions.

For example, you can simplify the expression $\left(\dfrac{2^5}{2^4}\right)^3$.

$\left(\dfrac{2^5}{2^4}\right)^3 = (2^1)^3$ Quotient Rule of Powers

$\quad\quad\; = 2^3$ Power to a Power Powers

LESSON 3

The Big and Small of It

Scientific notation is a notation used to express a very large or a very small number as the product of two numbers:

- A number that is greater than or equal to 1 and less than 10 and
- A power of 10.

In general terms, $a \times 10^n$ is a number written in scientific notation, where a is greater than or equal to 1 and less than 10, and n is any integer. The number a is called the **mantissa**, and n is called the **characteristic**.

For example, you can write the number 16,000,000,000 in scientific notation.

$$16{,}000{,}000{,}000 = 1.6 \times 10^{10}.$$

You can also write 0.00065 in scientific notation.

$$0.00065 = 6.5 \times 10^{-4}.$$

Scientific notation makes is much easier to tell at a glance the order of magnitude. The **order of magnitude** is an estimate of size expressed as a power of ten. For example, Earth's mass has an order of magnitude of 10^{24} kilograms.

When comparing numbers written in scientific notation, start by comparing the characteristic of each number. A number with a larger characteristic has a greater value. If the two numbers have the same characteristic, the number with the greater mantissa has the greater value.

For example, 7.7×10^{12} is greater than 7.7×10^{4} because $12 > 4$. Also, 9.3×10^{-3} is greater than 4.2×10^{-3} because $9.3 > 4.2$.

LESSON 4

How Much Larger?

The properties of exponents apply to numbers expressed in scientific notation.

To multiply two numbers written in scientific notation, multiply the mantissas of each factor. Then apply the Product Rule of Powers to the powers with the same base, 10.

For example, determine the product of 6.7×10^{-7} and 2×10^6.

$(6.7 \times 10^{-7})(3 \times 10^6)$
$(6.7 \times 3)(10^{-7} \times 10^6)$
$(6.7 \times 3)(10^{-7 + 6})$
20.1×10^{-1}

To divide two numbers written in scientific notation, divide the mantissa of the dividend by the mantissa in the divisor. Then apply the Quotient Rule of Powers to the powers with the same base, 10.

For example, determine the quotient of 6×10^8 and 2×10^3.

$$\frac{(6 \times 10^8)}{(2 \times 10^3)}$$
$$\left(\frac{6}{2}\right)\left(\frac{10^8}{10^3}\right)$$
$$\left(\frac{6}{2}\right)(10^{8 - 3})$$
$$3 \times 10^5$$

If you want to add or subtract numbers written in scientific notation that have the same characteristics, add or subtract the mantissas and multiply by a power of 10 with the same characteristic. If the two numbers have different characteristics, you must first rewrite either number so that the numbers have the same characteristic.

For example, determine the sum of 3.7×10^5 and 2.1×10^6.

$3.7 \times 10^5 + 2.1 \times 10^6$
$0.37 \times 10^6 + 2.1 \times 10^6$
$(0.37 + 2.1)(10^6)$
2.47×10^6

Volume of Curved Figures

Disco balls are spheres that reflect light in all different directions. They were really popular in dance clubs throughout the 1960s, 1970s, and 1980s.

Module 5: Applying Powers

TOPIC 2: VOLUME OF CURVED FIGURES

In this topic, students solve real-world and mathematical problems involving volume of cylinders, cones, and spheres. Students explore each figure in turn and determine the formula for the volume of each, they practice applying each formula, and then they solve problems requiring the use of multiple volume formulas. Students use the formulas for cylinders, cones, and spheres to determine volumes of composite figures and to compare volumes of two figures.

Where have we been?

As early as first grade, students learned about right cylinders and cones, and in grades 6 and 7, they learned to calculate volumes of prisms and pyramids and areas and circumferences of circles.

Where are we going?

This topic opens the door for students to engage in geometric design and to model real-world situations. As students study polynomial functions in high school, volumes of three-dimensional figures are applications that can be used to develop understanding of graphical characteristics and creating equations.

The Volume of a Sphere

A sphere is made up of all the points that are the same distance in three dimensions from a center point. The radius of a sphere, shown here as 4 meters, is the only measure you need to determine its volume. The volume of a sphere is given by the formula $V = \frac{4}{3}\pi r^3$.

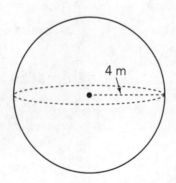

Myth: Some students are "right-brain" learners while other students are "left-brain" learners.

As you probably know, the brain is divided into two hemispheres: the left and the right. Some categorize people by their preferred or dominant mode of thinking. "Right-brain" thinkers are considered to be more intuitive, creative, and imaginative. "Left-brain" thinkers are more logical, verbal, and mathematical.

The brain can also be broken down into lobes. The occipital lobe can be found in back of the brain, and it is responsible for processing visual information. The temporal lobes, which sit above your ears, process language and sensory information. A band across the top of your head is the parietal lobe, and it controls movement. Finally, the frontal lobe is where planning and learning occurs. Another way to think about the brain is from the back to the front, where information goes from highly concrete to abstract.

Why don't we claim that some people are "back of the brain" thinkers who are highly concrete; whereas, others are "frontal thinkers" who are more abstract? The reason is that the brain is a highly interconnected organ. Each lobe hands off information to be processed by other lobes, and they are constantly talking to each other. All of us are whole-brain thinkers!

#mathmythbusted

Talking Points

You can further support your student's learning by asking questions about the work they do in class or at home. Your student is learning about the volume of cylinders, cones, and spheres.

Questions to Ask

- Does your answer make sense? Why?
- Can you show me the strategy you used to solve this problem? Do you know another way to solve it?
- Does your answer make sense? How do you know?

Key Terms

cone
A cone is a three-dimensional object with a circular or oval base and one vertex.

great circle
A great circle is the circumference of the sphere at the sphere's widest part.

Drum Roll, Please!

Volume of a Cylinder

WARM UP

Imagine a can of soup with a label.

1. Draw and describe a representation for the label if it were removed from the can.

2. Describe the sides and the top and bottom of a can of soup.

3. Describe how to determine the height of a can of soup.

4. If the radius of the top of the can is 3 inches, determine the area of the top of the can.

LEARNING GOALS

- Explore the volume of a cylinder.
- Write formulas for the volume of a cylinder.
- Use a formula to determine the volume of any cylinder.
- Use the formula for the volume of a cylinder to solve real-world problems.

KEY TERMS

- cylinder
- right cylinder
- radius of a cylinder
- height of a cylinder
- oblique cylinder

You know how to calculate the area of circles and the volume of rectangular prisms and pyramids. How can you use this knowledge to solve problems involving the volume of cylinders?

All About Cylinders

A **cylinder** is a three-dimensional object with two parallel, congruent circular bases.

1. Sketch an example of a cylinder. Explain how your sketch fits the definition of a cylinder.

A **right cylinder** is a cylinder in which the bases are circles and are aligned one directly above the other.

2. Compare your sketch with your classmates' sketches. Did everyone sketch the same cylinder? Explain how the sketches are the same or different.

The **radius of a cylinder** is the distance from the center of the base to any point on the edge of the base. The radius of a cylinder is the same on both bases.

3. Use your sketch to illustrate what is meant by "radius of the base."

The **height of a cylinder** is the length of a line segment drawn from one base to the other base, perpendicular to both bases.

4. Use your sketch to illustrate the height of a cylinder.

5. Identify the radius, diameter, and height of each cylinder.

a.

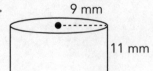

9 mm

11 mm

b.

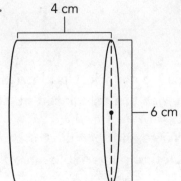

4 cm

6 cm

Volume Formula for a Cylinder

Analyze the prisms shown.

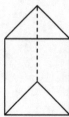
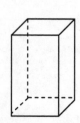
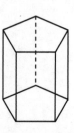
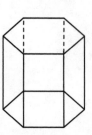

Triangular Prism   **Rectangular Prism**   **Pentagonal Prism**   **Hexagonal Prism**

1. What pattern do you see as the number of sides of the base increases?

Prisms and cylinders both have two bases and a constant height between the bases.

---

2. Because cylinders and prisms are similar in composition, their volumes are calculated in similar ways.

   a. Write the formula for the volume of any right prism. Define all variables used in the formula.

   b. Make a conjecture about how you will calculate the volume of a right cylinder.

Consider the cylinder shown. The radius of the circular base is 5 units and the height of the cylinder is 8 units.

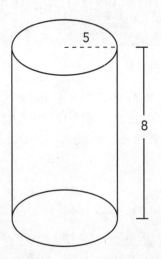

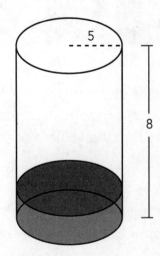

3. Suppose there is a circular disc of height 1 unit at the bottom of the cylinder.

   a. Calculate the area of the top of the circular disc.

   b. How many congruent circular discs would fill the cylinder? What is the volume of each disc? Explain your reasoning.

   c. Determine the total volume of the cylinder. Explain your strategy.

How is this formula like the volume formula for prisms?

4. Write a formula for the volume of a cylinder, where V represents the volume of the cylinder, r represents the radius of the cylinder, and h represents the height of the cylinder.

Cylinder Volume Problems

The director of the marketing department at the Rice Is Nice Company sent a memo to her product development team. She requested that the volume of the new cylinder prototype equal 602.88 cm³.

1. Two members of the marketing team claim to have created appropriate prototypes, but they disagree about the dimensions of the cylinder prototype.

Cassandra designed the cylinder prototype on the left, and Robert designed the cylinder prototype on the right. Who is correct? What would you say to Cassandra and Robert to settle their disagreement?

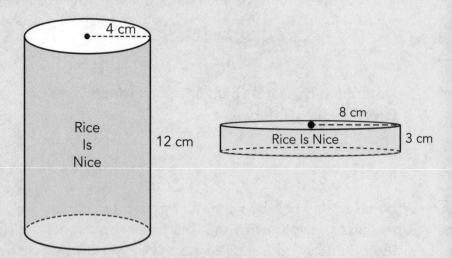

Use what you know about cylinders to solve real-world problems.

2. A circular swimming pool has a diameter of 30 feet and a height of 5 feet. What is the volume of the pool?

3. How many milliliters of liquid are needed to fill a cylindrical can with a radius of 3 centimeters and a height of 4.2 centimeters?

One milliliter is equivalent to one cubic centimeter of liquid.

4. Many newspapers are made from 100% wood. The wood used to make this paper can come from pine trees, which are typically about 60 feet tall and have diameters of about 1 foot. However, only about half of the volume of each tree is turned into paper.

Suppose it takes about 0.5 cubic inch of wood to make one sheet of paper. About how many sheets can be made from a typical pine tree? Show your work, and explain your reasoning.

5. The volume of each solid is 500 cm³. Calculate the unknown length in each figure.

a.

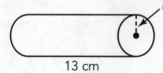

13 cm

b.

3 cm

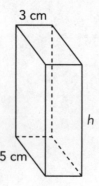

4.5 cm

h

c.

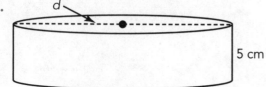

d

5 cm

Juan and Sandy are discussing the effect that doubling the length of the radius of the base has on the volume of a cylinder.

1. Juan insists that if the length of the radius of a cylinder doubles, the volume will double. Sandy thinks the volume will be more than double. Who is correct? Explain your reasoning.

2. Sandy and Juan wondered if the results from Question 1 were the same, regardless of the numbers they used. They created a table, hoping to see a pattern. Complete the table, and identify any patterns that you notice.

The pattern is easier to recognize if you leave your answers in terms of pi.

Cylinder Radius (cm)	Cylinder Area of Base (cm)	Cylinder Height (cm)	Cylinder Volume (cm³)
1		1	
2		1	
4		1	
8		1	

3. Juan and Sandy are also interested in the effect that doubling the height has on the volume of a cylinder.

Juan insists that if the height of a cylinder doubles, the volume will double. Sandy says the volume again will be more than double. Who is correct? Explain your reasoning.

4. Explain why the effect of doubling the length of the radius is different from the effect of doubling the height.

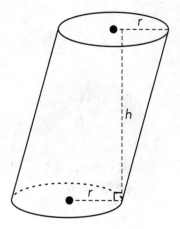

Not all cylinders are right cylinders. Consider the *oblique cylinder* shown.

1. **Explain how this cylinder is similar to and different from the right cylinders that you have explored in this lesson.**

Imagine taking cross-sections of a right cylinder and of an oblique cylinder.

2. **Compare the cross-sections that result from each slice for right cylinders and for oblique cylinders.**

   a. **slicing the cylinder parallel to its bases**

   b. **slicing the cylinder perpendicular to its bases**

3. Explain how the cross-sections created by slicing a right cylinder are related to calculating the volume of a right cylinder.

4. Apply your explanation from Question 3 to explain how to calculate the volume of an oblique cylinder.

You will learn to explain these volume strategies in high school.

An **oblique cylinder** is a cylinder in which the bases are parallel to each other, but they are not aligned directly above and below each other. The radius of an oblique cylinder is the radius of one of the bases, and the height is the perpendicular distance between the two bases. Its volume is calculated using the same strategies as other cylinders.

5. Determine the volume of each oblique cylinder.

a.

b.

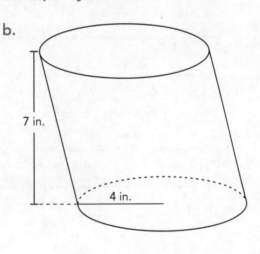

15 cm

7 in.

5 cm

4 in.

TALK the TALK 💬

The Prism Connection

Carrie was absent for the lesson on volume of a cylinder. However, she knows that the formula for the volume of a right rectangular prism can be written as $V = lwh$. Explain to Carrie how to use her knowledge of the volume of right rectangular prisms to determine the volume of a cylinder.

_____

_____

_____

_____

_____

_____

_____

_____

_____

_____

_____

_____

_____

_____

Assignment

Write

Explain the similarities and differences of right prisms, right cylinders, and oblique cylinders.

Remember

The volume of any cylinder can be calculated by multiplying the area of the circular base by the height of the cylinder.

Practice

1. Determine the volume of each cylinder. Round your answer to the nearest tenth, if necessary.

a.

b.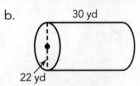

c.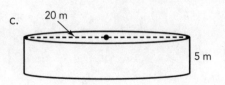

d.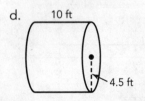

2. A cylindrical fish tank provides a 360° view. The height of the cylindrical fish tank is 30 inches, and the diameter of the base is 27.5 inches. If one US gallon is equal to approximately 231 cubic inches, calculate the amount of water the tank will hold.

3. Brittany's grandmother sends her to the store to buy a new flour canister for her kitchen. Brittany finds two canisters that she likes and is having trouble deciding which one to purchase.

   a. Calculate the volume of each canister.

   b. If the canisters cost the same, which one should Brittany purchase?

   c. A third canister has a radius of 2.5 inches and a height of 10 inches. How much less flour will this canister hold than Canister 1? Explain your reasoning.

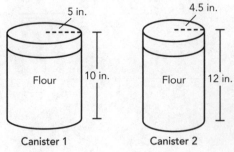

Stretch

Give the dimensions of a cylinder and a pentagonal prism that have the same volume and height.

Review

Use scientific notation to calcuate each product or quotient.

1. $(8.1 \times 10^{-4})(3 \times 10^9)$

2. $\dfrac{3.2 \times 10^8}{2.5 \times 10^3}$

Simplify each expression. Write your answer as a number raised to a power.

3. $(2^2)^3$

4. $-\dfrac{12^8}{12^4}$

Calculate the distance between the two given points.

5. $(-3, 8)$ and $(7, -16)$

6.

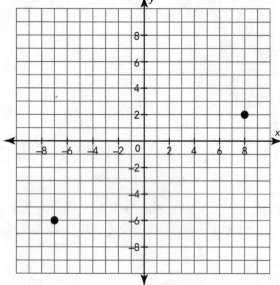

Cone of Silence

Volume of a Cone

LEARNING GOALS

- Explore the volume of a cone using a cylinder.
- Write formulas for the volume of a cone.
- Use the formula for the volume of a cone to solve real-world and mathematical problems.

KEY TERMS

- cone
- height of a cone

You have used what you know about prisms to determine the volume of cylinders. Is there a figure that can help you to determine the volume of cones?

All About Cones

All of the cones associated with this topic have a circular base and a vertex that is located directly above the center of the base of the cone.

A **cone** is a three-dimensional object with a circular or oval base and one vertex.

1. Sketch an example of a cone. Explain how your sketch fits the definition of a cone.

2. Compare your sketch with your classmates' sketches. Did everyone sketch the same cone? Explain how the sketches are the same or different.

3. How does the radius of a cone compare to the radius of a cylinder? Use your sketch to illustrate the radius of the cone.

The **height of a cone** is the length of a line segment drawn from the vertex to the base of the cone. In a right cone, this line segment is perpendicular to the base.

4. Identify the radius, diameter, and height of each cone.

a.
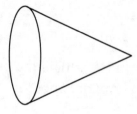

b.
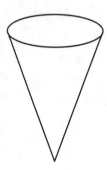

In previous courses, you explored how the volume of a pyramid is related to the volume of a prism. Let's explore how the volume of a cone is related to the volume of a cylinder. You can use nets to investigate this relationship.

A two-dimensional representation of a three-dimensional geometric figure is called a *net*.

1. Use the nets provided at the end of the lesson to create models of a cylinder and a cone.

   a. What is similar about the cone and cylinder formed from the nets?

   b. What do you think is true about the relationship between the cylinder and the cone?

2. Fill the cone with birdseed, and then pour the birdseed into the cylinder. Continue refilling the cone until you fill the cylinder with birdseed.

   a. How many cones of birdseed did it take to fill the cylinder?

Remember, the unit of measurement for volume is cubic units.

b. Compare the amount of birdseed that you used to fill the cone and to fill the cylinder. In other words, compare the volume of the cone to the volume of the cylinder. What fraction best describes this ratio?

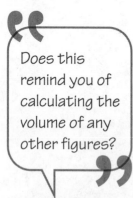

c. If you know the volume of the cylinder, how could you determine the volume of the cone?

3. Use a centimeter ruler to measure the length of the radius and height of the cylinder.

   a. Calculate the volume of the cylinder.

Does this remind you of calculating the volume of any other figures?

b. Using the volume of the cylinder, calculate the volume of the cone.

Analyze the pyramids shown.

1. What pattern do you see as the number of sides of the base increases?

Triangular
Pyramid

Because cones and pyramids are similar in composition, their volumes are calculated in similar ways.

Rectangular
Pyramid

2. Write the formula for the volume of any right pyramid and explain how it relates to your investigation with the nets.

Pentagonal
Pyramid

3. Use the formula for the volume of a pyramid to write a formula for the volume of a cone. Define all variables used in the formula.

Hexagonal
Pyramid

4. Write a second formula for the volume of a cone, where V represents the volume, r represents the radius of the base, and h represents the height.

5. Which of the two formulas do you prefer? Explain your reasoning.

Use what you know about the volume of a cone to solve each problem.

1. Joel owns a frozen yogurt and fruit smoothie shop. He just placed an order for cones, and the order contains three different sizes of cones. He wants to know the volume of each cup to help him determine how much to charge for each cone.

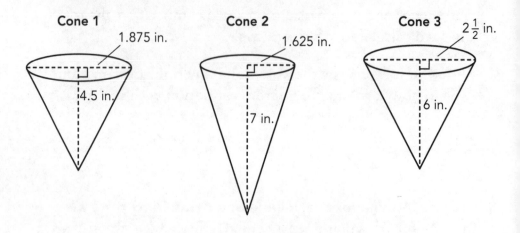

Cone 1   1.875 in.   4.5 in.

Cone 2   1.625 in.   7 in.

Cone 3 $2\frac{1}{2}$ in.   6 in.

a. Predict which cone has the greatest volume. Explain your reasoning.

b. Calculate the volume of each cone.

c. If Joel's market research reveals that he should charge $3.75 for the smallest cone, what prices would you propose for the other two cones? Explain your reasoning.

2. Mark and Alison are working on their homework and disagree on the volume of the cone shown.

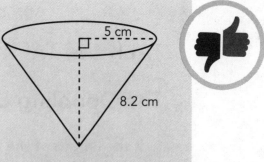

Mark says that the volume of the cone is $V = \frac{1}{3}\pi(5)^2(8.2) \approx 214.68$ cm³.
Alison argues that 8.2 cm is not the height of the cone, so they need to calculate the height before determining the volume. She says that the volume is $V = \frac{1}{3}\pi(5)^2(6.5) \approx 170.17$ cm³.
Who's correct? Explain your reasoning.

3. Calculate the volume of each cone. Round your answers to the nearest hundredth, if necessary.

a.

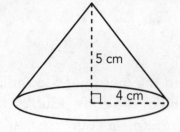

5 cm
4 cm

b.

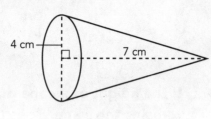

4 cm
7 cm

c.

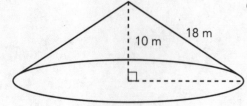

10 m
18 m

d.

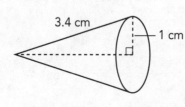

3.4 cm
1 cm

4. Use the formula for the volume of a cone to solve for each unknown dimension.

a. $V = 3042$ cm³, $d = 25.2$ cm, $h = $ _____

b. $V = 25\pi$ in.³, $h = 12$ in., $r = $ _____

TALK the TALK 💬

The Doubling Effect

1. If the length of the radius of a cone doubles and the height remains the same, does the volume of the cone double? If not, how does the volume change? Explain your reasoning.

2. If the height of a cone doubles and the length of the radius remains the same, does the volume of the cone double? If not, how does the volume change? Explain your reasoning.

Cylinder Net

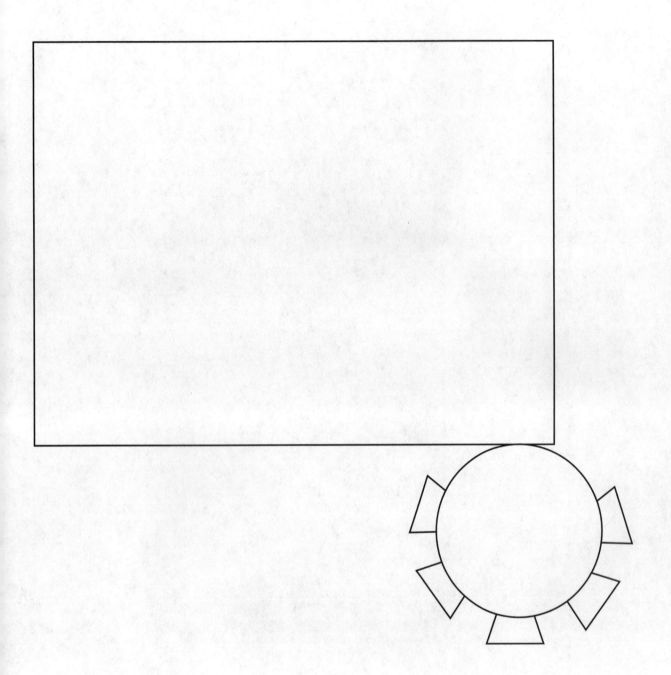

Cone Net

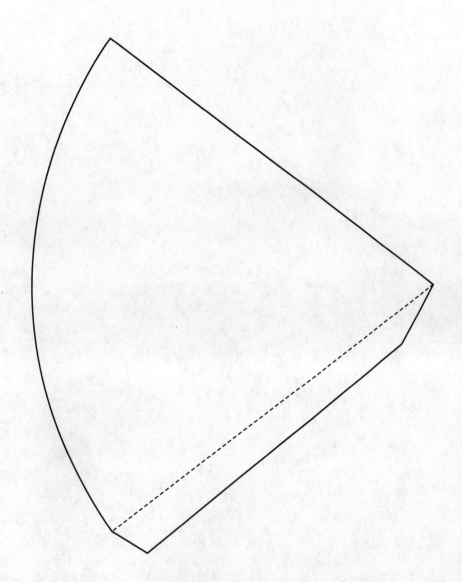

Assignment

Write

Explain when you need to use the Pythagorean Theorem to calculate the volume of a cone.

Remember

The volume of a cone is one-third the volume of the cylinder with the same base and height as the cone.

Practice

1. Determine the volume of each cone. Round your answer to the nearest tenth, if necessary.

a.

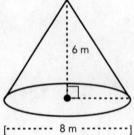

b.

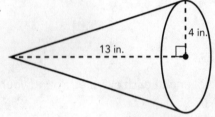

c.

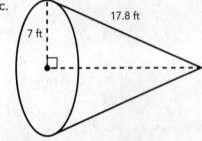

d.

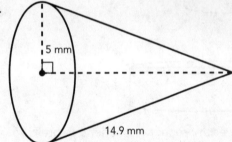

2. A company sells two sizes of cone-shaped party hats. The smaller hat has a radius of 6 cm and a volume of 376.8 cm³. The larger hats are double the volume of the smaller hats but have the same size radius. Determine the dimensions of the larger hats.

3. Cara asked her parents to make a piñata for her birthday party. Her parents decided to make the piñata in the shape of her favorite dessert, an ice cream cone. They stuffed only the cone portion of the piñata. The height of the cone is 34 inches, and the diameter of the base is 24 inches. (Note: 144 square inches equal 1 square foot, and 1728 cubic inches equals 1 cubic foot.) Calculate the amount of space (cubic feet) in the cone that will be filled with goodies.

Stretch

The frustum of a cone is the portion of a cone that remains after its upper part has been cut off by a plane parallel to its base. Calculate the volume of the frustum shown.

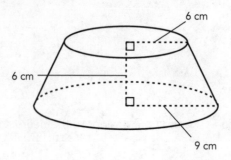

Review

Calculate the volume of each cylinder. Round your answer to the nearest tenth, if necessary.

1.

2.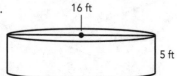

Determine each product or quotient. Express your answer in scientific notation.

3. $\dfrac{2.4 \times 10^4}{8 \times 10^{-4}}$

4. $(4.82 \times 10^8)(1.5 \times 10^{-5})$

Rewrite each expression without exponents.

5. $2^5 \cdot 2^{-2}$

6. $(10^2)^3 \cdot (-10)^2$

Pulled in All Directions

Volume of a Sphere

WARM UP

In June 2007, 7-year-old Jake Lonsway broke a world record, building the world's largest plastic wrap ball. It took him 8 months to make the ball, which weighed 281.5 pounds. The circumference of the ball was 138 inches.

1. Calculate the length of the radius and diameter of Lonsway's ball of plastic wrap. Use 3.14 for π.

2. Do you think a ball twice this size would weigh twice as much? Explain your reasoning.

LEARNING GOALS

- Identify a formula for the volume of a sphere.
- Use a formula to determine the volume of spheres in mathematical and real-world contexts.
- Use the formula for the volume of a sphere to determine an unknown length of a sphere radius or diameter.

KEY TERMS

- sphere
- center of a sphere
- radius of a sphere
- diameter of a sphere
- great circle

You have learned and applied volume formulas for a variety of different solids. In this lesson, you will learn and apply the formula for the volume of a sphere. How can you use the formula to determine both volumes and lengths of radii of spheres?

Getting to Know Spheres

A **sphere** is the set of all points in three dimensions that are the same distance from a given point called the **center of a sphere**. Like a circle, a sphere has radii and diameters. A segment drawn from the center of the sphere to a point on the sphere is called a **radius of a sphere**. A segment drawn between two points on the sphere that passes through the center is a **diameter of a sphere**. The length of a diameter is twice the length of a radius. A **great circle** is the circumference of the sphere at the sphere's widest part.

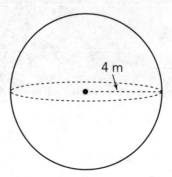

4 m

1. List all of the things that you know to be true about this sphere.

Modeling the Volume of a Sphere

Use the modeling clay and paper provided by your teacher to complete each step.

- Make a sphere using the clay. Measure and record the diameter of the sphere.

- Cut a long strip of paper so that its height matches the height of the sphere.

- Wrap the paper tightly around the sphere and tape the paper to make a sturdy cylinder with no bases.

- Squish the clay sphere so that it molds to the bottom of the cylinder.

- Mark the height of the clay in the cylinder with a marker.

1. Complete the first row of the table with the data from your sphere. Then, complete the other rows using data from three other classmates.

Sphere	Diameter	Cylinder Height	Height of Squished Sphere in Cylinder	Height of Squished Sphere —————————— Height of Cylinder
My Sphere				
Classmate A				
Classmate B				
Classmate C				

2. What do you notice about the ratio of the height of the squished sphere to the height of the cylinder?

3. What is the relationship between the volume of the sphere and the volume of the cylinder?

Recall that the formula for the volume of a cylinder is $V = \pi r^2 h$.

4. What is the height, h, of the cylinder in terms of the radius, r, of the sphere? Explain your reasoning.

5. Use this relationship and the formula for the volume of a cylinder to write a formula that describes the volume of the sphere in terms of r.

Applying the Formula for the Volume of a Sphere

Now that you know how to calculate the volume of a sphere, use the formula to solve each problem. Use 3.14 for π.

1. Earth has a diameter of approximately 7926 miles.

   a. Determine the length of the radius of Earth.

   b. Determine the volume of Earth.

2. The circumference of an NBA basketball ranges from 29.5 to 30 inches.

   a. Calculate the approximate length of the radius of a basketball with a circumference of 30 inches.

   b. Calculate the approximate volume of a basketball with a circumference of 30 inches.

3. The volume of a Major League baseball is 12.77 cubic inches.

   a. Calculate the approximate length of the radius of a Major League baseball.

   b. Calculate the approximate circumference of a Major League baseball.

4. Built in the 1950s by the Stamp Collecting Club at Boy's Town, the World's Largest Ball of Postage Stamps is very impressive. The solid ball has a diameter of 32 inches, weighs 600 pounds, and consists of 4,655,000 postage stamps.

   Calculate the volume of the world's largest ball of postage stamps.

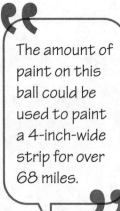

The amount of paint on this ball could be used to paint a 4-inch-wide strip for over 68 miles.

5. The world's largest ball of paint resides in Alexandria, Indiana. The ball began as a baseball. People began coating the ball with layers of paint. Imagine this baseball with over 21,140 coats of paint on it! The baseball originally weighed approximately 5 ounces and now weighs more than 2700 pounds. Painting this baseball has gone on for more than 32 years, and people are still painting it today.

   When the baseball had 20,500 coats of paint on it, the circumference along the great circle of the ball was approximately 133 inches. Each layer is approximately 0.001037 inches thick.

   Calculate the volume of the world's largest paint ball.

6. The world's largest disco ball hangs from a fixed point and is powered by a 5-ton hydraulic rotator. It weighs nearly 1.5 tons with a volume of approximately 67 cubic meters. Approximately 8000 100-square-centimeter mirror tiles and over 10,000 rivets were used in its creation.

   Calculate the length of the radius of the world's largest disco ball.

7. For over seven years, John Bain spent his life creating the world's largest rubber band ball. It is solid to the core with rubber bands. Each rubber band was individually stretched around the ball, creating a giant rubber band ball. The weight of the ball is over 3,120 pounds, and the circumference is 15.1 feet.

   Calculate the volume of the world's largest rubber band ball.

There are 850,000 rubber bands in the ball, and the cost of the materials was approximately $25,000!

8. The world's largest ball of twine is in Darwin, Minnesota. It weighs 17,400 pounds and was created by Francis A. Johnson. He began this pursuit in March 1950. He spent four hours a day, every day wrapping the ball. It took Francis 39 years to complete. Upon completion, it was moved to a circular open air shed on his front lawn for all to view.

   If the volume of the world's largest ball of twine is 7234.56 cubic feet, determine the length of the diameter.

At some point, the ball had to be lifted with a crane to continue proper wrapping.

TALK the TALK

Locker Room Math

Young people often attempt to break world records. Jessica is no exception. Today her math class studied the volume of a sphere, and she had a great idea. After working out the math, Jessica told her best friend Molly that they could stuff 63 inflated regulation-size basketballs into a school locker. The rectangular locker is 6 feet high, 20 inches wide, and 20 inches deep. The radius of one basketball is 4.76 inches. Molly also did the math and said that only 28 basketballs would fit.

1. **How did Molly and Jessica compute their answers? Who's correct? Explain your reasoning.**

Assignment

Write

Describe the similarities and differences between each pair of terms.
1. radius of the sphere and diameter of the sphere
2. radius of the sphere and center of the sphere

Remember

The volume of a sphere is given by the formula $V = \frac{4}{3}\pi r^3$, where r represents the radius of the sphere.

Practice

Solve each problem. Use 3.14 for π.

1. The diameter of a small red beach ball is 8 inches. Calculate the volume of the red beach ball to the nearest whole number.

2. The diameter of a large blue beach ball is 16 inches. Calculate the volume of the blue beach ball to the nearest whole number.

3. Spaceship Earth is the most recognizable structure at Epcot Center at Disney World in Orlando, Florida. The ride is a geodesic sphere made up of thousands of small triangular panels. The circumference of Spaceship Earth is 518.1 feet. Determine its approximate volume.

4. The Oriental Pearl Tower in Shanghai, China, is a 468-meter high tower with 11 spheres along the tower. Two spheres are larger than the rest and house meeting areas, an observation deck, and a revolving restaurant. The lower of the two larger spheres has a radius of 25 meters, and the higher sphere has a radius of 22.5 meters. What is the approximate total volume of the two largest spheres on the Oriental Pearl Tower?

5. A model of Earth is located 7600 meters from the Globe Arena in Sweden's solar system model. The volume of the model is approximately 3052.08 cubic centimeters. What is the length of the radius of the Earth model?

6. The Montreal Biosphere is a geodesic dome that surrounds an environmental museum in Montreal, Canada. The dome has a volume of 6,132,812.5 cubic feet. The structure is 75% of a full sphere. What is the length of its diameter?

Stretch

A typical orange has 10 segments and is composed of about 87% water. Suppose an orange has a diameter of 3 inches. What is the volume of water in each segment?

Review

Determine the volume of each cone described. Use 3.14 for π.

1. Cone with a radius of 4.1 cm and a height of 10 cm

2. Cone with a diameter of 8 in. and a height of 5.03 in.

Determine each quotient. Write each quotient as a power and in standard form.

3. $\dfrac{6^4}{6^5}$

4. $\dfrac{9^{-1}}{9^{-2}}$

Determine each quotient. Write your response using scientific notation.

5. $\dfrac{(6.4 \times 10^8)}{(2.0 \times 10^2)}$

6. $\dfrac{(1.6 \times 10^3)}{(2.5 \times 10^6)}$

Silos, Frozen Yogurt, and Popcorn

4

Volume Problems with Cylinders, Cones, and Spheres

WARM UP

You have been asked to supply the ice cream for a birthday party. Assume that each person attending the party will eat one ice cream cone. The local grocery store sells ice cream in rectangular half-gallon containers. Each container is 6.75 inches in length, 5 inches in height, and 3.5 inches in width. Your plan is to put two scoops of ice cream in each cone. Each scoop is a sphere with a radius of 1 inch.

1. What is the volume of one scoop of ice cream?

2. If 30 people attended the birthday party, how many half-gallons of ice cream should you buy?

LEARNING GOALS

- Use formulas for the volume of a cone, cylinder, and sphere to solve real-world and mathematical problems.
- Compare volumes of cones, cylinders, and spheres.

You have learned the formulas for the volume of a cylinder, the volume of a cone, and the volume of a sphere. How can you reason with these formulas separately and together to solve problems?

Formula Review

By now, you have determined some formulas for prisms, pyramids, cylinders, cones, and spheres.

1. Write the formula for the volume of each solid. Use V for volume, B for area of a base, h for height, r for radius, and π for pi.

Solid	Model	Volume Formula
Rectangular Prism		
Triangular Prism		
Rectangular Pyramid		
Triangular Pyramid		
Cylinder		
Cone		
Sphere		

Cylinder and Half-Sphere Problem

A silo is used to store grain that farm animals eat during the winter months. The top of the silo is a hemisphere (a half-sphere) with a radius of 8 feet. The cylindrical body of the silo shares the same radius as the hemisphere and has a height of 40 feet.

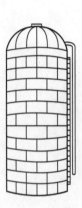

A truck hauling grain to the silo has a rectangular container attached to the back that is 8 feet in length, 5 feet in width, and 4 feet in height.

1. Determine the number of truckloads of grain required to fill an empty silo.

The word *fill* is often used to describe the volume of a solid. Consider how much you can fill the cones described in each question. Use 3.14 for π.

1. A frozen yogurt shop advertises that their frozen yogurt is now sold in cones that hold 25% more frozen yogurt than the old cones. The old cone has a radius of 3.75 centimeters and a height of 11 centimeters. The length of the radius of the new cone is the same as the length of the radius of the old cone. What is the height of the new cone?

2. A frozen yogurt cone is 12 centimeters in height and has a diameter of 6 centimeters. A scoop of frozen yogurt is placed on the wide end of the cone. The scoop is a sphere with a diameter of 6 centimeters.

   If the scoop of frozen yogurt melts into the cone, will the cone overflow? Explain your reasoning.

If you were to make a cylinder using a piece of paper, is the volume the same no matter which way you roll the paper?

Use the paper provided by your teacher to complete an investigation of cylinder volume.

- Roll one piece of paper along its longer side. This will form a cylinder (Cylinder A) with no bases that is tall and narrow. Tape along the edges without overlapping the sides of the paper.

- Roll a second piece of paper of the same size but a different color along its shorter side. This will form a cylinder (Cylinder B) with no bases that is short and wide. Tape along the edges without overlapping the sides.

1. **Do you think that the two cylinders have the same volume? Make a conjecture and explain your thinking.**

2. **Stand Cylinder B upright on your desk with Cylinder A inside it. Pour centimeter cubes into Cylinder A until it is full. Carefully lift Cylinder A so that the centimeter cubes fall into Cylinder B. Describe what happens.**

3. Consider your prediction about the volumes of Cylinder A and Cylinder B.

    a. Was your prediction correct? How do you know?

    b. If your prediction was incorrect, why do you think what actually happened was different from your prediction?

4. Measure the dimensions of the tall, narrow cylinder and enter them in the table as measures for Cylinder A. Then, measure the dimensions of the short, wide cylinder and enter them in the table as measures for Cylinder B.

Dimension	Cylinder A	Cylinder B
Height (in.)		
Diameter (in.)		
Radius (in.)		

5. Calculate the volumes of the cylinders.

6. By how much would you have to decrease the height of Cylinder B to make the volumes of the two cylinders equal?

Cone vs. Cylinder

Consider the popcorn containers: one is a cylindrical tub and the other is conical. When they are full of popcorn, the containers hold the same amount of popcorn.

1. Calculate the volume of the cylindrical tub.

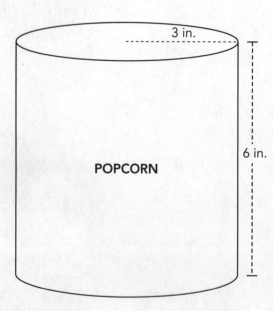

2. If the height of the conical container is 10.1 inches, what is the length of the radius of the cone?

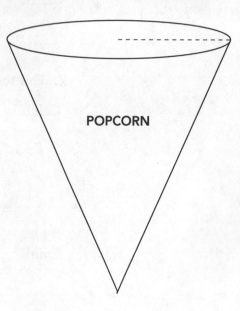

3. If the length of the radius of the conical container is the same as the length of the radius of the cylindrical tub, what is the height of the cone?

TALK the TALK

Composite Solids

Use what you know about the volume of curved figures to solve each problem. Use 3.14 for π.

1. The building shown is composed of a cylinder and a cone. Determine the volume of this building.

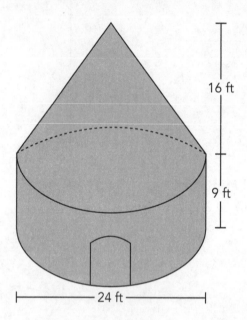

16 ft

9 ft

24 ft

2. The top of this model forms a half-sphere. Determine the volume of this model.

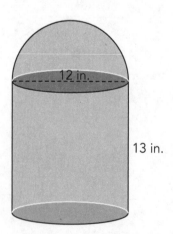

12 in.

13 in.

Assignment

Write

Describe the relationships among the volumes of a cylinder, cone, and sphere that have the same height and radius.

Remember

The formula for the volume of a cylinder is $\pi r^2 h$.

The formula for the volume of a cone is $\frac{1}{3}\pi r^2 h$.

The formula for the volume of a sphere is $\frac{4}{3}\pi r^3$.

Practice

Solve each problem. Use 3.14 for π.

1. Veronica is making a large sphere-shaped piñata for a party. The piñata is going to be 2 feet in diameter. In order to know how much candy she will need to fill the piñata, she needs to know the volume of the piñata. Calculate the volume of this large piñata.

2. A jeweler sold a string of fifty 8-millimeter pearls. He needs to choose a box to put them in. Which box should the jeweler choose?

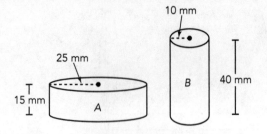

3. The drinking glass is not a cylinder, but is actually part of a cone. Determine the volume of the glass.

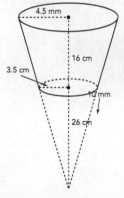

4. A tennis ball company is designing a new can to hold 3 tennis balls. They want to waste as little space as possible. How much space does each can waste? Which can design should they choose?

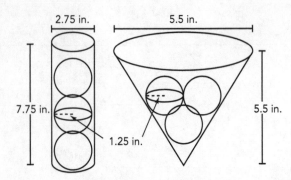

5. A candle company makes pillar candles, spherical candles, and conical candles. They have an order for 3 pillar, 2 spherical, and 1 conical candle. Wax is sold in large rectangular blocks. What are the possible dimensions for a wax block that could be used to fill this order?

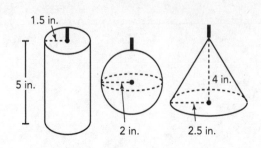

6. An ice cream shop sells cones with a volume of 94.2 cubic centimeters. They want to double the volume of their cones without changing the diameter of the cone so that the ice cream scoop will stay on top of the cone. What should the dimensions of the new cone be if the old cone had a height of 10 centimeters?

Stretch

A container in the shape of a half-sphere is on top of a cylinder. The container has a volume of 360π cubic inches. The total height of the container is the same as the diameter of the half-sphere. What is the diameter of the half-sphere?

Review

Calculate each volume. Use 3.14 for π. Round to the nearest hundredth.

1. What is the volume of a sphere with a diameter of 8.5 inches?
2. What is the volume of a sphere with a radius of 9 millimeters?

3.   6 m

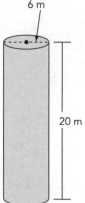

20 m

4.

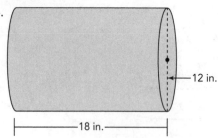

12 in.

18 in.

Determine each sum. Write each sum in scientific notation.

5. $4.1 \times 10^3 + 3.5 \times 10^4$

6. $9.9 \times 10^5 + 2.9 \times 10^2$

Volume of Curved Figures Summary

KEY TERMS

- cylinder
- right cylinder
- radius of a cylinder
- height of a cylinder
- oblique cylinder
- cone
- height of a cone
- sphere
- center of a sphere
- radius of a sphere
- diameter of a sphere
- great circle

LESSON 1

Drum Roll, Please!

A **cylinder** is a three-dimensional object with two parallel, congruent circular bases. A **right cylinder** is a cylinder in which the bases are circles and are aligned one directly above the other.

The **radius of a cylinder** is the distance from the center of the base to any point on the edge of the base. The length of the radius of a cylinder is the same on both bases. The **height of a cylinder** is the length of a line segment drawn from one base to the other base, perpendicular to both bases.

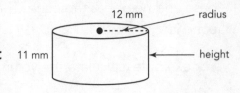

The volume of any cylinder can be calculated by multiplying the area of the circular base by the height of the cylinder. The formula for the area of a circle is $A = \pi r^2$, so the formula for the volume of a cylinder is $V = \pi r^2 h$.

For example, calculate the volume of the given cylinder.

$$V = \pi r^2 h$$
$$= \pi(12^2)(11)$$
$$\approx 4976.28 \text{ cubic millimeters}$$

Doubling only the length of the radius of a cylinder quadruples the volume of the cylinder, while doubling only the height doubles the volume.

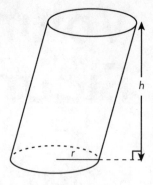

Not all cylinders are right cylinders. An **oblique cylinder** is a cylinder in which the bases are parallel to each other, but they are not aligned directly above and below each other. The radius of an oblique cylinder is the radius of one of the bases, and the height is the perpendicular distance between the two bases. Its volume is calculated using the same strategies as other cylinders.

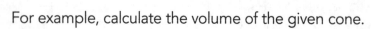

Cone of Silence

A **cone** is a three-dimensional object with a circular or oval base and one vertex. The **height of a cone** is the length of a line segment drawn from the vertex to the base of the cone. In a right cone, this line segment is perpendicular to the base.

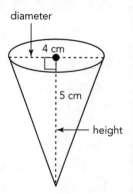

The volume of a cone is one-third the volume of the cylinder with the same base and height as the cone. Therefore, the formula for the volume of a cone is $V = \frac{1}{3}\pi r^2 h$.

For example, calculate the volume of the given cone.

$$V = \frac{1}{3}\pi r^2 h.$$
$$= \frac{1}{3}\pi \left(\frac{4}{2}\right)^2 (5)$$
$$\approx 20.94 \text{ cubic centimeters}$$

Pulled in All Directions

A **sphere** is the set of all points in three dimensions that are the same distance from a given point called the **center of a sphere**. Like a circle, a sphere has radii and diameters. A segment drawn from the center of the sphere to a point on the sphere is called a **radius of a sphere**. A segment drawn between two points on the sphere that passes through the center is a **diameter of a sphere**. The length of a diameter is twice the length of a radius. A **great circle** is the circumference of the sphere at the sphere's widest part.

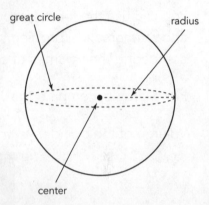

The volume of a sphere is given by the formula $V = \frac{4}{3}\pi r^3$, where r represents the length of the radius of the sphere.

For example, calculate the volume of a sphere with a radius length of 4.5 inches.

$$V = \frac{4}{3}\pi r^3$$
$$= \frac{4}{3}\pi(4.5)^3$$
$$\approx 381.7 \text{ cubic inches}$$

You can use the formulas for the volume of a cone, cylinder, and sphere to solve real-world and mathematical problems, including determining the volume of composite figures and comparing the volumes of cones, cylinders, and spheres.

For example, compare the volumes of the cylinder, sphere and cone.

Volume of the cylinder $= \pi r^2 h$

$\qquad = \pi(2)^2(5)$

$\qquad \approx 62.83$ cubic inches

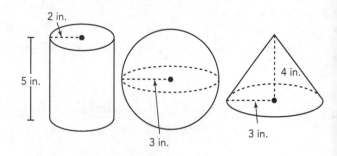

Volume of the sphere $= \frac{4}{3}\pi r^3$

$\qquad = \frac{4}{3}\pi(3)^3$

$\qquad \approx 113.1$ cubic inches

Volume of the cone $= \frac{1}{3}\pi r^2 h$

$\qquad = \frac{1}{3}\pi(3)^2(4)$

$\qquad \approx 37.7$ cubic inches

The volume of the sphere is the greatest, and the volume of the cone is the least.

Glossary

A

absolute value function

An absolute value function is a function that can be written in the form $y = |x|$, where x is any number or expression.

alternate exterior angles

Alternate exterior angles are angles formed when a transversal intersects two other lines. These angle pairs are on opposite sides of the transversal and are outside the other two lines.

Example

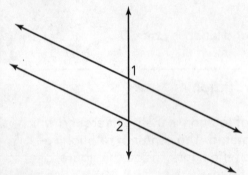

Angles 1 and 2 are alternate exterior angles.

alternate interior angles

Alternate interior angles are angles formed when a transversal intersects two other lines. These angle pairs are on opposite sides of the transversal and are between the other two lines.

Example

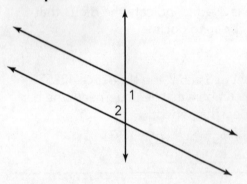

Angles 1 and 2 are alternate interior angles.

angle of rotation

The angle of rotation is the amount of rotation, in degrees, about a fixed point, the center of rotation.

Example

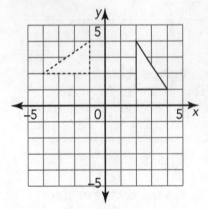

The angle of rotation is 90° counterclockwise about the origin (0, 0).

Angle-Angle Similarity Theorem

The Angle-Angle Similarity Theorem states that if two angles of one triangle are congruent to the corresponding angles of another triangle, then the triangles are similar.

association

A pattern or relationship identified in a scatter plot of a two-variable data set is called an association.

B

bar notation

Bar notation is used to indicate the digits that repeat in a repeating decimal.

Example

In the quotient of 3 and 7, the sequence 428571 repeats. The numbers that lie underneath the bar are the numbers that repeat.

$$\frac{3}{7} = 0.4285714285714... = 0.\overline{428571}$$

base

The base of a power is the factor that is multiplied repeatedly in the power.

Examples

$$2^3 = 2 \times 2 \times 2 = 8 \qquad 8^0 = 1$$
$$\uparrow \qquad\qquad\qquad \uparrow$$
$$\text{base} \qquad\qquad\qquad \text{base}$$

bivariate data

When you collect information about two separate characteristics for the same person, thing, or event, you have collected bivariate data.

break-even point

When one line represents the cost of an item and the other line represents the income from selling the item, the point of intersection is called the break-even point.

C

categorical data

Categorical data, or qualitative data, are data for which each piece of data fits into exactly one of several different groups or categories.

Examples

Animals: lions, tigers, bears, etc.

Colors: blue, green, red, etc.

center of dilation

The point from which a dilation is generated is called the center of dilation.

Example

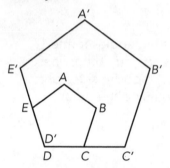

The center of dilation is point D.

center of rotation

The center of rotation is the point around which a figure is rotated. The center of rotation can be a point on the figure, inside the figure, or outside the figure.

Example

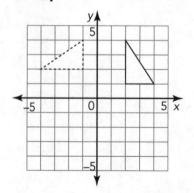

The figure has been rotated 90° counterclockwise about the center of rotation, which is the origin (0, 0).

center of the sphere

The given point from which the set of all points in three dimensions are the same distance is the center of the sphere.

Example

Point *C* is the center of the sphere.

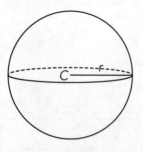

characteristic

In the expression $a \times 10^n$, the variable n is called the characteristic.

Example

$6.1 \times 10^5 = 610,000$

↑

characteristic

closed

A set of numbers is said to be closed under an operation if the result of the operation on two numbers in the set is a defined value also in the set.

Example

The set of integers is closed under the operation of addition because for every two integers *a* and *b*, the sum $a + b$ is also an integer.

collinear points

Collinear points are points that lie in the same straight line.

Example

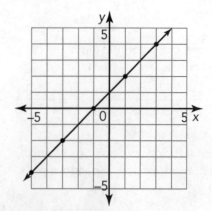

All the points on the graph are collinear points.

cone

A cone is a three-dimensional object with a circular or oval base and one vertex.

Example

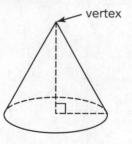

vertex

congruent angles

Congruent angles are angles that are equal in measure.

congruent figures

Figures that have the same size and shape are congruent figures. If two figures are congruent, all corresponding sides and all corresponding angles have the same measure.

congruent line segments

Congruent line segments are line segments that have the same length.

consistent system

Systems that have one or an infinite number of solutions are called consistent systems.

constant function

When the y-value of a function does not change, or remains constant, the function is called a constant function.

constant interval

When a function is constant for some values of the independent variable, it is said to have a constant interval.

Example

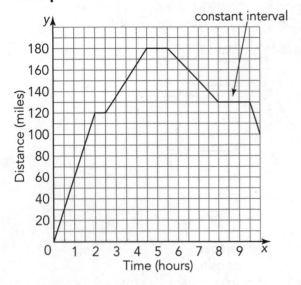

constant of proportionality

In a proportional relationship, the ratio of all y-values to their corresponding x-values is constant. This specific ratio, $\frac{y}{x}$, is called the constant of proportionality. Generally, the variable k is used to represent the constant of proportionality.

continuous

A continuous graph is a graph with no breaks in it.

Examples

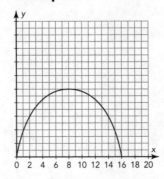 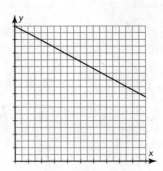

converse

The converse of a theorem is created when the if-then parts of that theorem are exchanged.

Example

Triangle inequality Theorem:

If a polygon is a triangle, then the sum of any two of its side lengths is always greater than the length of the third side.

Converse of Triangle Inequality Theorem:

If you have three side lengths, and the sum of any two of the side lengths is greater than the third side length, then the side lengths can form a triangle.

Converse of the Pythagorean Theorem

The Converse of the Pythagorean Theorem states that if the sum of the squares of the two shorter sides of a triangle equals the square of the longest side, then the triangle is a right triangle.

Example

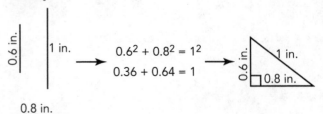

corresponding angles

Corresponding angles are angles that have the same relative positions in geometric figures.

Example

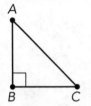 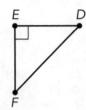

Angle *B* and Angle *E* are corresponding angles.

corresponding sides

Corresponding sides are sides that have the same relative positions in geometric figures.

Example

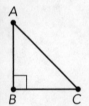 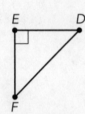

Sides *AB* and *DE* are corresponding sides.

cube root

A cube root is one of 3 equal factors of a number.

Example

The cube root of 125, $\sqrt[3]{125}$, is 5, because $5 \times 5 \times 5 = 125$.

cubic function

A cubic function is a function that can be written in the form $y = ax^3 + bx^2 + cx + d$, where each coefficient or constant *a*, *b*, *c*, and *d* is a real number and *a* is not equal to 0.

cylinder

A cylinder is a three-dimensional object with two parallel, congruent circular bases.

Examples

—————————— D ——————————

decreasing function

When the value of a dependent variable decreases as the independent variable increases, the function is called a decreasing function.

diagonal

In a three-dimensional figure, a diagonal is a line segment connecting any two non-adjacent vertices.

Example

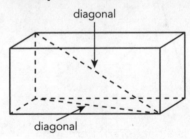

diagonal

diagonal

diagonal of a square

A diagonal of a square is a line segment connecting opposite vertices of the square.

diameter of the sphere

A segment drawn between two points on the sphere that passes through the center of the sphere is a diameter of the sphere.

Example

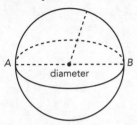

The diameter of the sphere is labeled.

dilation

A dilation is a transformation that produces a figure that is the same shape as the original figure, but not necessarily the same size.

Example

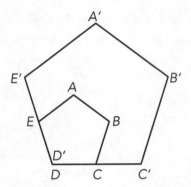

Pentagon *A'B'C'D'E'* is a dilation of Pentagon *ABCDE*.

discrete

A discrete graph is a graph of isolated points.

Examples

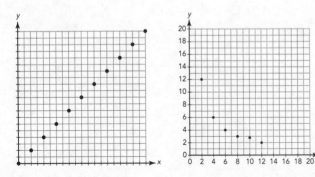

domain

The domain of a function is the set of all inputs of the function.

Example

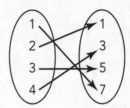

The domain in the mapping shown is {1, 2, 3, 4}.

—————————— E ——————————

ellipsis

An ellipsis is a set of three periods which stands for "and so on."

Example

3, 9, 27, 81, ...
↑
ellipsis

enlargement

When the scale factor is greater than 1, the image is called an enlargement.

explanatory variable

The independent variable can also be called the explanatory variable.

exponent

The exponent of the power is the number of times the base is used as a factor.

Examples

$2^3 = 2 \times 2 \times 2 = 8$ $8^4 = 8 \times 8 \times 8 \times 8 = 4096$
↑   ↑
exponent   exponent

exterior angle of a polygon

An exterior angle of a polygon is an angle between a side of a polygon and the extension of its adjacent side.

Example

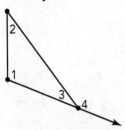

Angle 4 is an exterior angle of a polygon.

Exterior Angle Theorem

The Exterior Angle Theorem states that the measure of the exterior angle of a triangle is equal to the sum of the measures of the two remote interior angles of the triangle.

Example

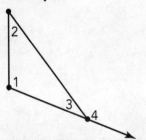

According to the Exterior Angle Theorem, $m\angle 4 = m\angle 1 + m\angle 2$.

extrapolating

Extrapolating is predicting values that fall outside the plotted values on a scatter plot.

first differences

First differences are the values determined by subtracting consecutive y-values in a table when the x-values are consecutive integers. When the first differences are equal, the points represented by the ordered pairs in the table will form a straight line.

Example

x	y	
1	25	9
2	34	
3	45	11

The first differences are 9 and 11, so the points represented by these ordered pairs will not form a straight line.

frequency

A frequency is the number of times an item or number occurs in a data set.

Example

Number Rolled	Tally	Frequency
2	IIII II	7

The number 2 was rolled 7 times, so its frequency was 7.

function

A function maps each input to one and only one output.

Example

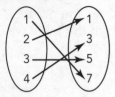

This mapping represents a function.

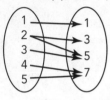

This mapping does NOT represent a function.

G

great circle

A great circle is the circumference of the sphere at the sphere's widest part.

Example

Point A is the center of the sphere. It is also the center of the great circle.

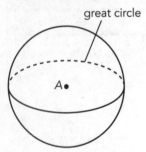

H

height of a cone

The height of a cone is the length of a line segment drawn from the vertex to the base of the cone. In a right cone, this line segment is perpendicular to the base.

Example

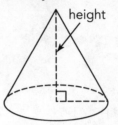

height of a cylinder

The height of a cylinder is the length of a line segment drawn from one base to the other base, perpendicular to both bases.

Example

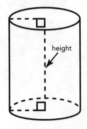

hypotenuse

The side opposite the right angle in a right triangle is called the hypotenuse.

Examples

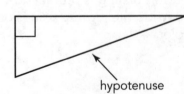

image

The new figure created from a transformation is called the image.

Example

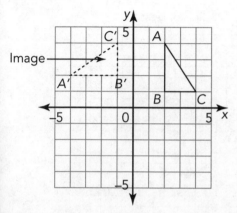

inconsistent system

Systems that have no solution are called inconsistent systems.

increasing function

When both values of a function increase together, the function is called an increasing function.

index

The index is the number placed above and to the left of the radical to indicate what root is being calculated.

Example

Index
↓
$\sqrt{3}\ 512 = 8$

input

The first coordinate of an ordered pair in a relation is the input.

integers

Integers are the set of whole numbers and their additive inverses.

Example

The set of integers can be represented as {... −3, −2, −1, 0, 1, 2, 3, ...}

interpolating

Interpolating is predicting values that fall within the plotted values on a scatter plot.

interval of decrease

When a function is decreasing for some values of the independent variable, it is said to have an interval of decrease.

Example

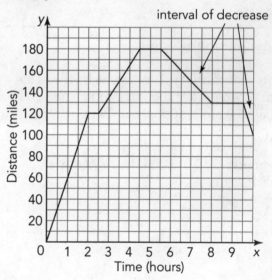

interval of increase

When a function is increasing for some values of the independent variable, it is said to have an interval of increase.

Example

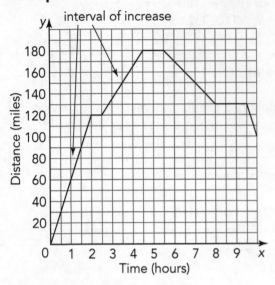

irrational numbers

Numbers that cannot be written as fractions in the form $\frac{a}{b}$, where a and b are integers and b is not equal to 0 are irrational numbers.

Examples

The numbers $\sqrt{2}$, 0.313113111..., and π are irrational numbers

— L —

leg

A leg of a right triangle is either of the two shorter sides. Together, the two legs form the right angle of a right triangle.

Examples

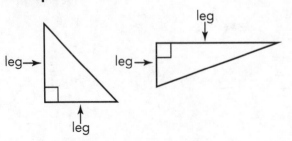

line of best fit

A line of best fit is a line that is as close to as many points as possible but doesn't have to go through all of the points.

Example

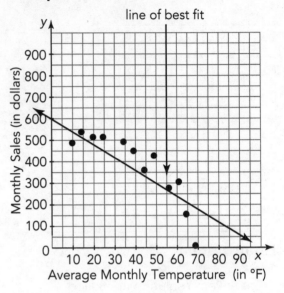

line of reflection

A line of reflection is a line that acts as a mirror so that corresponding points are the same distance from the line.

Example

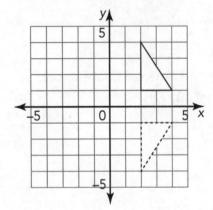

The x-axis is the line of reflection.

linear association

A linear association occurs when the points on the scatter plot seem to form a line.

Example

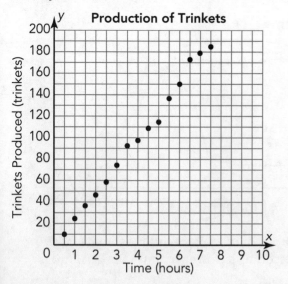

linear function

A function whose graph is a straight line is a linear function.

Example

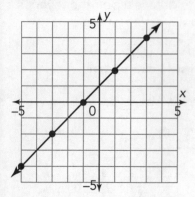

The function $f(x) = x + 1$ is a linear function.

mantissa

In the expression $a \times 10^n$, the variable a is called the mantissa. In scientific notation, the mantissa is greater than or equal to 1 and less than 10.

Example

$6.1 \times 10^5 = 610,000$

mantissa

mapping

A mapping represents two sets of objects or items. Arrows connect the items to represent a relationship between them.

Example

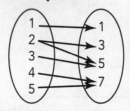

model

When you use a line of best fit, the line and its equation are often referred to as a model of the data, or a trend line. (See *trend line*.)

natural numbers

Natural numbers consist of the numbers that you use to count objects: {1, 2, 3, 4, 5, ...}

negative association

If the response variable decreases as the explanatory variable increases, then the two variables have a negative association.

Example

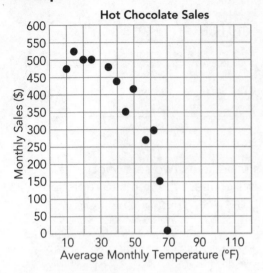

There is a negative association between average monthly temperature and hot chocolate sales.

non-linear

A non-linear graph is a graph that is not a line and therefore not a series of collinear points.

Example

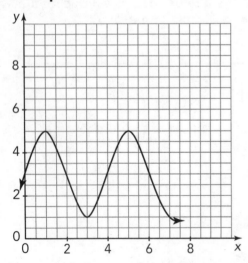

oblique cylinder

An oblique cylinder is a cylinder in which the bases are parallel to each other, but they are not aligned directly above and below each other.

Example

order of magnitude

The order of magnitude is an estimate of size expressed as a power of ten.

Example

The Earth's mass has an order of magnitude of about 10^{24} kilograms.

outlier

An outlier for bivariate data is a point that varies greatly from the overall pattern of the data.

Example

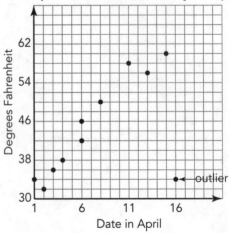

output

The second coordinate of an ordered pair in a relation is the output.

perfect cube

A perfect cube is the cube of a whole number.

Example

$4 \times 4 \times 4 = 64$ ← perfect cube

plane

A plane is a flat surface. It has infinite length and width, but no depth. A plane extends infinitely in all directions in two dimensions. Planes are determined by three points, but are usually named using one uppercase letter.

Example

Plane Q is shown.

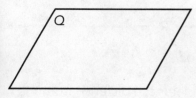

point of intersection

The point of intersection is the point at which two lines cross on a coordinate plane. In a system of linear equations, a point of intersection indicates a solution to both equations.

point-slope form

The point-slope form of a linear equation is $y - y_1 = m(x - x_1)$, where m is the slope of the line and (x_1, y_1) is any point on the line.

positive association

The two variables have a positive association if, as the explanatory variable increases, the response variable also increases.

Example

There is a positive association between the average monthly temperature and ice cream cone sales.

power

A power has two elements: the base and the exponent.

Example

base ——▶ $\underset{\text{Power}}{6^2}$ ◀—— exponent

pre-image

The original figure in a transformation is called the pre-image.

Example

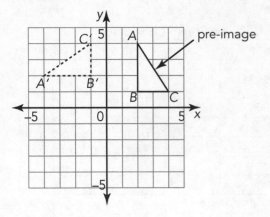

proof

A proof is a line of reasoning used to validate a theorem.

proportional relationship

A proportional relationship is one in which the ratio of the inputs to the outputs is constant. For a relationship to illustrate a proportional relationship, all the ratios $\frac{y}{x}$ or $\frac{x}{y}$, must represent the same constant.

Pythagorean Theorem

The Pythagorean Theorem states that the sum of the squares of the lengths of the legs of a right triangle equals the square of the length of the hypotenuse. If a and b are the lengths of the legs, and c is the length of the hypotenuse, then $a^2 + b^2 = c^2$.

Example

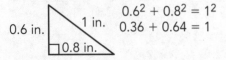

$$0.6^2 + 0.8^2 = 1^2$$
$$0.36 + 0.64 = 1$$

Pythagorean triple

Any set of three positive integers a, b, and c that satisfies the equation $a^2 + b^2 = c^2$ is a Pythagorean triple.

Example

3, 4, and 5 is a Pythagorean triple: $3^2 + 4^2 = 5^2$

Q

quadratic function

A quadratic function is a function that can be written in the form $y = ax^2 + bx + c$, where a, b, and c are any real numbers and a is not equal to zero.

R

radius of a cylinder

The radius of a cylinder is the distance from the center of the base to any point on the edge of the base.

Example

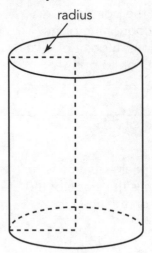

radius

radius of the sphere

A segment drawn from the center of a sphere to a point on the sphere is called a radius of the sphere.

Example

Point C is the center of the sphere, and r is the radius of the sphere.

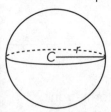

range

The range of a function is the set of all outputs of the function.

Example

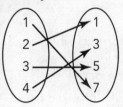

The range in the mapping shown is {1, 3, 5, 7}.

rate of change

The rate of change for a situation describes the amount that the dependent variable changes compared with the amount that the independent variable changes.

rational numbers

Rational numbers are the set of numbers that can be written as $\frac{a}{b}$, where a and b are integers and $b \neq 0$.

Examples

$-4, \frac{1}{2}, \frac{2}{3}, 0.67$, and $\frac{22}{7}$ are examples of rational numbers.

real numbers

Combining the set of rational numbers and the set of irrational numbers produces the set of real numbers. Real numbers can be represented on the real number line.

Examples

The numbers $-3, 1.25, \frac{11}{4}$, and $\sqrt{13}$ shown are real numbers.

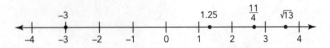

reduction

When the scale factor is less than 1, the image is called a reduction.

reflection

A reflection is a rigid motion transformation that "flips" a figure across a line of reflection.

Example

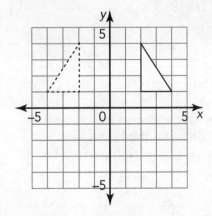

The figure has been reflected across the y-axis.

relation

A relation is any set of ordered pairs or the mapping between a set of inputs and a set of outputs.

relative frequency

A relative frequency is the ratio or percent of occurrences within a category to the total of the category.

remote interior angles of a triangle

The remote interior angles of a triangle are the two angles that are non-adjacent to the specified exterior angle.

Example

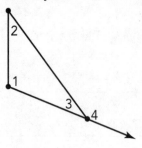

Angles 1 and 2 are remote interior angles of a triangle.

repeating decimal

A repeating decimal is a decimal in which a digit, or a group of digits, repeat(s) infinitely. Repeating decimals are rational numbers.

Examples

$\frac{1}{9} = 0.111...$ $\frac{7}{12} = 0.58333...$

$\frac{22}{7} = 3.142857142857...$

response variable

The dependent variable can also be called the response variable, because this is the variable that responds to what occurs to the explanatory variable.

right cylinder

A right cylinder is a cylinder in which the bases are aligned one directly above the other.

Example

rigid motion

A rigid motion is a special type of transformation that preserves the size and shape of the figure.

Examples

Translations, reflections, and rotations are examples of rigid motion transformations.

rotation

A rotation is a rigid motion transformation that turns a figure on a plane about a fixed point, called the center of rotation, through a given angle, called the angle of rotation.

──────────── S ────────────

same-side exterior angles

Same-side interior angles are formed when a transversal intersects two other lines. These angle pairs are on the same side of the transversal and are outside the other two lines.

Example

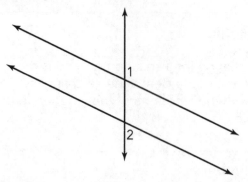

Angles 1 and 2 are same-side exterior angles.

same-side interior angles

Same-side interior angles are formed when a transversal intersects two other lines. These angle pairs are on the same side of the transversal and are between the other two lines.

Example

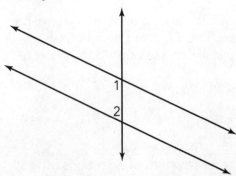

Angles 1 and 2 are same-side interior angles.

scale factor

In a dilation, the scale factor is the ratio of the distance of the new figure from the center of dilation to the distance of the original figure from the center of dilation.

Example

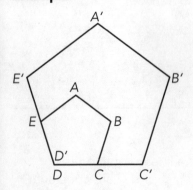

Pentagon *ABCDE* has been dilated by a scale factor of 2 to create Pentagon *A'B'C'D'E'*.

scatter plot

A scatter plot is a graph of a collection of ordered pairs that allows an exploration of the relationship between the points.

Example

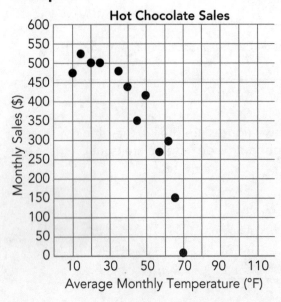

scientific notation

Scientific notation is a notation used to express a very large or a very small number as the product of a number greater than or equal to 1 and less than 10 and a power of 10.

Example

The number 1,345,000,000 is written in scientific notation as 1.345×10^9.

sequence

A sequence is a pattern involving an ordered arrangement of numbers, geometric figures, letters, or other objects.

Examples

Sequence A:

2, 4, 6, 8, 10, 12, . . .

Sequence B:

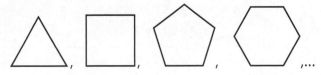

set

A set is a collection of numbers, geometric figures, letters, or other objects that have some characteristic in common.

Examples

The set of counting numbers is {1, 2, 3, 4, …}

The set of even numbers is {2, 4, 6, 8, …}

similar

When two figures are similar, the ratios of their corresponding side lengths are equal.

Example

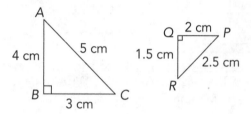

Triangle *ABC* is similar to Triangle *PQR*.

slope

In any linear relationship, slope describes the direction and steepness of a line and is usually represented by the variable *m*. Slope is another name for rate of change. (See *rate of change*.)

Example

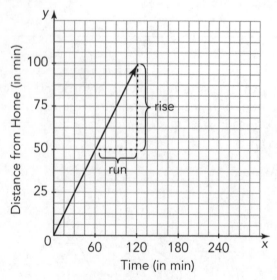

The slope of the line is $\frac{50}{60}$, or $\frac{5}{6}$.

slope-intercept form

The slope-intercept form of a linear equation is $y = mx + b$, where *m* is the slope of the line and (0, *b*) is the *y*-intercept.

solution of a linear system

The solution of a linear system is an ordered pair (*x*, *y*) that is a solution to both equations in the system. Graphically, the solution is the point of intersection.

Example

$$\begin{cases} y = x + 5 \\ y = -2x + 8 \end{cases}$$

The solution to this system of equations is (1, 6).

sphere

A sphere is the set of all points in three dimensions that are the same distance from a given point called the center of the sphere.

Example

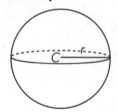

standard form

The standard form of a linear equation is $Ax + By = C$, where *A*, *B*, and *C* are constants and *A* and *B* are not both 0.

substitution method

The substitution method is a process of solving a system of equations by substituting a variable in one equation with an equivalent expression.

system of linear equations

When two or more linear equations define a relationship between quantities they form a system of linear equations.

Example

$$\begin{cases} y = x + 5 \\ y = -2x + 8 \end{cases}$$

---------------- T ----------------

term

A term in a sequence is an individual number, figure, or letter in the sequence.

Example

2, 7, 12, 17, 22, 27, 32, ...

↑

term

terminating decimal

A terminating decimal has a finite number of digits, meaning that after a finite number of decimal places, all following decimal places have a value of 0. Terminating decimals are rational numbers.

Examples

$\frac{9}{10} = 0.9$ $\frac{15}{8} = 1.875$ $\frac{193}{16} = 12.0625$

transformation

A transformation is the mapping, or movement, of a plane and all the points of a figure on a plane according to a common action or operation.

Examples

Translations, reflections, rotations, and dilations are examples of transformations.

translation

A translation is a rigid motion transformation that "slides" each point of a figure the same distance and direction.

Example

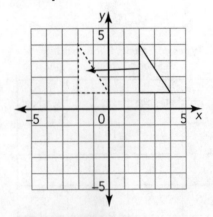

transversal

A transversal is a line that intersects two or more lines at distinct points.

Example

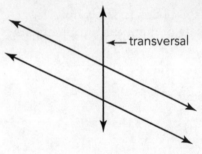

trend line

When you use a line of best fit, the line and its equation are often referred to as a model of the data, or a trend line. (See *model*.)

Triangle Sum Theorem

The Triangle Sum Theorem states that the sum of the measures of the interior angles of a triangle is 180°.

two-way table

A two-way table displays categorical data that shows the number of data points that fall into each group for two variables. One variable is divided into rows, and the other is divided into columns.

Example

Types of Snacks Purchased

	Snack Types			
	Popcorn	Nachos	Hot Dog	Candy
5:00 PM	200	125	75	100
7:00 PM	350	175	150	125
9:00 PM	425	225	175	125
11:00 PM	100	65	10	75

(Movie Showings)

— V —

Venn diagram

A Venn diagram uses circles to show how elements among sets of numbers or objects are related.

Example

Factors of 18   Factors of 30

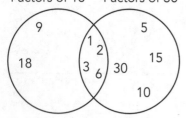

vertical line test

The vertical line test is a visual method used to determine whether a relation represented as a graph is a function. To apply the vertical line test, consider all the vertical lines that could be drawn on the graph of a relation. If any of the vertical lines intersect the graph of the relation at more than one point, then the relation is not a function.

Example

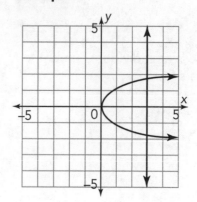

The line drawn at $x = 3$ crosses two points on the graph, so the relation is not a function.

— W —

whole numbers

Whole numbers are made up of the set of natural numbers and the number 0, the additive identity.

Example

The set of whole numbers can be represented as {0, 1, 2, 3, 4, 5, …}.

y-intercept

The *y*-intercept is the *y*-coordinate of the point where a graph crosses the *y*-axis. The *y*-intercept can be written in the form (0, *y*).

Example

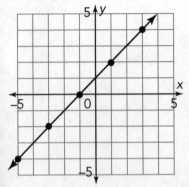

The *y*-intercept of the graph is (0, 1).

Index